FIRST AID AND
CARE OF WILDLIFE

FIRST AID
AND CARE OF
WILDLIFE

RICHARD MARK MARTIN
with Jill Nute MRCVS
and Geoff Nute MRCVS

DAVID & CHARLES
Newton Abbot London North Pomfret (Vt)

British Library Cataloguing in Publication Data
Martin, Richard Mark
  First aid and care of wildlife.
  I. Wildlife conservation
  I. Title   II. Nute, Jill
  III. Nute, Geoff
  639.9   QL82

  ISBN 0–7153–8444–9

Photoset by Photo-Graphics, Honiton, Devon
and printed in Great Britain
by Butler & Tanner Ltd., London and Frome
for David & Charles (Publishers) Limited
Brunel House   Newton Abbot   Devon

Published in the United States of America
by David & Charles Inc
North Pomfret   Vermont 05053   USA

Contents

Preface

Due to a rock solid belief in empiricism and because unconventional techniques are often astonishingly successful, in addition to the central veterinary chapters it has been my aim to awaken interest, stimulate thought and observation, and encourage sensible research and experiment. All thought and opinion expressed in the following pages is entirely my own responsibility and must not necessarily be attributed to my collaborators.

This book is indeed founded on the bedrock opinion that unless we care for our environment we do not and cannot care for our wildlife.

R.M.M.
Hellandbridge, June 1983

To Sam

*May he and his generation be more enlightened
stewards of this Planet Earth*

Foreword: Our Responsibility

The progression of mankind pushes on relentlessly, and leaves behind it a wake of casualties. Some are on the grand scale: the atmosphere contaminated, the Earth ravaged, the seas and lakes poisoned, the forests slash-burnt and the extinction, it is feared, of one species of animal or plant each and every day. Looking back along this dismal path we feel helpless, we blame someone else, we shrug our shoulders and turn away in the hope that we may learn from our mistakes and do better. But man is discovering that Earth management – the manipulation of nature – is not as easy as it sounds; we might as soon try to rewrite a Mozart late symphony.

Compared to the sheer sublimity of nature, even high technology appears crass and narrow-minded – a means to just one often fairly dubious end, rather than the drawing together of all ends into one colossal purpose. Now that we have blundered up to the ultimate death-producing trick the question is do we survive with nature or die with her? And we find we are totally unprepared to face this awful dilemma. Yet, as we dither on the brink, and I wonder about the futility of worrying about some of the minor casualties left behind, life goes on ever optimistically.

For the heart of all living matter – from man to microbe – is *the individual organism*. When one dies the world ceases, only to be reconstituted slightly, becoming microscopically different with each new birth. Were this not basically sound, the human condition would be different, births and deaths outside our immediate family would be meaningless, and we would be concerned with the human race only as an abstract phenomenon. And although we are no different to any other animal in our preoccupation with our own condition, we do differ thanks to our sentiment and consciousness. The greater our grasp, moreover, of the living world, the harder it is to ignore the existences of other life-forms and, as many a relationship between hostage and terrorist has indicated, intimacy engenders mutual sympathy. Since the Victorians it has been tempting to deride sentiment; after all, there are connotations with sentimentality. Yet the possession of sentiment or sensibility – thought tinged with emotion – is a mark of humanity. Along with humour, it is to be cherished, for in it lies a glimmer of hope, and a guard against abstract or cold ambition.

The analytical scientist is often surprised and embarrassed to find himself calling a research subject 'Sid', 'Eddie' or 'Cleopatra' in preference to, say, 34/B. The motorist in a hurry is pricked by his conscience into turning back to find a maimed thrush. This is evidence of something profound and valuable in humanity. Take it away, and Orwell's 1984 is surely here. But, happily, confronted by a helpless wild creature, the priorities of many an inherently selfish person undergo a surprising change and sensitivity, repressed by a veneer of toughness or swamped by busyness and business, responds unerringly.

So far I have intimated that all animal casualties are the result of human action. Of course, this is not so, but natural circumstances hardly ever occasion waste and most such victims are for one reason or another inefficient, and die to further other life. Accidental injury in nature is rare and will not be allowed to incapacitate the victim for long. It stems from some inadequacy and seldom affects those in peak condition.

Natural outbreaks of disease or premature mass mortality such as happen during severe winter conditions, although regrettable to us, have a role to play; no animal ever died a death which was both natural and needless. At worst, a life is sacrificed for the health and regulation of the species lest the population grows too large and unsustainable.

The flail of modern man however lays waste indiscriminately; and it is reasonable to suppose that it scythes down the cream of the species which is up and about, rather than the old and inefficient lying low. And so it is that this book is mostly concerned with the victims of man. It is the work of three concerned individuals seeking to help others help the casualties.

1 The Danger Areas

Animals fall victim to man wherever he or his effects are to be found, that is inevitable, but it is essentially techno-man that is most dangerous, and techno-man is protected and sustained only by such technology. In this chapter we try to identify the main areas of physical conflict between man and wildlife, so that by looking at the dangers they present we may be better prepared. We begin with the most wasteful and blighted area of all.

The Roadside

To venture like an eighteen-month-old toddler onto a road, oblivious of the rules which govern and control its traffic, puts a man utterly at the mercy of his brethren. Fortunately it seems instinctual for the average driver to take any option including crashing his own car and putting himself in increased danger before he will mow down a fellow human being. This altruism however does not extend so often to other species, although I am reminded of a well known racing-driver who killed himself in an ordinary car on an ordinary road while trying to avoid an ordinary dog; and a scientist who daylong was concerned with pest control and yet could not bring himself to run down a rabbit caught in his headlights.

But many humans do fall on the highway, and incalculably more animals; the modern road is the battleground on everyone's doorstep. I say 'modern' because it is not so much the road as the horrific kinetic energy of modern powered traffic that wreaks the havoc on flesh and bone. Road victims are known to us all. The city street, the suburban avenue, the bypass, the trunk road, the country lane – they all exact their toll. 'Battleground' is probably the wrong word because it suggests a fight or contest, and there is none; animals live or die by luck alone. The most unlucky are maimed to limp away and die in a verge or gutter.

11

The toll is collected continuously, perhaps the early hours of Sunday and Christmas mornings are the only relatively safe periods. The victims may change with the hour and the season, but overall carnage and the car age will not be separated.

Hard winters see desperately hungry, thirsty and exhausted migrants congregating on verges to seek food exposed by the slightly increased ground temperature, and water provided by melted ice and snow following de-icing operations. The deadly trap could hardly be better laid: for if animals are not simply struck by vehicles they risk being poisoned by the high salinity of the water they drink (which causes nervous derangement leading to disorientation and fits). During the winter of 1981–2 while I was researching this book I watched helplessly as small foraging parties of weakened Redwings were thrown up by the turbulence of passing lorries to be run down by following cars. The efficiency of the trap was such that it might have been designed by a malicious Heath Robinson; and yet no one was to blame. It was the hard winter that set the problem, and technology which executed the sweeping solution. The traffic was hardly speeding; even I on my bicycle represented a threat for so desperate were these Redwings – pushed farther south to Cornwall than they would normally travel – that they scarcely moved as I passed but a pump's length away. One, more engrossed than the others, panicked as I came upon it and actually flew between my wheels; thereafter I whistled and even sang lustily.

Apart from this danger, the short days and dull conditions of winter require use of headlights, and there is evidence that many animals fall when dazzled, including owls, the Fox and deer.

When the surviving migrators have departed north and spring beckons summer, residents are fatigued and yet face the prospect of a vigorous breeding season, some in competition with incoming migrants. Birds in particular are vulnerable for they become engrossed in prospecting, the building of nests and later the feeding of young. Hibernating animals such as the Hedgehog emerge; and amphibians move along ancient routes – often now intersected by roads – to and from their breeding grounds. At the same time, more and more motorists respond enthusiastically to the burgeoning spring and drier road surfaces. As fledglings first test their wings in the harsh real world beyond the nest, those unfortunate to do so alongside a road face a peril much less worthy and of far greater omnipresence than a lone predatory Sparrowhawk or even a cat.

High summer brings maximum populations of all species. The great competition for food and territory now begins and necessitates the fullest exploitation of the countryside and, in particular, its wilderness areas. Road margins with their attendant hedges and rank vegetation form a great network supporting much wildlife across many countries. It is as well they do, otherwise the wildlife in such regions or, at least, in the more developed areas, would be greatly depleted. However, as we have seen, it is a habitat which extorts its toll and in full-blown summer as lush vegetation endeavours to invade the tarmac it overhangs it, blurs the edges, obscures the vision of road-user and road-trespasser, and in times of economic cutbacks and increasing ecological awareness gets trimmed less frequently – certainly to the benefit of the flora, which is reason enough.

Autumn sees scarcely fewer numbers of animals and also extensive movements of territories and populations. Moulting birds are subjected to extra stress, impaired manoeuvrability and a surtax on energy just as reserves of fat are to be laid down for the lean months ahead. Mammals, though less mobile than birds, suffer almost as much. Most birds are hit by vehicles as they fly up from verges (as with my Redwings) or emerge without warning from a hedge, bank or gap; once they gain height they are reasonably safe. Mammals, except bats, are earthbound and sooner or later in their perambulations will likely encounter a road. Indeed, the nightly excursions of Badgers and Hedgehogs for instance take them regularly along the same route which may well include a length of road; their survival then becomes a matter of chance in the coincidence of dark night, blind bend and careless driver.

In an area admittedly of high Badger density in Gloucestershire between 1973 and 1976 inclusive, 460 road traffic casualties were examined at the Gloucester Veterinary Investigation Centre compared to 70 found dead from natural causes. Though many chronically sick Badgers may die below ground, from the low proportion of sickness seen in culled and road victims there seems little likelihood that the toll due to natural causes can in any way approach that due to the motor vehicle. Inexperienced juveniles are on their own in the autumn and looking for new territories; all are preoccupied with hunting or foraging, and headlights suddenly present a glaring hazard. I have, however, just seen a Badger apparently waiting on a verge for my car to pass before crossing over.

Roads then, from byway to bypass, are a likely source of injured

13

fauna. Motorways are rather less so. They have a broad open aspect and lack nearby dense vegetation; besides, their hard-shoulders provide a valuable buffer-zone out of bounds to both vehicle and animal. Of course, hits do occur, and motorway margins and central reservation strips are heavily contaminated with lead, but we are usually only aware of the larger animals: deer, Foxes, stray dogs and predatory or scavenging birds such as Buzzards and corvids lured by the foregoing casualties, which could be as small as amphibians and invertebrates. Owls, such as the Barn owls which hunt largely by sound are attracted by the build-up of voles along the verges but are confused by the traffic noise and headlights; this is a major reason for the Barn owl's decline.

A long-distance lorry driver friend, admittedly sympathetic to animals, fears he accounts for about half a dozen (noticeable) birds and mammals per year or 100,000 miles. Possibly less interested drivers account for more although there is little safe evasive action you can take when in control of a heavy goods vehicle. It would be foolhardy in the extreme, quite apart from blatantly illegal, to stop on a motorway to retrieve a wounded animal. Should such an animal be seen and judged to be a hazard either by wandering or as an obstacle, the police should be informed from one of the emergency telephones located at frequent intervals.

On quieter roads I occasionally alarm passengers by swerving to avoid caterpillars (which they never seem to have seen) in much the same way as a friend engaged in research on birds' parasites would career off backwards down the road in order to recover a dead source of specimens before another vehicle had the chance of compressing it yet further into the tarmac. Incidentally, the hazard lights now apparently fitted as standard equipment to vehicles could not be better designed as an aid to roadside research into mortality or to on-the-spot first-aid in relative safety.

Perhaps a bicycle provides the best means of surveying the roadside battleground. And yet it can also be tedious for although it enables considerable mileage to be covered at little or no cost, there are few more irksome experiences than to have gained full speed on some swooping descent (accumulating valuable cheap energy to help ascend the next looming hill) only to flash past, usually nearer the bottom, some forlorn creature heading resolutely out to take on the next car or lorry. There follows an inner conflict in which conscience usually triumphs over selfish interest, and the splendid down gradient

14

becomes a hill to be regained. This errand of mercy can end even more irritatingly if the creature has vanished altogether or reveals itself to be no more than a leaf or fragment of stick engaged in animal mimicry.

Road systems are designed to link or bypass towns, cities and villages. These conurbations create their own kind of problems: the roads themselves and even roofs as they shine in wet weather can dupe waterbirds into landing on them, with perilous consequences not difficult to imagine. Towns always have high populations of dogs, cats and children – all of which are dangerous to wildlife. Empty buildings are death traps to many small birds which enter in search of secure roosting and nesting quarters and are unable to find their way out, attracted and baffled as they are by the windows.

Countryside and Watercourses

Away from the arterial road system, the patchwork of fields and copses stitched together by lanes, streams and hedgerows will hold less wildlife maimed by man directly. True, there will probably always be birds winged by incompetent 'guns' and boys with catapults and airguns. And unfortunately casualties resulting from traps and self-locking snares set despite their prohibition under the Wildlife and Countryside Act 1981 by gamekeepers and countrymen with nineteenth-century attitudes, still persist as we approach the twenty-first century. Even the entanglement of birds' legs in fishing-line abandoned along river banks is seldom the result of an accident.

Natural death in the countryside is an everyday occurrence, merci-fully it is usually clean, quick and efficient in the higher forms of life and always necessary; where it is not, man, alas, is often to blame. For example, the swan hitting overhead power-cables and the deer entangled in barbed-wire – a twentieth-century barbarity – are not natural casualties.

In a needless and starkly visible way the human being marks its territory with garbage and litter: the country village, farmland, beauty spot, roadside and railway embankment all attract their own brand of rubbish – rubbish that can be deadly to wildlife apart from being highly offensive to most visually aware people. Broken glass, bottles, tin cans, ring-tops, polythene bags and wrappers and the debris of farming and angling are all more dangerous than the traditional mattress, cooker and refrigerator. Farmers, always quick to denounce the towny, often offend as much, especially in the careless disposal of brightly coloured fertiliser bags and the pervasive residues they contain. Virtually all the remaining 'freshwater' pools near my home have their resident populations of such debris.

Whatever the prevailing law and codes of practice, farmers also cause unnecessary suffering, and indeed the elimination of localised pockets of wildlife, by straw- and stubble-burning. In one study, it reduced the numbers of insects living above ground by 85 per cent, the numbers of insects appearing in the following year by 71 per cent, and the number of species present by 61 per cent. Apart from the inevitable deaths, burns and abandoned young of larger species, straw- and stubble-burning causes the destruction of habitat along marginal land in just the same way as gorse and brushwood fires which flare up after prolonged dry weather. The latter, now that steam-trains are a thing of the past, are usually caused by the foolish and irresponsible actions of members of the public.

The hazards of broken glass to wildlife are obvious. Milk bottles or others with wide necks make effective small mammal traps from which it is often impossible to escape due to the slippery camber inside. Opened cans and plastic yoghurt containers are a danger to curious mammals such as Hedgehogs which, tempted by the possibility of gleanings inside, have been known to get them wedged on their heads. And however amusing the idea of a Hedgehog with a hat, it condemns the wretched creature to panic and starvation. The sharp edges of cans are also a menace to all tongues, snouts and paws. The pull-rings off cans of drink are well known for the damage they have caused to mammals and birds with their razor-sharp edges.

Intentional vandalism, now making itself apparent even in quite small villages, causes much distress, injury and death particularly to semi-wild birds such as the Mute swan, Mallard and pigeon, plus ornamental birds in public parks.

Poisons deliberately or accidentally put down must have accounted for millions of deaths over the years. Pesticides and herbicides are a curious combination of the two – intended usually for specifics but often with a potential reaching much further than desired, intended or anticipated. Synthetic pesticides developed after World War II from research into nerve gas and chemical warfare have had far-reaching and disastrous consequences to wildlife. There are two main groups. The organophosphates or organo-phosphorous compounds (parathion, malathion and so on) work by destroying enzymes and are highly toxic to all animals (man included), but they break down speedily in the environment into harmless compounds. The chlorin-ated-hydrocarbons or organochlorines are a quite different matter; they are highly persistent, accumulating not only in the individual – especially in the fatty tissues – but also in prey species, where they become more and more concentrated.

DDT, the first and best known, has been scattered all over the world since 1939 on a comparatively massive scale – most notably in programmes of mosquito/malaria eradication. Its greatest use was as an insecticide and it is still used sometimes to control insects at sewage plants. Although the dangers of its uncontrolled use became apparent, its efficiency questionable in the face of resistant strains and its control subsequently tightened, the unbroken-down residue of the hundreds of thousands of tons manufactured and remaining in the earth (and animal tissue) has still not found its way into the sea. And there it can kill aquatic life in concentrations greater than 0.1ppm. But even worse, the emergence ten or more years later of other chlorinated-hydrocarbons highly toxic to higher forms of life, in particular birds, had horrific consequences.

Dieldrin, aldrin and, most lethal of all, endrin, among others were virtually outlawed in the 1960s; but in the meantime had been responsible for untold deaths of seed-eating birds, their predators such as birds of prey and scavengers such as the Fox. The problem arose simply because in the forties and fifties it seems to have been assumed that dieldrin and its related compounds were no more lethal to birds than was DDT. Yet it is about fourteen times more so – at least to the principal groups at risk, gamebirds and pigeons, which will take dressed grain. Endrin is unique in being equally toxic to both mammals and birds and to the latter is a staggering fifty times more toxic than DDT, 10mg per kilo of bodyweight proving to be a lethal dose to 50 per cent of those tested (LD_{50}). But there is little to choose between the other organochlorines in mammal toxicity and this is where the original error occurred; for the principal test case was the rat not a bird: the LD_{50} being around 100mg.

Pesticide	LD_{50} as milligrams per kilo bodyweight	
	rat	*quail*
Endrin	10	10
Dieldrin	100	35
DDT	113	500

(from Mellanby)

To sum up, whereas 10mg of endrin and 35mg of dieldrin were, and are, sufficient to kill outright many birds (quail were subsequently used in American experiments), the LD_{50} for DDT was as much as 500mg.

This major problem has receded greatly since the mass deaths of granivorous birds in the late fifties, although sporadic toxic outbursts may occur as long as some farmers dispose of containers in an irresponsible way. Now that the chlorinated-hydrocarbons have largely disappeared we might have hoped that the whole pesticide problem would have done the same, but this is not the case. At the ends of food chains or, more graphically, at the apices of food pyramids, birds-of-prey like the Sparrowhawk and Peregrine falcon which specialise in eating seed-eating birds – and to a lesser extent scavengers like the Buzzard, Fox and crows – are still susceptible to contamination through accumulating in their bodies the insidious combination of organo-phosphorous insecticides and mercurial fungicidal seed-dressings which are taken by many granivores in sub-lethal doses. Such carnivores and omnivores may still be affected by low fertility and (in birds) clutch depletion. See Chapters 5 and 7 for symptoms and such treatment as there is.

Deadly poisons such as strychnine can be frighteningly abused. Nowadays it is sold only against permit for the destruction specifically of the Mole *underground*, and yet more than enough is issued annually to put paid to the entire Mole population of the country once and for all. And the Mole is still common and widespread. I know from sad personal experience of this abuse for a young Jack Russell terrier of mine picked up and ate a poisoned egg left in open view. He died in convulsions hours later. The intended victim was probably a Rook, Carrion crow or even a Fox; but instead of a pet dog it could have been picked up by a child and taken home and eaten.

Poisons are not always so spectacular: pure alcohol, ethylene glycol (anti-freeze), detergent and soap are all common pollutants and toxic, while a glance at the range of killing chemicals on display in any garden centre gives some idea of the amount of death there is for sale. Behind brand names are concealed a range of poisons (herbicides, insecticides, molluscicides, rodenticides, fungicides and nematocides) deadly enough to impress any adherent of chemical warfare. You have to search hard, usually in vain, to find one not marked 'keep out of reach of children', 'avoid contact with the skin', 'dangerous to pets, fish and domestic animals' or something similar.

The most dangerous in concentrated form are the famous paraquat and 2,4,5,T together with other petrochemical based herbicides which produce pulmonary oedema, and against which there is no effective treatment. One of the commonest is the molluscicide metaldehyde. Literally tons, suitably baited, are sprinkled over countryside and gardens annually, presumably killing tons of slugs and snails which are immobilised and die of desiccation the following day when unable to return to cover. Their populations seem able to withstand such inroads with equanimity, but vertebrates too are affected by the poison – in particular domestic dogs and some species of birds. For instance slug pellets are picked up and eaten by some gallinaceous birds and waterfowl causing severe disturbances, mainly to the liver and the brain, which result in inco-ordinated movements. And one wonders, despite a lack of evidence, about the effects on thrushes and the Hedgehog if and when they are tempted to sample such dead or dying molluscs in large numbers.

Gardens, attractive with flowers and productive with vegetables, harbour other dangers to wildlife besides chemicals. The domestic cat is a terrifying and efficient predator of small vertebrates but presents a quandary, for although I would like to see far fewer about because away from busy roads most people will certainly encounter their wildlife casualties by courtesy of the cat, it is also true that our predatory British fauna is so reduced from former times that the cat – more so our latest favourite *bête noire*, the Mink – living wild, help to redress the balance. With cats it is a highly wasteful depredation as few victims are eaten or even left for scavengers; almost as wasteful as fruit-nets, which can entangle birds and the Rabbit and long-suffering Hedgehog. Loose or slack nets are most dangerous, so peg them tautly to the ground and store carefully when not in use.

The on-going story of human conflict with nature in the cause of commercial food production and even gardening is complex and, with the exception of the misuse and side-effects of chemicals and the casualties so caused, must be left to the professional monitors and experts. It must, however, be suspected that an animal acting abnormally, which does not seem to have been physically injured, may have been poisoned in some way or other. Every effort must be made using commonsense and deduction to discover the source and nature of the incident.

Another insidious pollutant is lead. It invades the environment by diverse routes and is one of the most worrying and least controlled

19

poisons today, probably accounting for more fatalities than any other single agent. It is estimated for instance that 100,000 ducks may die each year from lead poisoning. Lead has several domestic uses and threatens people – especially young ones – as well as wildlife. Its evil is masked by a certain innocuousness and, moreover, it seldom advertises its presence. It lurks in old paint on railings in children's playgrounds, maybe covered by leadfree overcoats but rarely removed and waiting to be exposed by flaking, picking or chipping; it is a component of batteries which are often discarded on rubbish dumps or, worse, on roadsides. In the UK it is still regrettably used as an anti-knocking petrol additive, though it is due to be phased out this decade.

A fine spray of inorganic lead compound – 150 tons a week – is emitted in the exhaust fumes of British cars. These particles are breathed in by roadside animals and fall onto vegetation and soil, some ending up in drainage ditches. It is therefore a part of all towndwellers of whatever species and also of the food chains begun by plants and insects along all roadways, particularly trunk routes. Ten years ago, British cars poured into the atmosphere 6 million tons of carbon monoxide, 300,000 tons of hydrocarbons, 210,000 tons of nitrogen oxides, 20,000 tons of sulphur dioxide, 10,000 tons of aldehydes and 7,000 tons of lead, not to mention great quantities of smoke, asbestos brake-dust etc.

Even longer ago, in 1967, Kenneth Mellanby said: 'Recent findings on the effects of low doses of lead in man are disquieting and more harm may be being done to other forms of life than is usually recognised.' Fifteen years later, lead is still ineffectively controlled in Britain, unlike in Japan and America. Industrial leadworkings in Britain may now be virtually obsolete, but the ground and even the atmosphere around such sites are heavily contaminated as are watercourses passing through them.

Lead in a more recognisable form is introduced into the environment by anglers and 'guns'. Leadshot is a massive problem, particularly in North America, and has been for decades, especially where shooting is heavy and sustained such as over favoured lakes and, in Britain, estuaries. Shot is taken up as grit, which is used by birds as internal teeth to aid the breaking down of coarse fodder in the crop. Wildfowl, as we have seen, are highly vulnerable to the cumulative effects of lead poisoning as the metal builds up in the tissues, but even granivorous land birds such as gamebirds, pigeons and crows are at risk and can be killed by consuming a very small amount. As few as two pieces of shot have been known to kill a dove.

The contamination of ground around traditional grousebutts and clay-pigeon ranges is comparable to heavily hunted stretches of water. The problem here is aggravated by fishing tackle, some anglers seeming to mark their territory with a system of discarded nylon line and lead weights whose durability is a virtue to the fisherman but an unmitigated liability when abandoned. Currently of great concern is the poisoning of swans (see Chapter 7); the Nature Conservancy Council (NCC) estimate 3,000–5,000 deaths a year. The leads lie concealed in the silt of estuaries and riverbeds until found and swallowed by waterfowl – usually after having been stirred up by pleasure craft – in just the same way as shot. Now, late in the day, great efforts are being made to find an acceptable substitute for anglers' lead split-shot, possibly by the use of steel or tungsten.

Rocky coastlines criss-crossed with line are particularly dangerous, for here the line becomes snagged and the sinkers jam in crevices or their grapnel hooks become entangled in vegetation. Again it is difficult to conceive a more dastardly hazard to birds. The problem could be alleviated if those anglers responsible would wait for the tide to recede and retrieve their equipment. One such stretch of coastline I know well on the northern side of Morecambe Bay along the Kent estuary could be guaranteed to yield miles of line and pound upon pound of weights.

Considering the stress it undoubtedly causes in various ways, it is a little surprising that fish-hunting under the guise of angling enjoys the reputation for peacefulness that it does. Similar tormenting of any other harmless and sensitive animal would probably not be tolerated by the public at large; but then fish have always been conveniently seen as non-flesh flesh. The lucky ones are despatched quickly and cleanly; others are thrown back to withstand their injuries as best they can, out of human sight. But there is another side to the story, for the popularity of angling makes it a redoubtable lobby for clean water. The Anglers' Co-operative Association (ACA) fights tirelessly against pollution, and deserves support even from non-anglers.

The problem – as in most things – is the irresponsible element – the thoughtless, ignorant or arrogant angler or 'gun'. Causes of death in the 630 swans dealt with in 1982 by the Swan Rescue Service operating from Norfolk were as follows: 72 per cent directly attributable to coarse fishing (eg lead poisoning, line entanglement resulting

21

in mandibles being bound together, leg amputations/gangrene etc, and impaled or swallowed fish-hooks); 18 per cent from collision with power cables (outright death, legs or wings ripped off and severe burns, possibly when vision is impaired and reactions dulled by high lead levels); 5 per cent shot – illegally – by farmers and 'cowboys'; and 5 per cent from other forms of vandalism (air rifles, crossbows, knives etc). An example of the sort of vandalism to which swans seem particularly prone befell one pair: the cob was peppered with shot while the pen was dragged from her nest, stretched out on a path and repeatedly run over by a gang of youths on cycles until dead.

Len Baker who runs Swan Rescue tells me that of the 317 rescues carried out from June to September 1983 inclusive, 278 received their injuries through coarse fishing; 213 of these had lead poisoning and there have been 129 deaths. For those swans and geese which can be treated and do recover, the question always remains: where can they be released in safety given the risks of lead poisoning, discarded line and impoverished or disturbed water short of natural food? In the Norfolk Broads the average Mute swan weighs only 7.7kg (17lb) compared to a correct weight of about 11.8kg (26lb); it is forced to beg for junk food from picnickers. Water can be polluted by natural causes such as drainage from land with seams of copper and lead and even coniferous woodland, but it is our old adversaries the chlorinated-hydrocarbons which cause the most serious mass fish mortality.

In mining districts river water tends to carry large quantities of coal dust in suspension. Elsewhere, detergents of various kinds make their presence felt, and there is a massive and frightening land run-off and leaching of nitrogenous fertilisers and other nutrient materials such as animal slurry which may contain zinc, copper, hormones and antibiotics which are used wholesale. When such pollutants aggravate or are aggravated by deoxygenation, extremely complicated effects ensue. The discharge of raw, untreated sewage such as happened on a large scale during the 1983 water strike is a major cause of deoxygenation as bacterial populations erupt.

The effect of pollutants on the life in a watercourse depends largely on whether materials in suspension are organic or inorganic. If there is a large quantity of organic particles their decomposition could produce gas bubbles which buoy up the material to form an evil-smelling sludge on the surface. The most common forms are proteins, fats and carbohydrates derived from food-processing, eg dairies, and from slaughterhouses, and sewage disposal. Alternatively, if the particles are inorganic, they may settle en masse onto the riverbed forming a stifling blanket over plant and animal life. Another effect of highly turbid water is to cut down the amount of sunlight reaching the bed, which severely restricts plant life and, thereby, the amount of oxygen released into the water by photosynthesis.

However, the biggest threat to wildlife is simply the continual retraction of its living space. The countryside is under pressure from many powerful commercial lobbies: agriculture, mining, coniferous reafforestation, housing, industry, communications and leisure. Some animals are able to adapt and take advantage of man's developments but, while there may be many individuals, they account only for a minority of species which is frequently of pest status due to this very adaptability and vigour. The town Fox, Cockroach, House sparrow, Collared dove, Brown rat and various gulls all come to mind. Evolution itself cannot cope with man's rate of technological progress. The harsh truth is that most of our wildlife will continue to decrease and gradually, unspectacularly, disappear until we acknowledge that the countryside was not created solely for our economic benefit.

The Sea and Seashore

With his land-based view of the world, man has a bias which blinkers him to aquatic matters: water is for drinking, swimming, surfing, fishing, gardening, sailing and so on. It is an 'amenity', and thus rarely gets the respect it deserves and needs. And yet it covers about 70 per cent of the Earth's surface.

Along the margins of this 140 million square miles we confront a vast alien world, and may at any time meet a creature from it – a creature to whom dry land is as inexplicable and inhospitable as outer space is to us. The littoral zone is a real biological frontier, the animals and plants confined there are utterly dependent on the tidal ebb and flow, and it collects some of the sea's casualties.

Occasionally, a whale or other cetacean is stranded. Thus beached, this air-breathing mammal is as much out of its element as any fish for, deprived of the buoyancy of water and its cooling properties, the whale's lungs can collapse under its own weight or it may overheat. Seals are marine mammals that have not altogether relinquished their ties to dry land. An adult caught in a salmon-net will likely drown or be despatched by the fisherman who finds it. They also have to haul out to moult and to breed; and the pups are often orphaned either by natural means or by well-meaning people who cannot approach a wild animal without 'rescuing' it. The same syndrome exists with leverets, baby deer and, most commonly, nestling birds (see Chapters 7 and 8).

Specialist sea creatures from whales to whelks are never easy to maintain artificially, and more often than not are past redemption. On the other hand, I have amused myself and considered time spent ferrying small animals from rapidly evaporating rockpools to deeper ones not entirely wasted. In the same way, starfish abandoned by a high tide and found still alive may be reprieved. It should, however, be appreciated that when one interferes thus with nature another creature is being deprived of a meal and maybe its own life. In a similar spirit and with no thought of interfering with natural cycles, early morning walks along country lanes near my home are forever punctuated by scooping suicidal snails, worms and even slugs from the tarmac and lobbing them gently into the safety of herbage.

Of course, one does not usually go out especially to look for casualties; but all good naturalists programme themselves to notice any creature around, and one of Murphy's last-minute laws decrees that injured animals present themselves when most unexpected and least convenient to the finder. Additionally, it is important to keep quiet about all interest in wildlife, especially any past successes at treating casualties, unless you want to open a full-time rescue centre; for the telephone summonses intermingled with assorted callers clutching mysterious boxes and bundles come at all hours. With the best will in the world, caring for a continuous supply of wild animals is exacting work – time and space consuming, and expensive; a quite different matter to dealing with the occasional victim found by family and friends. Several large animal hospitals have begun in such a way, for instance the famous one at Mousehole in Cornwall.

Mention of Mousehole brings to mind the *Torrey Canyon* disaster of 1967. When this tanker went aground off Lands End I was a young zoological worker in north Lincolnshire, and felt the overwhelming urge for the first (and probably last) time in my life to 'do good'; and in a small way I organised public collections of money to send to the appeal fund. It was, I suppose, the first major oil disaster of its kind and seemed to me the first strike presaging the end of the world, or at least my world. During the despair of the grim news, I imagined, as did many others, the horrendous deaths of untold thousands of seabirds, the ruination of an ecosystem, even the extinction of bird species I had hitherto romantically worshipped as independent spirits

– wild and free. Since those bleak days in 1967, we have been amazed at the ability of nature to heal herself; have become more hardened to tanker and rig disasters, blow-outs and the rest; grown to accept our own helplessness in such calamities and leave the cleaning up to experts and their techniques, which have improved beyond measure.

But notwithstanding the millions of seabird fatalities which have occurred – perhaps 1 million a year in the North Atlantic alone – there remain few sights more pathetic or wretched than that of a lone Guillemot or Razorbill huddled on a winter tideline, nonplussed by its evil black overcoat which has reduced it in a trice from master of its domain to a sick and feeble derelict. Many such birds, even were they to survive – and about 65 per cent can if properly treated (see Chapter 8) – might, for all we know, be ostracised for life from the company of their peers.

Crude oil pollution – whether from ship as a result of accident or the deliberate and illicit flushing out of tanks on the high seas, or from chronic leakage at the well-head or via defective pipelines – is by no means the only source of marine contamination, though it is likely to go on being the most widespread as long as oil is coveted from the seabed. Surprisingly, perhaps, lighter oils such as fuel oil and diesel oil are much more toxic even though their effects on skin and plumage are less apparent. Most oiled birds are lost at sea through chilling and drowning; for the 'lucky' few which make it to coast their external condition, providing they are cleaned very thoroughly and kept warm, can become secondary to their internal poisoning. So, apparently lightly oiled birds may be more seriously affected than seems apparent. Light oils may also be responsible for the burn marks which have been found on seals, and which have been attributed to chemicals.

The emulsifiers used to disperse oil slicks are themselves highly toxic, particularly to lower forms of marine life; but fortunately their long-term effects are not thought to be great. Some industrial chemicals used in the 1960s presented a far more sinister prospect; these were, or rather are, the infamous PCBs (polychlorinated biphenyls). I say 'were' because moves to control their use following recognition of their danger to the environment in 1968 were remarkably rapid considering their importance, especially to the plastic industry. By 1972 controls were in force, and less than two years later the levels monitored in North Atlantic surface waters were much reduced. But the residue must remain in sediment layers on the seabed, for PCBs are highly persistent; therefore, like the chlorinated-

25

hydrocarbon pesticides of which PCBs are an ingredient, they accumulate in the individual and also in food chains.

Industrial toxic effluent has been conveniently flushed into the sea for generations, and over the years man's ambiguous attitude towards water in general and the sea in particular has resulted in a terribly convoluted series of contradictions. Ever since he first used water to wash in, sluice down and flush away, he has increasingly abused it and assumed its ability to self-purify. It is impossible to think of another substance which is universally sought both as a fundamental of our life-support system required in as clean and pure a form as possible, and at virtually the same time as a vehicle for everything from cleansing our bodies, dishes, cars and drains to diluting and dispersing industrial effluent and cooling radioactive isotopes.

It is estimated by the Keep Britain Tidy group that 6½ million tons of garbage is dumped overboard from vessels each year, but this traditional use for the sea is no longer acceptable with so much indestructible plastic around. Especially dangerous are the monofilament nylon gill-nets which are not only designed to eliminate fish altogether but which, when adrift, can go on 'ghost-fishing' for years either on the surface representing a hazard to birds and marine mammals or on the seabed. In ghost-fishing the net sinks and collapses under the weight of fish, re-erecting when the bodies decay. Curious sea mammals investigating such an apparition become entangled and either starve or drown or their bodies may actually grow around the net.

The sea beckons us with its promise of unending treasures and at the same time represents a convenient waste-disposal unit – out of sight, out of mind. And though nature is remarkably resilient, those of us with septic-tanks tend not to abuse them in the way that society, abrogating individual responsibility, abuses its sea. And yet the sea is more than just a gigantic septic-tank or storehouse of wealth, it is a vital biosphere.

However, because we do not live in it, we have this blinkered attitude; dolphins and whales would speak with a different perception and, for all we know, do just that. The great whale and its smaller cousins and even the less-committed seals can bear witness to our despoilment of the marine environment; and so it is to be expected that wholly aquatic lifeforms, which never need to surface, are affected still more. Shellfish, in particular, are effective monitors of marine pollution because of their filtering feeding technique.

26

Every summer around our coast there are outbreaks of food-poisoning caused by the discharge of untreated sewage which contaminates by its concentration and consequent deoxygenation. This form of pollution is at least understandable, more difficult to explain to a gallactic visitor would be the use of the sea as a cesspit for the waste chemicals and metals of modern processes. Toxic metals are numerous. Chromium, nickel, copper, arsenic, mercury, cadmium and zinc are now quite strictly controlled in Britain but the middle three are still used in agriculture and horticulture, copper and mercury being insidious but lacking the infamous reputation of arsenic. The dangers of persistent chlorinated-hydrocarbons have already been mentioned, as has the leaching of nitrates from heavily used inorganic nitrogenous fertilisers. In industry on the other hand, metal-plating shops for example produce forms of cyanide as a by-product; this is lethal to aquatic life in doses as low as 0.1ppm. Aluminium affects sexual reproduction in animals and root growth in plants.

The concentration of such pollutants is likely to be highest in streams and rivers adjacent to their source, and in the sea adjacent to the estuaries of large rivers. Wildlife attracted to such places plus, of course, the residents, are most at risk. Fish and fish-eating animals are the best examples. The cellular levels of these elements in the main food chains are significantly rising.

The Atmosphere

The effects on *individual* animals in Britain of atmospheric pollution tend to be localised and confined to scenes of accidents, specific industrial areas and roadsides whose contamination from exhaust fumes has already been mentioned. Fluorine, for instance, seen as a pale greenish-yellow gas, causes chronic poisoning in the countryside around aluminium plants, brickworks and large potteries.

Acid rain, though, knocks into a cocked hat the poet's 'sweet rain from heaven doth fall' as forests are killed off in Germany, and fish vanish from lakes in Sweden and Canada. In Germany, 1,500ha (3,700 acres) of 'evergreen' forest were already dead by mid 1982 with a further 80,000 ha (30,900 acres) threatened; and a leading expert has predicted that whole forests will die in the next five years. In Sweden, over 18,000 lakes have been affected, 4,000 so seriously that most life in them has been destroyed.

We in Britain were deluded and selfish in thinking that prevailing westerly winds blowing over our factories and power-stations carried away our sulphur-dioxide and nitrogen-oxide emissions. It has now been shown that even south-west Scotland and parts of the Lake District are affected, as well as more easterly regions.

2 Identification

It seems inevitable that we endeavour to identify or investigate anything unusual we happen upon – no doubt prompted by the curiosity innate to all higher primates, and which has helped to sustain, protect and advance mankind. Our progress as a species has allowed the luxury of humanitarianism to flourish – only in the whales do we find anything similar – and when we confront a helpless representative of another species which appears to be beseeching our help, we do not automatically capitalise on its misfortune. Rather, and even before we try to find out what is wrong with it, our first question is 'What exactly is it?'. But it is a question which need not always be answered exactly.

The purpose of this chapter is in fact to discover how much we need to know about an unknown disabled animal in order to take immediate positive action. Time, energy and possibly enthusiasm can be wasted on specific identification when familial knowledge would suffice. It is this general knowledge which is important: that we know instinctively that a Badger is an omnivorous carnivore; that a Robin is a thrush is an invertebrate feeder; that a vole is related to a mouse and is vegetarian; that a shrew though it may approximate a mouse is quite different and highly insectivorous; that a tern is not truly a gull; that a Slow-worm is not a snake; that a Hedgehog dietetically is more like a thrush than a hamster; and so on. More precise cognition can follow later after correct *first* aid has been administered.

I do not propose to imitate a fieldguide to species; such books are readily available. It is more important to set down certain guidelines which, having been assimilated, can be carried around in one's head. As was pointed out earlier, we come upon casualties when we least expect to, and even the committed wildlifer doesn't always want to have to carry a book of reference.

General knowledge combined with commonsense is of inestimable value. Mammals and birds can clearly be differentiated and this forms

29

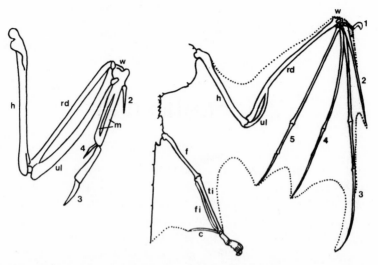

Fig 1 Comparative anatomy of bird *(left)* and bat *(right)*: **c** calcar; **f** femur; **fi** fibula; **h** humerus; **m** metacarpals; **rd** radius; **ti** tibia; **ul** ulna (reduced in bats [horseshoe] or absent altogether); **w** wrist. Numerals refer to phalanges or digits; in birds, (1) and (5) have atrophied *(after Kingsley, Comparative Anatomy of Vertebrates 1917, and Joanna C. Webb).* See also *Fig 27*

a useful starting point, bats being the only overlap in countries with no flightless birds. These two groups will give us most of our treatable casualties (Fig 1). But in some ways this is not such a useful distinction for, as has just been shown, a mammal can have more in common with a bird than with another mammal when it comes to captive management. Obviously their mode of locomotion is characteristically different but since a bird will likely have been rendered flightless to have been caught in the first place, airborn restraint is less a problem at first than might be thought. The dashing and scurrying or the bite, run and hide technique are used by birds and mammals alike.

Once the casualty has been taken to secure, warm and quiet quarters, and after initial fears have been soothed, nutrition is the major problem of maintenance and goes on alongside and irrespective of veterinary treatment. Nutrition (see Chapter 4) is not just a matter of providing the right sort of food in a manner appropriate for the particular species. The nutritional and dietary demands made on an animal determine to a large extent its character and anatomy and – although it is something of a chicken-and-egg conundrum – its distribution.

Unless it is on migration, an animal ought not to be found where there is no food for it (see also page 55). So it is important to note the site exactly together with any other relevant local information. The theme of this chapter, while certainly not ignoring speciation, is more concerned with fostering a slightly deeper perception or insight into those groups and species which might cause confusion. The thing to remember is that an experienced naturalist confronted by an unknown animal from a foreign land could deduce its character and basic needs from a survey of its anatomy and basic physiognomy.

Mammals

The larger land mammals, there being so few left in Britain, are immediately recognisable: deer, 'wild' ponies, the Badger, Fox and certainly the wallabies living feral in certain localities, notably the Peak District. Deer are the most difficult to place in species. The layperson possibly cannot immediately tell one from another while identifying their young is even more difficult. It is the new-born spotted young – usually of the little Roe deer – that are most likely to be picked up in appreciable numbers each spring under the mistaken assumption that they have been abandoned by their mothers (see Chapter 9).

Even though there are only two species of deer (Red and Roe) truly indigenous to Britain, the Fallow has long been established as part of our fauna. All of these, when adult, are actually easily distinguished. Three more recent introductions are less easy, but it is sufficient initially to recognise all as 'deer'. The first and most successful of the Asiatic newcomers was the Sika deer last century. Although well scattered over Britain, it stays very much in pockets and is consequently to a certain extent self-limiting. The New Forest and Wareham groups, for example, have never joined up; nor have the Yorkshire, Cumbrian and Mull of Kintyre groups. The only places where the Sika deer seems to be extending its range is in Invernessshire and Ireland. The Muntjac or Barking deer is also fairly comfortably established, yet still more thinly, following its introduction early this century by the 11th Duke of Bedford in his estate at Woburn in Bedfordshire. In the 1940s, some Chinese Water deer were also released or escaped; this species appears to have done least well of the three, has spread less far from the Midlands and is seldom seen even where relatively numerous.

31

Fig 2 Outlines of deer showing antlers and relative sizes. Months in parentheses are dates of shedding (where applicable). Top (*left to right*): Red deer (February–March); Fallow deer (April–May); Roe deer (November–December). Bottom (*left to right*): Sika deer (April); Chinese Water deer; Muntjac

As shown in Fig 2, the size of deer and the form of the males' antlers vary considerably. Of whatever species, they prefer to inhabit woodland, sometimes more open spaces but always with cover nearby. The grand Red deer has taken to high moorland in Scotland, Exmoor and elsewhere with feeding excursions to low ground from winter until early summer as it seeks to avoid man. Many have now got into the large Forestry Commission plantations where they stay permanently, reverting to a more natural existence. All adult deer present very real dangers to handlers (see Chapter 3) and problems of management due to their temperament though not their diet.

Of similar size and distribution but typically preferring more open country, the 'wild' ponies of Dartmoor, Exmoor, the New Forest, the Lake District, the Welsh uplands, the Northumbrian fells etc are possibly *pro rata* the most susceptible of all animals to road accidents. Familiarity with humans makes them tame and the foolishness, not to mention the illegality in National Parks, of roadside feeding acts as an irresistible lure during the summer when traffic at such beauty spots is at its heaviest. It is important to remember that these ponies are not wild but the responsibility of their owners, even though much cruelty and misery is caused by irresponsible ones.

That really is the score for large mammals in Britain, and we can see

Plate 1 Waterfowl, and swans in particular, are very susceptible to the poisoning of water-systems, contamination by lead-weights, and discarded fishing-tackle. This Mute swan starved to death; fishing-line can be seen at the base of the bottom mandible *(Paul Scheller/Swan Rescue Service)*

Plate 2 An adult Badger bites the tarmac early one damp and dismal winter morning; the car driver drove on, leaving her mortally wounded. Bleeding from the nostrils and mouth indicates severe internal damage *(Geoff Nute)*

Plate 3 A farmer marks his territory *(author)*

Plate 4 Death for sale: a chemical arsenal for the private gardener *(author)*

that there are few problems in their essential identification. The Badger and Fox are hardly large by mammalian standards though on the reduced scale of British fauna they seem so. But although they are actually only medium sized, the Badger is immensely powerful and on no account should be trifled with. The Fox is more wiry, but it too has useful teeth and can inflict a nasty bite.

Both occur coast to coast – commonly in suitable areas. I know of a dozen Badger sets near my home and there are no doubt more. Broadly speaking, the Badger prefers wooded country near to arable land and water; the Fox is much less choosy and although it may prefer more open country to hunt over, its presence increasingly in urban areas, where it has discovered an easy existence exploiting man's wasteful habits, is now well known. Since both are largely nocturnal or crepuscular and shy and retiring, they are most often seen as road victims. One- and two-year old Badgers are vulnerable to attack from other Badgers, and especially vulnerable to road traffic when forced to seek new territories. It is estimated that at least half of all those born never make it to three years of age, thereafter, though, survival prospects are good.

Medium-small mammals tend to be carnivorous because that size-range allows the fundamental combination necessary to most lone predators: sufficient speed and agility to catch an active prey with size and strength enough to dominate and kill it. By this criterion, the larger varieties, like the Badger and Fox, have to eke out animal protein with whatever else they can get – to such an extent that they should really be regarded as indiscriminating omnivores – and are robust and manageable in captivity. The smaller we go, the more problems we are likely to encounter, both in essential identification and treatment.

The smaller the predator, the more it compensates with pugnacity and specialised habits: its behavioural options are fewer and it is more likely to flee or attack. If retreat is denied, either through injury or being cornered, there is only one course left to pursue. This 'highly-strung' condition is also bound to complicate their acceptance of captivity and its conditions.

Excepting the appropriately named Scottish Wild cat, Britain is sadly bereft of respectably sized out-and-out terrestrial carnivores, and the Wild cat itself is an even more infrequent apparition these days than the Otter which, though highly aquatic, is its only rival. The latter presumably presents no great problem of identification but as its

Fig 3 Scottish Wild cat, showing characteristic tail

numbers are decreasing almost everywhere due to human encroach-
ment, general disturbance and pollution, its chances of being seen in
any condition are remote. It was never a common sight: many
countrypeople have never seen one despite many years of looking; and
only on some remote stretches of the Wester Ross and Irish coasts can
one be confident of a sighting.

The Otter is a strange 'fish' indeed – it is virtually unique in being
as much at home in water as on dry land. This versatility eases captive
maintenance since it will accept almost any kind of flesh; however,
with the possible exception of the Badger, I can think of no other
animal that I might be expected to, but would less like to get grips
with. It has the strongest yet most supple and sinewy frame imagin-
able and a terrible array of teeth backed up by immensely strong jaws.
It is the ultimate hunter killer and its decline across the European
continent is nothing short of tragic and scandalous.

The true Wild cat, when it comes to recognition, possibly has as
much difficulty in distinguishing between its own kind and the feral
tabby as we do (Fig 3), or maybe it just doesn't care. With the
consequent reduction in purity, many of today's so-called wild cats
represent a jumble of genes – both wild and domesticated. One has to
go to the remotest parts of Scotland to reach true Wild cat country,
and even then a sighting is far from likely. It is an animal that since
early childhood has fascinated me more than any other, and it has
taken several excursions far from human influence and long periods of
solitary watching at dusk and dawn to catch so much as a few glimpses

of this remarkable, solitary, wary and ferocious killer. Few Scottish readers will have the doubtful privilege of getting to grips with a Wild cat: 'doubtful' because if any animal can be said to be virtually untameable it is this one, even hand-reared kittens generally remaining intractable and highly suspicious. Sadly, the only humans likely to come into contact with it are gamekeepers and shepherds who, though attitudes are slowly changing, seem not to ask questions at all before or after despatching such 'vermin'.

This, then, is Britain's unhappy selection of 'large' land-based predatory mammals. Mustelids smaller than the Badger – the Stoat, Weasel, Pine marten, Polecat and Mink – form a much more impressive cross-section of wide distribution. The first two are the most likely to be seen, either scurrying across a road (occasionally though not commonly found there as a victim) or hunting along a hedge or bank.

Since escapes began to occur regularly in the 1930s, the American Mink has found the British Isles to its liking; but it favours a waterside home – its principal food is fish – and is by no means the threat to the countryside that its detractors would have us believe. Like any other predator, its numbers are pretty much self-determining and are not about to swamp all prey fauna. Many are trapped and killed by unyielding countrypeople who may well, at times, have cause to view askance this successful little predator. It is a shame, though, that anything thought of as out-of-control appears as a thrown gauntlet to so many; whether it is an area of scrubland or watermeadow ('wasteland'), an unkempt stretch of hedge or ramshackled old barn ('untidy'), ivy or a magnificent splash of Dandelions ('weeds') or the Woodpigeon and Rook ('pests').

If the Mink is unlikely to intrude into the average person's life, the rare Pine marten certainly will not as it keeps to comparatively few areas of remote woodland and hillside chiefly in the Scottish Highlands; some still managing to hang on in north-west England, Wales and Ireland. The Polecat is of similar occurrence although crosses known as 'polecat-ferrets' are widely recorded and are the most likely mustelid to be seen near human rural habitation.

In a manner of speaking, the insectivores are carnivores too though the prospects of specialist insect-eaters in captivity are as dodgy as those of most of their bird counterparts – hirundines, warblers etc. Bats, despite belonging to their own order (Chiroptera = 'winghanded') are actually more strictly insectivorous than many members

Fig 4 Outlines *(left to right)* of shrew, mouse and vole, with the Dormouse below (to scale)

of the Insectivora. Typical mammalian insectivores are the Hedgehog, Mole, shrews and, by our definition, the bats – at least the British representatives.

Insectivores are characterised by their simple sharply pointed teeth and are easily told; even the shrews, which can be confused with small rodents (Fig 4), are readily identified by their medium tails, their sensitive, mobile, pointed snouts and their almost invisible ears. Problems of caring for the smallest insectivores concern mostly the suitability, quantity and presentation of their nutrition and the already mentioned nervousness. Specific identification of bats and shrews for our purposes is frankly pointless (at this stage). Of the four shrews present in Britain the most likely to be encountered is the Common followed by the Pygmy. Shrews usually see only one winter, as immatures, breeding and dying the following year. Since they seem to come 'up to the surface' to die, unlike rodents, and are unpalatable, large numbers of corpses are quite a common sight in the autumn. The little Pipistrelle is the commonest of fifteen British bat species. The Long-eared bat gathers non-flying food from foliage and branches and would, therefore, be more likely to take suitable food from a raised dish.

Difficulties can occur in splitting the two main families of terrestrial small rodents: mice (Muridae) and voles (Microtidae). Voles are most easily differentiated by their small eyes, short tails and blunt muzzles (Fig 4). Although appreciably different, members of both families will consider varying their basically vegetarian diet with animal protein and are much more manageable than the volatile predators. Of variable occurrence and habitat, there are five species each of mice and voles in Britain. Needless to say, the House mouse is best known although the Yellow-necked fieldmouse also enters dwellings in

38

southern England and Wales; the Wood or Field mouse is of nationwide distribution. Happily, the Harvest mouse though seldom seen is thought not to be so rare as hitherto feared. Three species of voles are also widespread: the Short-tailed, Bank and Water voles. The Water vole can be twice the size of the other two – with a body length of up to 220mm (8¼in); it is slightly larger than the Ground vole and appears to have driven this species north to Scotland. The remaining species is the Common vole but is only so on the continent – occurring in the UK as a relict form on some islands. The Dormouse (Fig 4) (Gliridae) hibernates from late October to April in a range thinly spread and probably retreating. Dormice are almost exclusively nocturnal, much more so than even the Muridae.

Considerably larger and squirrel-like with its bushy tail is the Edible dormouse introduced by Lord Rothschild at the turn of the century and now comfortably ensconced in the Chiltern countryside around Tring. It is perhaps best distinguished from squirrels by its larger, more lustrous eyes. Deciduous woodland is its natural haunt in warmer latitudes; in England it takes advantage of buildings, especially their lofts, where it is likely to betray its presence by making noises which have been likened to those one might expect from 'a small herd of tiny elephants'.

Before turning our attention to the true squirrels and those other medium-sized rodents, the rats, whose history tends to damn all introductions, we must first consider the Coypu: an even larger though less significant rodent newcomer, this time to East Anglia where it thrives and yet is still more or less confined. It undoubtedly does come into conflict with man, causing serious damage to crops, riverbanks and the indigenous flora. It is an official pest and the subject of an extermination programme, expected to be completed by the end of the decade.

Whatever the pros and cons of the Coypu, no one takes pity on a rat (though plenty do on the House mouse) and they certainly do not need it. Rats not only live off man but are a significant and sometimes deadly threat; they are in direct competition and, let it be said, far from losing the battle. As G. I. Twigg (1980) put it: 'In terms of parasites which seriously affect man and his domesticated animals, the rat carries more dangerous pathogenic organisms than does any other species.' The Black rat, confined in Britain to a few mainly dockyard areas, is far less common than the Brown rat which is increasingly becoming known as the Common rat, and is widespread in city, town and country. To quote Twigg again: 'There is no doubt that the introduction of the Brown rat to the British Isles markedly increased the range of human and domestic animal pathogens.' D. M. Jones in a lecture in 1978 (see References and Further Reading) said: 'Rodents are a major source of disease communicable to man. Lymphocytic choriomeningitis and Listeriosis are less commonly encountered but Weils disease or Leptospiral jaundice is a frequent problem where there is regular contact with rat urine.'

Their anti-social propensities apart (anti-social that is to human society) or possibly because of them, rats are fascinating creatures and worthy of intensive study. But it is not surprising or unhealthy that we dread a deadly threat. An injured rat is a dangerous but, thankfully, highly improbable customer and one to be given a wide berth, except under very special circumstances.

It is perhaps no coincidence that rats and squirrels come to be rubbing shoulders here if little in actuality. Much to foresters' chagrin, a squirrel – even the introduced and invading North American Grey – presents an attractive and popular image; to the forestry worker, on account of the damage it can do to growing trees, it is little better than an arboreal rat with a bushy tail. Moreover, in its successful colonisation of Britain, despite man's concerted efforts to the contrary, the Grey squirrel could almost be said to rival the Brown rat, although it presents no health hazard. And similarly under The Destructive Imported Animals Act 1932 (Grey Squirrels Order 1937) it is, despite my bad example below, illegal to keep or release specimens except under licence.

Altogether more enchanting and less troublesome, the native Red squirrel is a quite different proposition, but sadly due to disease and the usurping expansion of the Grey it occurs in relatively few of its former coniferous haunts. A dark morph, which could be mistaken at a glance for the Grey squirrel, occurs more in deciduous woodland (as does the Grey) than does the typical red form. Seen clearly, the more petit Red squirrel should not be confused with the Grey (Fig 5).

Fig 5 Grey squirrel (*left*) and Red squirrel (*right*)

Rats and squirrels differ chiefly in their diet and habits. The former are gregarious, opportunistic, firmly omnivorous and no mean predators; the squirrels follow a more conventional rodent line, feeding principally on nuts and seeds, fruits and berries apart from the browsing which alienates foresters. Some Grey squirrels have a carnivorous bent, eggs and young birds being particularly favoured.

One of the best things that can be said for the rat is that it represents useful protein to several predators, both mammalian and avian, with much need for it. And, as already intimated, it is very unusual to see one save in a very live or very dead condition. Squirrels are less valuable as prey species due mainly to their more specialised habits and skilled tree-climbing. Some, however, are caught by mustelids, the Fox and Wild cat; and it is possible that domesticated distant relatives of the last two catch one occasionally – a lurcher I knew specialised in catching Grey squirrels as her mistress rode out hunters. But it is unlikely, given the squirrel's strength and pugnacity, that one so caught would ever be recovered in a viable condition. It is the creature that lies passively that is least likely to be harmed by a playful and well-fed captor.

Baby squirrels are more likely to be recovered in a sound state and quite often are when trees housing their dreys are felled. Several years ago, when I was climbing a tree to investigate an irresistible hole, a half-grown Grey squirrel in fact issued from the hole and scampered round to the blind side of the tree. Not wishing to cause further alarm, and my curiosity being satisfied, I descended to the ground and awaited developments. Soon the youngster reappeared in that nervous staccato manner typical of all squirrels, and promptly lost its grip to land at my feet. As I picked it up and felt it snuggle into the warmth of my hand, connotations with vermin didn't enter into it. Here was an opportunity to study the beast.

He was reasonably enough named 'Humpty', and reared without difficulty on weakened milk, mashed fruit and baby cereal. Humpty proved a good companion, riding on my shoulder, in a pocket or inside my shirt. The animal collection in Buckinghamshire where I then worked had a Land Rover and on local trips Humpty would spring to the top of the steering-wheel and sit gazing out of the windscreen, the movement of the wheel even when cornering sharply or manoeuvring not bothering him in the least. He could not be dislodged this way, and was able to maintain effortlessly his position at the summit. On one long journey to Wales, he alternated between his position on the wheel and naps in my lap – climbing up and down as the fancy took him. When he could not accompany me away from the vehicle, he would happily remain in the cab where he could gather an audience by perching on the wheel and flicking his tail provocatively, and then entertain it by frantic high-speed circuits of the seats, windows and ceiling interspersed with periods of wistful contemplation.

As he grew older and more serious he reverted to type, and I found I could take him with me less often. After sustaining some nasty bites on my hands I decided to rehabilitate him back to the wild, which was accomplished easily enough. Thereafter, for a while, if I went to the wood where I had found and released him, and called his name, he would reappear on a branch and peer down curiously at me. Later still, there was always one squirrel in the wood tamer than all the others, but I could never have approached him again.

Mention of bites calls to mind the formidable chisel-like teeth of rodents, constantly honed by virtue of tough enamel on just the outer side. And all, save the absurdly well-mannered Dormouse, do not hesitate to bite if handled unwisely.

Once classed as rodents but now established in an order of their own, Lagomorpha, the Rabbit and two species of British hares will also bite strongly while the sharp claws on their powerful hind limbs can cause painful scratches (see Chapter 3). Hares are represented across the British Isles by the Brown or Common hare but its numbers are declining alarmingly due mainly to modern farming practices; in the mountains of the north, and Ireland, it is replaced by the Blue or Mountain hare which has the famous white winter coat. The Rabbit – that common tenant of agricultural land, as was once the hare – is distinguished by its shorter ears which lack the black tips which hares' ears always have. Hares are also longer-limbed and have an altogether more rangy appearance, but except for pronounced differences in development at birth – a blind, naked, helpless baby is always a Rabbit because leverets are born in a comparatively advanced state and are soon independent – there are few effective distinguishing features (see Chapter 9).

Those special marine mammals, the whales and seals, remain to be considered. Only two species of seals frequent British waters (Fig 6): the Common or Harbour seal seeks sandy, gently shelving coastal areas and river estuaries, notably around Scotland and Ireland; the Grey or Atlantic seal on the other hand reveals a preference for more

Fig 6 Note the concave profile of the Common seal's snout *(left)*, compared to the convex profile of the Grey seal *(right)*. Seals seen 'bottling' like this appear dark and shiny

exposed, precipitous and rocky coastlines. The Grey seal moves the easier of the two on dry land.

Whales and their smaller cousins, the dolphins and porpoises, come ashore only when in trouble or accidentally; whereafter they rapidly get into trouble. Fortunately, it is not a frequent occurrence. As a child growing up near the north Wales coast, and with an awakening interest in these gentle and paradoxical warm-blooded, sea-dwelling, air-breathing creatures, I explored the tideline assiduously yet did not find one dead or alive until much later.

There may be forty British strandings in an average year – really very few. Usually the animals are already dead when one finds or hears of them; if not, they attract so much interest nowadays that the local RSPCA, police or coastguard, museum, Ministry, university or some other such official body has already been summoned. Their classification as 'royal fish' requires their notification anyway, and the British Museum (Natural History) keeps a record of all strandings.

Fig 7 False killer whale *(above)* and Pilot whale or Blackfish *(below)*. These two species of dolphin, mostly black in colour, occasionally strand in large numbers

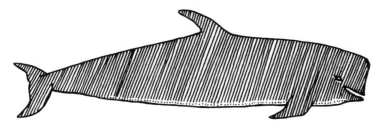

It is useful to know that significant differences exist between the giant baleen whales (Mystacoceti) which feed by filtering microscopic plankton – surely the ultimate zoological paradox – through plates of fringed baleen (whalebone) suspended from the roof of the mouth and the smaller fish-catching toothed whales (Odontoceti). Including the dolphins and porpoises at the smaller end, these progress up to the huge Sperm whale, one of several transitional species, at about 20m (22yd) long.

The Pilot whale or Blackfish (Fig 7) – a variably sized but always large completely black dolphin – is the one which mysteriously seems to want to drive ashore quite regularly in entire schools. The False killer is another; this whale is the same shape as the well-known Killer whale but lacks its characteristic white markings and is smaller at about 5m (5½yd) long. All these three are closely related, in the subfamily *Orcinae*. The limited assistance available to beached whales is mentioned in the next chapter.

Birds

Apart from bats, which significantly are much more successful *as a family* than generally appreciated, birds compared to mammals present a far more complex and efficient capability. And there is no doubting the benefits, now that our domination of the planet has put them to the test, of their super-mobility, their rapid life-cycles with quick maturity often enabling more than one brood per year, and their general opportunism which enables them to exploit fully all those options bestowed by the blessing of flight.

It is no coincidence that the birds with the most problems today are the flightless and more specialised ones. For instance although some birds-of-prey are benefiting now from more enlightened attitudes and pollution control, only the Kestrel can be said to represent more than a patch on its former status. The Dartford warbler, Nightjar, Wryneck, Chough, Great bustard, Corncrake, Bittern and Puffin are among the British birds which have found the going tough in the twentieth century, especially if on the edge of continental ranges.

The commonest British birds are vigorous by contrast, for example the Chaffinch, Starling, Wren (surprisingly, perhaps, at peak numbers Britain's commonest bird), House sparrow (compared to the much less robust Tree sparrow), Dunnock, Blackbird and the other utilitarian thrushes, most of the titmice (though not the specialised

Crested tit), the gulls (though not the gentle Kittiwake – much more a *sea*gull than any other), Fulmar petrel, the crows (including the Magpie but not the above-mentioned Chough), and the Woodpigeon and Collared dove (though not the little Turtle dove).

During some twelve years spent working with a wide variety of different sorts of animals from many parts of the world, the one thing that impressed me over and over again was the fundamentally omnivorous disposition of most. Stomach analysis of wild specimens confirms this, as does even modest fieldwork. Wild animals can no more afford to be finicky about their food than can the majority of the world's human population. Those which have no choice but to be selective because their very existence depends only on exploiting some offbeat ecological niche are less dynamic and more vulnerable to environmental instability. It is these peripheral species which feel the wind of change most acutely, and which find it more difficult to adapt to captivity. Specialisation has so refined their outlook that they simply may not see opportunities when they do present themselves – such as in captivity. In the avian world, therefore, we must learn to differentiate between the specialists and the non-specialists when designing a captive programme.

Beak design is a crucial clue for it, more than any other feature of a bird's anatomy, provides evidence of its ecological position and diet. There is a sort of universal beak possessed with slight alterations by a wide cross-section of birds: its essential qualities combine strength with versatility, and sensitivity with, of course, a business tip. Divergence from this standard implies specialisation; it would be nice

Fig 8 Dipper (cf **f** Robin in *Fig 9*)

Fig 9 Adaptive radiation of beaks: **A** Rook; **b** Song thrush; **c** Great tit; **d** Green woodpecker; **e** Pied wagtail; **f** Robin; **g** Dunnock; **h** Treecreeper; **i** Blackcap (warbler); **j** House martin; **k** Pied flycatcher; **l** Nightjar; **m** Moorhen; **n** Oystercatcher; **o** Woodpigeon; **p** Goldfinch; **q** Pheasant; **r** Canada goose; **s** Herring gull; **t** Razorbill; **u** Kingfisher; **v** Grey heron; **w** Red-breasted merganser; **x** Peregrine (falcon)

to argue that the greater the divergence the greater the specialisation, but this is only broadly true. For example, a bird as specialised as, say, the Dipper (Fig 8) has a beak that could conceivably be mistaken for that of a small thrush. It can also happen that two utterly different bird-types have, coincidentally, similar mandible shapes: for example, the divers and woodpeckers. And it is not unusual for two or more groups feeding on much the same kind of food to obtain it in very different ways or from very different habitats. For instance, a wader

46

with a long mud-probing bill (straight, decurved or up-tilted) seeks similar food to the shorter-billed plover which feeds on alluvion or damp meadows rather than mudflats. In this way, thematic bill variation ('adaptive radiation') helps to prevent intra-family competition. So while bill or beak design is not sufficient on its own, it may help us to understand this categorisation of birds if we look at the fundamental shapes shown in Fig 9, and briefly describe their function.

Radiating out from the universal omnivore beak of the thrushes, crows, rails etc there are the precision implements of a wide range of confirmed insectivores like the Dunnock, warblers, wagtails, chats and Treecreeper; the airborne insect-gatherers such as the Swift, hirundines (see also Fig 13), Nightjar and flycatchers (which have short rictal bristles around the gape to help them collect their prey); and the more versatile though still delicate seed- and insect-gleaning apparatus of the titmice. Delicate and sensitive on a quite different scale are the various probes of the waders (see above).

Sharply pointed and much more rigid, the weapons of the fish- and amphibian-catching herons, cranes, grebes, divers, kingfishers, terns and so on, combine the attributes of dagger and pincers. Variations for other piscivorous techniques are displayed by the gulls (reflecting their omnivorous tendencies), cormorants, auks and sawbilled ducks. Also heavily built, the woodpeckers' and nuthatches' beaks are often referred to as 'chisel-like' though this is much better suited to describing rodents' teeth; 'pick-like' is more analogous to these battering birds. Extremely stout, short and strong, the standard finch beak is designed for gathering and opening seeds etc, but note specialised extremes like the Crossbill's fircone device. The doves and pigeons also gather seeds but they swallow them whole and, therefore, require only a gleaning tool. Likewise the gamebirds; but their beaks are more robust and chicken-like, reflecting their rooting and grub-

Fig 10 Bird-of-prey beak (*left*) compared to shrike (*right*)

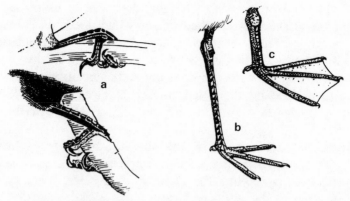

Fig 11 Perching feet (a), compared to a running/walking foot (b) and a swimming foot (c). Note the development of hind toes

bing habits. The spatulate bill characteristic of many ducks, and used for sifting and sieving mud and filtering water (hence 'dabbling-duck') is adapted for differing functions as in the marine ducks, and in the various grazing and browsing waterfowl like the shelducks, geese and swans.

The truly carnivorous birds (Fig 10) have a cruelly hooked beak used for both killing and rending down though not usually the actual capture. This is achieved by the talons, which are the true weapons, and are refined to a piercing degree of efficiency with consummate gripping, and very often killing, potential – as can be confirmed by anyone who has attempted to handle one carelessly.

Concomitantly with beak structure then, we are also on the lookout for other clues. While the feet of raptors represent a deadly extreme of grip, we might regard the ordinary passerine or perching foot and leg as standard, and compare its average tarsal length and sinewy mobile toes (Fig 11a) able to grip firmly thanks to an opposable hind digit – completed by serviceable claws, with the equipment of running and wading birds (Fig 11b). We can see from a glance at the weaker profile and particularly the hind toe – which can be higher, smaller or even absent altogether – and small claws, that they have a different job to do.

On the other hand, extreme tarsal shortness, almost to an extent suggesting complete atrophy, firmly indicates lack of use and must mean a bird like the Swift. Here all four toes are directed forward (Fig 12) and the claws are all-important, ruling out any kind of terrestrial locomotion. Such an airwards orientated creature must inevitably be

48

Fig 12 Foot of the Swift, with all four toes pointing forward (*left*)
Fig 13 Broad-based beak of the Swallow (*right*)

largely, if not exclusively, dependent on airborne insects, as is confirmed by the broad-based, wide-gaped beak (Fig 13) which enables it to virtually vacuum up or dredge-in all its needs. However, the Swift, Swallow and martins – all summer visitors to Britain – can suffer badly when prevented from feeding for more than a day or two by rainy weather. Swifts can be literally beaten to the ground by a storm, whence they cannot take off unaided even were they to survive long enough for their plumage to dry out.

Birds designed for wet conditions often have webbing between the toes (Fig 11c). It may be complete as in the cormorants; complete between three toes as in waterfowl, auks and a few swimming waders like the Avocet; or reduced as in the phalaropes. In the absence of webbing, toes which are elongated as in the Moorhen and rails, or lobed as in the Coot, also indicate a watery or marshy environment.

The feet and legs of habitually terrestrial birds are, as one might expect, plain, sturdy and well-developed – more like a hiker's than a fashion model's. There is no mistaking the scratching, stamping foot of a pheasant or fowl for that of any bird other than one with its feet firmly on the ground; and if we relate to it the hen-like rooting beak (Fig 9), we are well on the way to understanding the bird itself. Even the smaller quails and partridges have, in proportion, the same equipment.

Tail and wing structure tell us yet more about the owner's lifestyle. Most non-specialist flying birds have tails based on the standard passerine type – not too broad, short or long. Extreme length or

Fig 14 The Swallow in flight; terns (cf *Fig 15*) give a similar appearance, due to convergence, and are sometimes known as 'sea-swallows'

ornamentation is likely to be evidence of male courtship behaviour; but a forked tail (Fig 14) can give fast-flying species, which normally have very short tails, extra control such as would be required by hawkers of insects.

High air speed or streamlining is achieved in birds by flat, long, sweptback wings, which cause minimal drag, and the absence of 'wing-slots' – the spaces made at the extremities of the wings by the fanned-out primaries. These give enormous lift and thrust to game-birds and others which require great acceleration and speed over short distances, and yet which need short broad wings due to environmental considerations, ie living in woodland. Generally, the broader the surfaces of the wings and tail, the more manoeuvrable the bird can be. These features reach perfection in bush-hawks like the Sparrowhawk and Goshawk which, unlike the gamebirds, can superbly combine high sustainable speed, manoeuvrability and, for example in the Buzzard, great soaring ability.

Specialist *slow* flyers like the owls have long broad wings with a convex upper surface. In long-winged birds it is instructive to note the form the elongation takes. For instance, gliding specialists like the Fulmar petrel (the albatrosses are the supreme example) have a lengthened humerus and shortened manus (Fig 15) while the opposite applies in aerobatic species like the terns and Swift which require long primary feathers.

To compare intra-family types, the Rook is a great aerobat with its broad tail and wings, the effective length of which is greatly increased by deep wing-slots, while the woodland Jay has short broad wings and

50

Plate 5 and 5a (inset) Red fox restrained by a dog-grasper prior to safe scruff immobilisation (*Phil Hunt*)

Plate 6 Holding a small biting mammal by the scruff; in this case, an Edible dormouse (*Les Stocker/The Wildlife Hospitals Trust*)

Plate 7 Grey seal pups have substantial dental equipment and must be handled with care – at the rear end with gloved hands *(Cornish Seal Sanctuary/Richards Bros)*

Plate 8 Vixen caught in a gin trap (outlawed since 1954) with paw almost severed. She died after several days of struggle when she became tangled in a fence. Gin-traps are still used frequently by some callous country people *(Ray Bishop)*

Fig 15 Wing and tail figuration of the Fulmar (*top*) and tern (see also *Fig 14*)

a conventional tail. Even though the 'jizz' of a bird-of-prey can only rarely be confused with anything else, the long tapered wings and narrow tail of the falcons (in ordinary flight) is in direct contrast to those of the bush-hawks. To sum up so far: if we take the wings and food-gathering equipment of a typical hirundine like the Swallow, and set them alongside its delicacy of build, atrophied legs – yet with well-developed toes and claws – there is little else it could be. The basically short tail, which manages to gain the best of both worlds by the forking modification, reinforces our assessment.

Extremely short and stumpy tails have little mechanical use, and they tend to denote a ground, scrub or aquatic bird. For example, crakes, rails, all diving birds – with the exception of the cormorants which use their long stiff tails as rudders, and their feet more than their wings for propulsion – and the Wren and Dipper would find a conventional tail a positive disadvantage. A long heavy tail would be as much a liability in flight, and the presence of one *all the year round* (disregarding seasonal nuptial plumage) suggests a sedentary bird. Ground birds with long tails, like the pheasants, carry them raised to prevent soiling in the same manner as long-tailed perching birds (eg the Magpie) when they visit the ground in search of food. But there is one 'group' of birds to which a short, stiff tail in the form of a balancing organ – in this case, a prop – is indispensable. I refer, of course, to the trunk-climbing group: the woodpeckers and treecreepers, though not the nuthatches.

Convergent evolution (Figs 10, 14, 15, 17) is said to occur when two or more quite separate and distinct groups of animals evolve to resemble one another due to the selective forces of equivalent existences. In a sense it completes the circle begun by 'adaptive radiation', and is most useful as back-up evidence. I inferred before that a bird-of-prey could not be mistaken for anything else; this is not strictly true unless we unhyphenate the noun (which, otherwise, limits it to a member of the order Falconiformes) and address ourselves to a more poetic birdlover or a naturalist not hidebound by nomenclature. This applies on two levels: on one, and quite unconnected with convergence though there may be vague behavioural similarities, the Cuckoo mimics the falcon or hawk to enhance its own success rate, ie to alarm potential hosts to its young. And what is a Cuckoo if not a bird of prey? I have also mistaken the pantropical tree ducks in flight for owls but that is another story – much more the result of chance. Owls, of course, are birds of prey too but they compose a quite separate order (Strigiformes) and are not hyphenated in polite company without qualification, ie 'nocturnal birds-of-prey'; this despite the fact that by no means are all nocturnal. The introduced Little owl and very often the Short-eared owl are positively diurnal.

There is a cost in being a recognisable baddie: many birds mistakenly perceive the Cuckoo as a threat and mob it mercilessly; however, a quick glance at its beak (Figs 10, 16) would immediately

Fig 16 Profile of the Cuckoo

Fig 17 Silhouettes *(left to right)* of Swift, martin, Nightjar and falcon

reveal an impostor to the finder of an injured one. Not so – on the
second level – with the passerine shrikes which have converged with
hawks not only in appearance – strongly hooked beaks (Fig 10),
longish broad tails and broad rounded wings – but also in behaviour,
flight and diet. Shrikes are scarce summer migrants to southern and
eastern England. In the unlikely event of one being found injured,
treatment as for a small hawk would be more or less correct; and this
could be deduced, using the sort of detective work I have outlined, by
someone who has never heard of a shrike.

Another remarkable example of convergent evolution, capable of
confusing a novice systematist but leaping to our aid in understanding
the animal, affects the hirundines (Passeriformes), the swifts (Apodi-
formes) and, this time, the nightjars (Caprimuliformes) (Figs 9, 17) as
well: a convergence born of their superb adaptations for the 'hawking'
of airborne insects.

Confronted by an unknown bird of uncertain dietary tendencies –
even using the above guidelines and in the absence of a fieldguide –
there is more information to consider: finding place (locality, habitat
etc); time of year (summer or winter visitor or passage migrant?);
nature of injury (eg a gunshot wound *might* indicate a 'pest' or
'sporting-bird'); whether there is a zoo or bird collection near by
which might indicate an escapee. Of these, location is obviously highly
significant even though nature plays tricks with passage migrants and,
yet more baffling, 'wrecks' – ie birds blown off course by strong
winds, a spasmodic phenomenon affecting, or most often noticed
with, seabirds carried inland. One winter while I worked at The
Wildfowl Trust near Peterborough, both a Little auk and a Manx
shearwater were recovered from Huntingdon after a severe storm; the
latter from the main street where it caused considerable bewilder-
ment. Petrels are also frequent casualties of this sort. Such wrecks are

inevitably exhausted, but usually after a few days feeding-up in peace and quiet are ready for release on a suitable stretch of coastline. Wrecks, migrants and escapees apart, the habitat in or near which a bird is found should yield useful information regarding its behaviour, diet and requirements.

Cold-blooded Fauna

Apart from preventative measures and rescue from cats, it is unlikely that you will have much opportunity to practise first aid on fauna other than mammals and birds. Fish, reptiles and amphibians may often need our help – more often than we probably realise – but the problems of actually treating these cold-blooded vertebrates are, in contradistinction, as complex as we are ignorant.

Lizards suffering attack have a bizarre but useful tail-shedding mechanism; this writhing trump card being played with the aim of distracting the predator for long enough to allow the owner to escape. I have occasionally assisted a lizard in this predicament when it was by no means certain that, in the absence of nearby cover, it would escape the second assault of the cat. But other than being taken to a safe place – some stones, a wall or bank – no medical attention is needed. Even though the lizard will never be as beautiful again, it will automatically grow another tail. A Slow-worm is sometimes found in a similar

Fig 18 Identification of the Grass snake *(top)*, Adder *(bottom)* and Slow-worm *(centre)*. A melanistic form of the Adder appears almost black

predicament, which reminds us that this creature is a legless lizard and not a snake (Fig 18).

Snakes are in need of our consideration and understanding too. Signs warning one of adders are designed to have the same effect as the large brightly coloured burglar alarms currently mushrooming on the outsides of houses and 'Beware of the Dog' notices – ie to keep people out. But for everyone's sake, including the snakes', they are best watched from a respectful distance, and they will seldom, if ever, be found in difficulties. Recognition of the two principal species is usually easy (Fig 18).

Frogs differ from toads in having a smooth as opposed to a warty skin; but amphibians, like reptiles, really ask only for some undisturbed habitat. Alas, that little word 'only' assumes vast significance for, given such undisturbed habitat, nature conservation could happily be left to nature.

3 Handling

This chapter could alternatively be entitled 'Approach and Capture' since this, in the case of dangerous and/or awkward animals, covers the initial critical phase for *both* participants; however, eventually, 'handling' affects all animals – itself a regrettable fact. There are two prime general considerations: the captor's safety, and the stress imposed on wild animals by the utterly unprecedented experience of being approached by an alien creature from which it cannot flee despite the desperate orders issued by its brain. There is no doubt that the physical act of handling is the culmination of a terrifying ordeal, and something that should be achieved successfully first time in as sympathetic and yet as firm and confident a manner as possible.

Most wild animals detest being manhandled (but see page 83): if inexpertly or roughly done it disturbs fragile integument, and must seem like the death grip of a predator. Moreover, the close proximity it represents to the one thing the animal fears above all others, would never otherwise be contemplated. Those animals which have cause and are able to recognise in man their mortal enemy, can only be approached openly when forcibly restrained in some way or when in a very serious condition for all animals, particularly prey species, must hide any disabilities for as long as possible. As a consequence, it is unlikely that a success rate of over about 20 per cent is obtainable in wild-animal veterinary treatment.

The safety of workers with wildlife is something that no regulation or factory act controls; it is an area as little understood as the animals themselves. We can only surmise what goes on in the heads of creatures with which we cannot communicate – which includes all. The history of mankind offers little convincing evidence that we can understand even our own brothers and sisters let alone relationships over genetical boundaries. Individuals of the higher species vary in their reactions to paranormal stimuli almost as much as humans do,

58

perhaps just as much, and are usually difficult to anticipate. It is best not to try but, literally, to approach each new case with as open a mind as possible: to be prepared for the unexpected and the worst, all the while endeavouring to appreciate the creature's predicament and viewpoint, and interpret its mannerisms, gestures and character.

Perhaps the first mistake, and one invariably made by the inexperienced or unthinking on seeing a small, incapacitated animal, is to rush up and sweep it off the ground. This moment on, much is lost forever particularly the chance to observe the animal exactly as rendered by its incapacity, ie its posture and manner before distressed by the terrifying ordeal that might well aggravate any physical injury or disease already present. Clearly, aggravation and even injury itself can be caused by handling; less obviously, the stress and distress imposed can precipitate a pathological condition such as coccidiosis.

Visual contact precedes the physical, but the vastly superior senses of animals compared to those of humans are liable to betray our presence through scent or sound, if not sight, long before the animals themselves are seen. I think there is little doubt that unless in imminent danger of even worse injury, the initial sequence of actions when confronted by a possible casualty should be: stop, look, listen and think. *Stop*, hopefully, before the animal is disturbed and made wary and before it has altered its position; if not, gradually withdraw out of 'flight distance' – the distance which will trigger a flight response in an animal perceiving a threat. *Look* for any peculiarity or awkwardness of posture, movement or mannerism. *Listen* for distressed respiration, involuntary sounds, thwarted predators retreating etc. *Think* about the foregoing; most importantly about whether there is any need to handle at all, for example a young animal only resting can be effectively killed if impregnated with human scent or moved from where it has been left by its parents. Before intervention, consider methods of approach, capture, restraint, transport, caging – in short, all future problems. In other than desperate circumstances, unless a positive and unqualified answer can be found for all these questions, it may be better to leave the animal alone and further assess the situation.

These considerations will be examined more thoroughly in Chapter 5, but it cannot be overstressed that any attempt to catch and restrain a wild animal causes further distress and, if bungled, severely lessen its chances of a natural recovery. An abortive first attempt, moreover, results in a forewarned and more frightened target which will be even

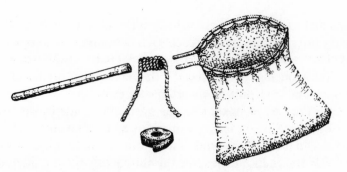

Fig 19 Construction of homemade catching net; a pillow-case may be used for the bag

more difficult to approach second time round. Adequate preparation and confident handling alone avoids the prejudicial lunge which usually ends in a handful of feathers or teeth, and an incensed animal disappearing beyond reach.

Water-birds, for instance, will prefer the devil they know – and which they have been forced to leave – to the one approaching in human guise; and if allowed to regain the water may stay there until they succumb to exhaustion or chilling. If unable to cut off this escape route, possibly by using a long-handled, wide-mouthed net (Fig 19), do not try to catch at all but maintain a watching brief. Excessive chasing is always harmful, and it is worth bearing in mind with other sorts of animals that, if they can escape you, they may recover naturally.

In the meantime, let's assume that we consider 'handling', whether direct or indirect, regrettable but necessary. With large or 'difficult' animals, there must be at hand some means of restraint allowing closer inspection plus any other equipment deemed necessary, (eg wire cutters). A plan should already have been formulated for getting the animal to a place of safety or for treatment; if the latter, make sure the essential equipment to obviate risk to life and limb of all participants is to hand. It is undoubtedly wise to expect every new case, always excepting the baffling cetaceans, to attempt to bite, kick, scratch or otherwise damage you. Never expect gratitude, always remember that, however worthy your intentions, to the victim you are an approaching enemy with evil in your eye. The eye is the mark of a predator.

Whales deserve special mention for many reasons, but particularly because of their 'humanity' and the inexcusable squalor our brand of humanity has heaped upon them. There is little the lone amateur can do to ease the distress of a beached whale clinging to life except talk to

60

it soothingly (recommended for all nervous subjects) while moistening the skin, especially about the fins and tail-fluke. Wet towels or clothes are preferable to splashing, and the animal must be shielded from the pernicious effects of direct sunshine. The blowhole is the whale's nostril and must be kept clear of water.

A healthy, small whale stranded in shallow tidal water can be eased back into deeper water by standing astride it with a knee behind each fluke; each wave as it breaks and recedes will help to take it out about six or eight feet until it can swim. With a stranded school, choose the largest animal; this may be the leader bull.

The calming effect of the soft human voice cannot be overemphasised especially when accompanied by gentle, unhurried movements, a confident friendly manner, and *never* the direct stare which, as mentioned above, to all animals (humans, except in courtship, included) is seen as premeditated aggression. After all, the voice is for communication, and we have to try with every means at our disposal to reach out over the gulf that separates us from our fellow visitors to this planet. Similarly with body language, and maybe in the same way that a smile and an open palm is understood by all cultures however remote from one another, it is perfectly reasonable to assume that even different species can comprehend a non-hostile attitude; certainly they fully recognise and understand the contrary. Perhaps already the difficulty of giving any further useful general advice about approaching, capturing and handling wildlife in all its bemusing and individualistic manifestations can be appreciated.

Size alone is not a foolproof guide to assessing possible handling hazards as anyone who has been bitten by a Budgerigar, large finch, rabbit, shrew or vole, or kicked by a little Roe deer can confirm. Any wound which breaks the skin is a potential source of infection so that handlers of wildlife, and this incidentally includes gardeners, should be protected against tetanus.

Birds

I have little hesitation in citing as the most dangerous of all birds those which use their beaks as weapons (note this excludes birds-of-prey, which have another method of attack: see page 65). The birds in question, it would seem, are mainly the fish- and amphibian-catching species. Even a medium-sized gull's beak – which may not look special – is sharp, strong and dangerous and, as with all snatching types, can be used with a speed greater than the human eye can assimilate. My nose has suffered one or two excruciatingly painful bites from gulls' beaks and there is no more effective way of learning the arm's length rule; a colleague once nearly lost an eye in the same way. The Greater black-backed gull, weighing twice as much as the Herring gull, is a formidable adversary, and should be accorded almost as much respect as the Gannet. A gull, though, however long its reach, is restricted by a short neck, and such biting birds can be easily rendered less dangerous by taping their mandibles together.

The dangers represented by a dagger-like beak aimed with unerring cold-eye accuracy and propelled by a whipcord neck are much more terrible. Apart from the Gannet and Greater black-back, the most dangerous British birds are the Heron, Bittern, Great crested grebe, Cormorant, Shag, Raven and possibly the divers. These birds will, given the slimmest opportunity, lunge for the face, probably the eyes, with a speed as deadly as evolution over the millennia has been able to devise – certainly equalling a snake strike. The 'cruel' eye of such birds ought in itself to be sufficient warning, but it is very easy to underestimate their phenomenal reach. Such a bird is most safely grabbed from behind, just below the head, after its attention has been engaged, and its fire drawn, by one's other hand. Once grasped, a cork impaled on the point of the taped mandibles makes them entirely harmless. I cannot recall ever having handled grebes and divers but I see no reason why their capabilities should be any less though their armaments seem somewhat less intimidatory. This is attested to by Peter Fitchie (1983), who affirms that a Great crested grebe can inflict as severe an injury as a Guillemot.

The poor old swan has a worse reputation than any other British bird; if some stories are to be believed, it roams the countryside looking for children, their arms to break. Slanderous of course, for however resolutely a Mute swan will legitimately defend its nest and cygnets, it will attack usually only as a last resort, and then it will likely be a display of threat rather than a followed through attack. If, in the face of such a warning, some idiot persists in interfering in a swan's affairs, he (usually it is a 'he') has only himself to blame. Unfortunately, a swan cannot distinguish between an idiot threatening its family and a well-meaning idiot trying to help it, and certainly someone intending to catch hold of a swan should be aware of the dangers, and not retaliate violently, as does happen, believe it or not, if struck.

Fig 20 Method of holding and carrying a large bird; note the legs, gripped between the fingers

All waterfowl (ducks, geese and swans) use their extremely power-ful wings as weapons. Actually, it is the hardened and calloused carpal joint – the leading, outer or wrist joint (Fig 34) – which is employed; indeed some species, though not British ones, go so far as to include on it a vicious spur. It is this joint which even in a duck can inflict quite a painful blow to a part of the body not protected by clothing or flesh, and in a swan could conceivably break an arm though a nasty bruise is more likely.

Ducks and geese should first of all be fettered by a firm hand or two over their backs and wings, pinioning them to the ground, then carried as shown in Fig 20. If approached sideways on and back-handedly as it were, the forearm can parry the head allowing the other hand to come round to do the actual pinioning. A swan, though approached in the same way, has its long neck as an additional weapon; but one which can be turned to your advantage because in hissing and attempting to bite you, the swan will extend its neck and keep it rigid. Your approaching forearm again parries the head, shields your body and enables the *same* hand to grab the neck just below the head; this is when the swan will endeavour to use its wings. However, if, in the same movement, you turn almost full circle towards the swan, keeping as close to its body as possible, so that you both are facing the same direction, your rear will protect your face and groin, and it is then simple to drop on the bird, effectively smothering its fire. Alternatively, a staff can be used to parry the head and neck, allowing you to rush in and smother the wings before they can do any damage; this method, though, brooks no hesitation.

During my days at The Wildfowl Trust, I had to catch up many

63

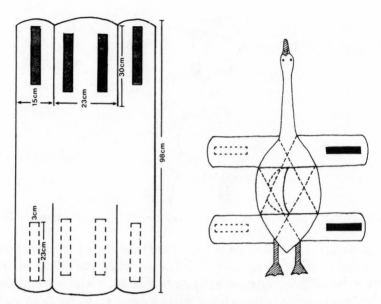

Fig 21 Swan transporting sheet (fastened with Velcro strips)

swans and can confidently say that I never received a single serious blow. Once held off the ground with its head and neck projecting between your arm and back, a swan generally does not struggle. Such a basically phlegmatic attitude also serves it well during transportation over longer distances than can be undertaken manually. A large sack with one corner cut off and placed over the head like a poncho will cause the bird actually to walk into it, whereupon the neck (of the sack!) can be secured. If injured or poisoned swans are likely to be a regular event, a 'swan jacket' made of tough plastic or polythene sheeting, canvas or similar, as devised by the Trust and shown in Fig 21, would be well worthwhile making.

A wildlife worker stands a good chance of coming into contact with vagrant birds or escapees due to their often spectacular appearance and environmental alienation. I have seen more 'wild' flamingos, for example, than I have many native British species. By our definition, among the dangerous ones are the cranes (which have been known to cause even death by stabbing through the eye into the brain), storks and exotic herons such as the Night heron and Squacco heron. Feral parrots, even budgies, are rarely encountered; but their hooked beaks can delve into flesh like a spoon into semolina.

Maybe, despite its shorter reach, the Guillemot should be included in the 'most dangerous' category, if only because it is the most likely of all to be found regularly – on the coast due to oil pollution. The Razorbill is more of a biter than a stabber, but nevertheless it can inflict severe and painful gouge-wounds. Both have a longer reach than might seem possible. The Fulmar petrel also has a useful beak but its foul-smelling secretions should be avoided too. Old clothes are always desirable when handling animals of all kinds. The smaller auks, grebes and divers are more akin to the medium to small gulls, such as the Black-headed gull. Sawbill ducks (mergansers etc) have serrated bills as their name suggests, but they do not have the jaw muscles or lunging neck sufficient to make them a threat. For the medium-sized biters, in the absence of gloves a handkerchief wrapped around the hand protects it well.

Plainly, all birds can bite. The most significant of those reluctant to do so are, of all things, the raptors including the owls, despite their fierce and sharply hooked beaks. Were they not so conditioned to fighting with their feet, the damage their beaks could do to unprotected human flesh is not difficult to imagine. Unable to fly and feeling itself cornered, a bird-of-prey rolls over onto its back and strikes out with its talons, which are as sharp as cats' claws. Having given the captive a thick cloth or towel to attack in this way, I have even been able to examine the mouths of eagles and hawks so preoccupied, and still they have not realised the potential of the formidable weapon they have literally at hand. A towel wrapped around these birds will also help to militate against the talons.

The old falconer's trick of hooding birds-of-prey can come to our assistance, particularly in their transportation; for a handkerchief placed over the head and tied snugly around the throat will keep most diurnal birds quiet indefinitely. Not so with the nocturnal owls, but in their case they may be transported loose since they will scuttle into some dark niche and remain there just as long.

However silly it may sound, I do urge all those expecting to come into contact with birds equipped with lunging beaks to acquire a stout fencing mask or else be very, very careful and take absolutely no risks. Unless you are experienced in handling dangerous birds, the old standby of a coat can be useful in handicapping a malevolent subject.

Due to their habit of lying doggo until one is almost on them and erupting startlingly, great difficulty can be had in collecting injured small birds. And rather than begin a long and frustrating game of hide-and-seek, which will undoubtedly make you and the bird wish you had never seen each other, it might be wise to take time to assess

65

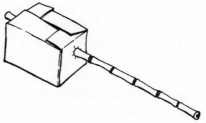

Fig 22 Makeshift box-net – made by pushing the pole through a tight hole in the cardboard box

the situation. A light cloth or shirt can expedite capture, or a makeshift box-net can be made as shown in Fig 22. A proper net can be run up quite quickly from a small-gauge garden net or pillowcase fitted on a wire coathanger formed into a circle, and many households have a fishing net of one sort or another.

Apart from the 'odd' mammal like the Dormouse and the beached porpoise, the only other warm-blooded animals either reluctant to bite or incapable of doing much damage are birds other than those already mentioned. Even a Blackbird will fasten onto a piece of flesh and tweak it vigorously, but it is unable to leave any permanent impression. The problems they present to handlers fade into insignificance, and we are able to concentrate on imposing the minimum amount of stress to the patient. However much birds detest being handled, it is my feeling that they hate much more the act of being caught, and this is the operation which needs to be carried out quickly, efficiently and with as little fuss and fluster as possible.

Small birds in cages needing to be caught up can be greatly stressed by, in the first place, being approached by a person and then, horror upon horror, having a huge hand thrust into the only refuge it has left. It goes without saying that it is an ordeal to be inflicted only when there is no alternative. Again placing in the dark helps; such birds may be picked up cleanly by a hand approaching from above and behind. Some will co-operate by cowering on the perch just as they do in the wild on seeing a bird-of-prey; others will flutter at the bars whereupon they can be quickly gathered in. Incidentally, in the experience of Peter Fitchie, the Cormorant and Shag will also cower when approached; but this does not nullify their powerful beaks when they do decide to have a go.

Once in the hand, the instinctual way in which one holds the bird is all down to knack, sensitivity, call it what you will. I have demonstrated to my own satisfaction that the same bird will lie passively in one person's hand, and yet struggle frantically when held – in apparently exactly the same way – in another's. I do not really find this surprising, and am more surprised that others do: no doubt we can all think of people whom the prospect of holding, or being held by, makes us recoil in horror, while with others we may not be able to imagine a more pleasurable way of spending our time. It is less to do with superficial beauty than an underlying spontaneity, what the Italians call *simpatico*. Disregarding one's vibes, a bird will feel more secure if held just tightly enough for it to realise there is no chance of escape: one held in too powerful a grip will panic and either be hurt or asphyxiated, while one held limply will sense the possibility of escape and endeavour to do so.

Birds while being handled must be prevented from beating their wings. Besides the risk of damage to the wings themselves (mainly bruising of the carpal joints) due to the powerful pectoral muscles, they will expend energy they can ill afford to lose, incur nervous tension, and more than likely exacerbate any existing injury. The wings must be folded comfortably in their natural resting position. Birds under or awaiting treatment can be immobilised by wrapping in a towel as recommended for birds-of-prey, or inserted in a poncho cum body-stocking of appropriate size, eg an old sock with the toe cut off, a child's pullover or the sleeve of an adult's (see also Chapter 6).

The actual grasp in which a bird is held depends utterly on its size. The smallest fit snugly into a palm and can be restrained by gentle pressure on the legs, which convinces a bird that it is not flying and therefore doesn't need to flap its wings. The largest require both hands and often an arm as well.

Most passerines of small to medium size can be satisfactorily held with the back to the palm and the head projecting between the two forefingers which should grip the neck firmly but not tightly or roughly (Fig 23). Those larger can be carried by being turned round 180° so that the tail is forward and, with the hand turned palm upward, the legs gripped between the fingers (Fig 20). This method has several advantages: the bird usually sits placidly because its head is either under or into one's arm – or in the case of a long-necked bird like a swan, projecting posteriorly – and cannot catch the glance or gaze of its captor's eye. The spare hand can be used to restrain the wings should it be necessary, or to stroke gently the nape and back, which does seem to have a calming influence. The feet of corvids are particularly strong, and the sharp claws can be painfully clamped into

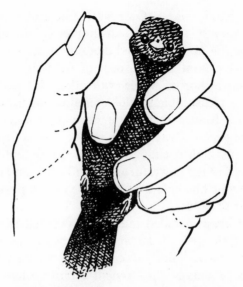

Fig 23 Method of holding a small bird securely

exposed flesh, and this method also reduces the risk of being bitten. The grazing mandibles of a goose are sharp and hard and well capable of inflicting painful bites to the inside of the thigh as one lifts or examines them. Other waterfowl will hang onto exposed flesh too, and swans given the chance may well lunge for the face. The way in which most people naturally endeavour to hold a bird – gripping it firmly around the body and wings with both hands and facing forwards – although not wrong is only really convenient for large birds being lifted or under examination.

Mammals

These present a far more versatile and unpredictable threat. Not being nearly so prone to resignation as birds, most will try every possible avenue of counter-attack and evasion before, if ever, accepting the situation – biting, snapping, scratching, kicking, clawing, butting, squirming and so on in just the same way as you or I when in mortal terror. Even the tail, so tempting as a 'handle', is not to be relied on because many small to medium mammals are able when suspended by the tail to climb up it and administer the *coup de grâce* with their teeth. By its strength and extreme suppleness, even an animal the size of an otter can overcome its weight to achieve this, its or your end – as I

68

Plate 9 The author demonstrates a technique for forcefeeding a Gannet single-handed: *(top)* with one knee gently pinioning the bird to the ground, the beak is opened with a stoutly gloved hand; *(centre)* the free hand introduces the fish (with medicament) into the oesophagus or gullet; *(bottom)* the beak is closed and the fish gently massaged down *(sequence: Mij Meyer)*

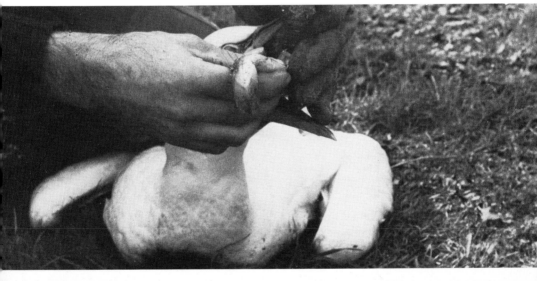

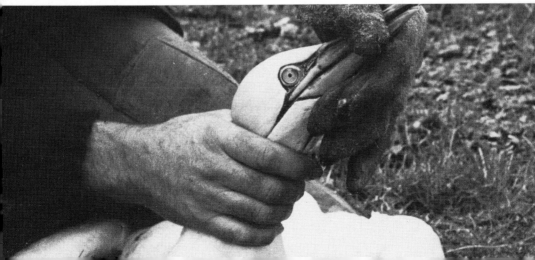

Plate 10 In controlled conditions, wirenetting can be a hazard to long bills. The upper mandible of this White-naped crane *(Grus vipio)* was successfully re-fashioned with epoxy resin on a stainless steel plate *(author)*

Plate 11 The top mandible of this Raven was ripped off by a Buzzard; it now survives admirably by swallowing whole day-old chicks *(Les Stocker/The Wildlife Hospitals Trust)*

nearly discovered once the hard way.

A large Indian Smooth otter at a zoo where I once worked escaped and I happened to see it disappearing beneath a building raised on pilework about a hundred yards away from its pen. Peering after it, I was just able to reach its tail and haul it out. So there I was, unable to do anything sensible except try to convey this heavy irate otter back to its pen at arm's length. The animal soon worked out what was going on and began slowly to do something about it. Clearly it was going to be touch and go whether I reached the enclosure before the otter's teeth reached my hand or before my arm held straight out ahead of me, and already beginning to sag, refused to suspend it any longer. By running the last twenty-five yards I just made it; had I not done so, I could easily have lost some fingers. On reflection, it was a foolish thing to do, but this is often the case in moments of crisis. In the unlikely event of having to transport the so-called Common otter, no difficulty should be experienced once it is safely within a container or sturdy hessian sack, for the ailing Otter is more likely to welcome the seclusion than resent imprisonment.

In the absence of specific information, I would not encourage an inexperienced person to pick up any mammal with an unprotected hand. The sort of maimed or helpless small mammals where this might be considered are best gripped around the neck behind the head, either between the two forefingers in much the same way as recommended for birds (Fig 23) or between the thumb and forefinger for larger subjects up to about the size of a Stoat, thus avoiding the teeth. Such advice is soon complicated when we realise that few small conscious mammals (or large ones for that matter) sit quietly about waiting to be picked up; the Dormouse seems the only one which might. Larger types, those about the size of an Edible dormouse, may be picked up by the scruff of the neck.

Far better, and causing less distress to both participants, is the early de-stimulation of the animal either by using a long-handled cloth net (Fig 19) or by dropping over it a handkerchief, headscarf, pullover, coat or something else of appropriate weight and size. Even highly olfactive animals often instantly quieten down when so enclosed. Some individuals may then be bodily picked up, others can be manoeuvred into a sling or bundle.

Unconscious animals must be approached and handled with equal caution for they may suddenly regain consciousness and snap. Do not carry them except in a secure container; it is hardly conducive to road safety to have a Polecat come round loose in the back of a car or inside a motorcyclist's leather jacket, as one was once brought to Geoff Nute. Pick the animal up, in as natural a position as possible, and place it in an appropriate or makeshift container like a cat-basket, picnic hamper or strong box. When there is no alternative, a sack tied up with cord might suffice, but endeavour to carry the casualty as flat as possible, perhaps using a rug or coat as a stretcher.

Large and potentially dangerous mammals clearly require extra caution – as my otter story showed. To begin with, let's assume the worst, and that we come upon a disabled animal when least expected and totally unprepared. To hypothesise a fairly desperate encounter, a solitary adult (children must *never* approach a cornered wild animal) on a country walk in summer finds a Badger caught in a snare. The wire has cut into the leg plainly over a period of more than twenty-four hours, flies cover the wound, and Brock is in a mean mood. Bear in mind that snares are not necessary *illegal*, although self-locking traps now are, and they do have to be visited once every day; also that, however distasteful, Badgers can be caught for various sound reasons by landowners and officials.

Assuming the worst again: foul play is suspected, and there is no help at hand nor any prospect of finding any. The immediate task is to de-stimulate the victim, relieve its distress and release the snare. Easier said than done.

Approach with care for unless the wire is snagged, the enraged animal can swing round and, as Eunice Overend (1980) graphically puts it, 'crunch through hand or foot till the bone breaks'. Try to immobilise it by pressing the wire to the ground with a forked branch. An animal as nocturnal as the Badger may not be calmed by a hood to the same extent as a diurnal one, but at least it permits the finder a certain freedom of action. A stout branch with one end stood upon or weighted down with rocks could be used to pinion the forequarters to the ground. Since, in our perversity, we have chosen summer for our drama, we have abandoned the advantages of thick anoraks, old sweaters and heavy overcoats, but it should be possible to spare some suitable item without frightening too many horses. Personally, I seldom go anywhere without my old sketching-bag, which would suffice admirably if manoeuvred over the head. Try distracting the animal by giving it something to bite on.

No amount of stealth can disguise human scent – so terrible to such a wild creature as a Badger – therefore quick, effective and positive

72

action is crucial. With a full-grown Badger, still strong and otherwise healthy, once the snare is slackened and the leg released (self-locking devices need to be turned to the same axis as the wire; which permits the wire to be pushed, not pulled, through), there will be little more one can do. If necessary, an improvised bandage of leaves could be wrapped around the wound, perhaps tied loosely with a couple of strands of grass; this should last until the Badger gets home or to some secluded spot where it can attend to the wound itself in nature's own time-honoured way. But use nothing that could make the situation yet worse, like cloth, string or elastic bands.

A very weakened or sickly specimen could be left in a quiet, dark spot until aid is summoned. One that is active yet weak can be released to take its chances as best it can, or hobbled by trussing together the two forelegs with a large handkerchief or length of material (a stocking or pair of tights is difficult to better in this type of emergency) until help comes or the animal is removed for treatment.

On-the-spot attention is always preferable, especially if the casualty is a lactating mother. A dustbin can be used to protect and contain many wild animals and, if removal is necessary, makes an ideal travelling-crate for a Badger or Fox. According to Phil Hunt – a vet with much experience of these species in the Westcountry – it cannot be bettered. The heavy-duty rubber kind of bin is best for it is strong and quiet, but even sturdy plastic ones are safe because the incarcerated animal is unable to gain purchase on any part of the smooth interior. Some have locking lids in which air-holes may be burnt; in others the lid can be secured by rope or twine to the two side handles (see also Chapter 4).

These suggestions are not foolproof, but are appropriate to desperate circumstances. Things are seldom so bad: usually one has company or there is a friendly habitation, or tools such as wire-cutters, a length of tubing and some rope, transport and a telephone within reach. However, anyone able to cope with such a crisis could cope with· most situations likely to be encountered in Britain. A more difficult decision involves the past-caring or past-help animal, in which case you have the task of despatching it once and for all as humanely as possible (see Chapter 11). But don't be too hasty, for Badgers are incredibly tough, and have been known to recover from frightful injuries in their own good time. It may even be kinder to let a mortally injured Badger limp away to die in peace and quiet; this is the sort of thing that can be decided only at the time. It is the moderately disabled one that provides most problems. Quite often Badgers get caught around the abdomen by the snare-wire. When they get tired from struggling, they often curl up and go into a deep sleep, which may last a week or more, and is nature's way of allowing injuries to heal. Beware; they can wake up suddenly.

If it is decided to remove the animal, with time and facilities a dog-catcher or -grasper can be made (Plate 5) so that with care, for neither the Badger nor the Otter has a canine-like neck, the business end can be rendered ineffective. A Badger can then be lifted, with a handful of the loose hide on the rump giving additional support; hoisted thus, it will seldom struggle even if the head swings free. Alternatively, as it tucks its head between its forelegs grasp the fur hard at the scruff and rump simultaneously, it may now be lifted reasonably safely and deposited in a receptacle. It is an operation that should be carried out quickly and confidently to reduce risk to the operator, and stress to the patient. Heavy-duty netting is unsurpassable (see page 76) as a means of rendering dangerous mammals defenceless while still allowing examination and the opportunity of giving injections and sedatives. Phil Hunt (1976) has successfully sedated the European badger using ketamine hydrochloride (Vetalar: Parke, Davis) subcutaneously at dose rates of 26mgm/kg as a prolonged but light anaesthesia, and 14mg/kg as a mild sedative allowing examination. It is, though, difficult to safely extricate from nets those fully conscious.

A Badger is more difficult to lure or guide into a travelling-crate than a Fox. Like the Badger, the Fox only attacks under severe provocation, but its bite, though nasty, cannot match that of a Badger, Otter or dog. Its jaws are comparatively weak and more suited to snapping and to prey much smaller than itself. Such anatomical evidence, quite as much as the absence of reliable eye-witnesses, tends to exonerate the Fox when it comes to those well-beloved sheep-killing stories. Lambs already dead or dying will certainly be snaffled up, otherwise it is generally a case of a rogue or desperate first-year animal (see Chapter 11). Such local incidents cannot of course be ignored, and one Sussex vet saw five Foxes attending a ewe in labour. But, seeing that Foxes are opportunist scavengers, the wool found in some stomachs, particularly those of hill Foxes, is neither mystery nor wholly incriminatory.

Care of wildlife in a broader context has, of course, to include care of its living space – the environment – and naturally this is achieved by the wonderful integration of all nature's forces. I say 'naturally' because many of mankind's more so-called sophisticated activities cannot be so dignified. In a healthy dynamic ecosystem, there is usually a better representation of large herbivores than exists in Britain's present manipulated countryside. And a virile waste-disposal force of scavengers from eagles and bears to burying-beetles and flies is of vital ecological importance. That the Fox (and the Badger) is ready, willing and able to help in this task – providing in the estimation of all open-minded countryfolk, a service which deserves to elevate rather than denigrate – is still occasionally evident when a sheep dies and lies unfound by the farmer. Unfortunately, as in human society, the reformer often attracts the blame for the deeds he seeks to ameliorate. Whatever the merits of the foxhunting tradition as a sop to some sheep-, game- and poultry-producers, it cannot be justified if we coolly and sensitively assess the Fox and its crimes. Farmers, anyway, are well capable of sorting out any rogue Fox that is annoying them.

The Fox, at least, lacks the Badger's knack for getting into awkward situations: centuries of human persecution on top of aeons of experience in the craft of opportunist survival have given this splendid beast an unpredictable versatile independence unequalled, probably, in the animal kingdom. Not for the Fox the insular routine of the Badger on its regular path; it prefers a furtive twilight existence, sensitive and shy of its own image, to such an extent that even the town Fox is seldom seen by its human neighbours. Sadly, most sightings in both town and country involve road victims, for Foxes seem to have difficulty in judging the speed of motor vehicles, and a variety of injuries ensue.

Foxes and Badgers that are only slightly injured will always endeavour to creep away and heal themselves. Only snared or severely crippled or diseased animals remain approachable. Lacking the Badger's strength, and always on the lookout for a bolthole, the Fox is far less formidable. Even a partially mobile Fox will likely avail itself of a dark crate, for example a tea-chest, especially if something like a piece of sacking covers most of the entrance. In the absence of such a facility or a dog-catcher (Plates 5 and 5a), a Fox can be grasped by the scruff of the neck once its attention has been gained by the captor advancing one hand towards the snout – obviously not so close that a snap could reach it – in a similar way to that recommended for dangerous birds. Immediately following a snap, the spare hand can be quickly and firmly brought to grasp the scruff of the extended neck, whereupon a Fox invariably becomes passive and allows itself to be carried a short distance or lifted into a container or sack; the main weight of the body being supported by a hand or arm beneath the rump. If the muzzle is taped, a Fox can be carried in relative safety.

In describing the hazards of foolhardiness and the resourcefulness of mammals, I have already touched on the Otter. As an expression of its impetuosity, the term 'a handful' would be woefully inadequate, indeed it would be dangerous in its implications. The dog-catcher, so useful with mammals of this size, can be used on the Otter but not around the neck for it would shrug it off much as, one imagines, an eel would. With an Otter, the noose must be passed over the shoulders before it is tightened.

It is unlikely, outside of a zoo, for a rope- or nylon-net of the necessarily fairly robust gauge to be lying about conveniently. But with forewarning, if one can be found or borrowed, I can think of no better way of dealing with a recalcitrant Otter or Badger. As evidence that this is true, I once had to move single-handed except for a torch held at a safe distance, in torrential rain, a Leopard badly injured after some feline wife-battering inside to where she could be treated. A good net sufficed – just – and illustrates why all zoos housing dangerous animals will have some handy.

A Wild cat with even a modicum of savoir-faire remaining would be another customer for the net if my imagination serves me well. I cannot see such a beast meekly retreating into a proffered hidy-hole, but, as was mentioned in the preceding chapter, it is not a drama, for better or worse, likely to see production.

Seals may belong to a different order (Pinnipedia) on account of their marine specialisation, but they descend from the Carnivora and, when it comes to contemplating handling, it would be extremely stupid to forget it. Fortunately, when a seal leaves the sea and hauls out onto dry land, its wonderful fluidity of movement seems to ossify – quite unlike the Otter, which is equally at home in both environments. It becomes reasonably and quite safely manoeuvrable when grasped just below the tail. However, adults – even of the Common seal which is more docile, aquatic and moves less freely of the two indigenous British species out of water – allowing close approach are not common. Because they are animals requiring co-operative effort, expensive care and sophisticated accommodation, their predicament should be brought to the attention of a zoo, marineland, aquarium, one of the specialist sanctuaries scattered round the coast near seal-frequented waters, the RSPCA or police, or perhaps a university with a faculty engaged in marine biology or oceanography. I have excluded seal pups so far not because they are any less likely to use their extremely sharp teeth and strong jaws but because their occurrence is rather more likely (see Chapter 9).

To move away from the sea, deer, due to their classic beauty and because they are sociable grazing animals – in short possessing all the attributes of what American workers call the 'Bambi syndrome' – evoke no fear in the public mind. And yet each autumn during the rutting season, male deer (stags or bucks) become aggressive and have the potential to cause more trouble than all our snakes and sharks put together. Where herds of semi-wild deer, usually Red or Fallow, live in parkland with public access, a problem could arise if an unsuspecting passer-by or curious child strayed too close to an irritable male.

When one considers that even the little Roe deer can cause fatal wounds with its strong legs and sharp hooves, the threat should injudicious handling be attempted imposed by the Red deer – Britain's largest terrestrial mammal, standing up to 1.4m (4½ft) tall at the shoulder and weighing about 200kg (440lb) – jumps into focus. Make no mistake, the antlers of male deer (Fig 2), grown for and shed after the rut, are no mere ornaments. Normally their use is in fairly equally matched trials of strength like human males arm-wrestling on a pub table; but should danger threaten or should a male feel that one of his does or hinds is vulnerable, he will attack with his head, antlered or not. Any cornered deer will stand its ground and confront its persecutor, hence the romantic image of 'the stag at bay'. In the case of a female, this will involve rearing up on her hindlegs and lashing out with her sharp front hooves. Even a prone deer – one too injured or sick to stand up – must be treated with the utmost respect, and no liberties taken near legs however innocent they may look.

Partly for reasons of safety and partly for reasons associated with their temperament and need of spacious enclosures, deer are seldom suitable cases for the amateur keeper despite the not infrequent incidence of their sustaining injury and, in the absence of predators, old age and disease. A deer caught fast in a wire-fence can be freed by two or more people provided one of them at least appreciates the dangers presented by the sharp hooves and is strong enough to hold the frightened animal firmly. Most deer do not bite, but the introduced Muntjac and Chinese Water deer have very useful teeth and tusks which they are not slow to use. Koreans used to believe that the bite of the Water deer was fatal.

Deer are occasionally caught in snares, and are regularly hit by motor vehicles, and maimed by poachers and other country vandals. The exact position of all seriously incapacitated deer should be reported to a local person competent and equipped to deal with such an emergency. There are generally such people domiciled in deer regions, and a local vet should know of them; alternatively, the British Deer Society (see Appendix 3), local police or RSPCA can be contacted.

As intimated above, deer are sometimes found with injuries so horrendous and in such a feeble and emaciated condition that they survive only because our ancestors exterminated all wolves, bears and lynxes, and reduced our eagle populations to relict proportions. Nature never seems quite so cruel viewed from this angle. In managed herds, marksmen have to assume this role of beneficial predator, and hunts attempt to justify their survival in today's slightly more aware society in much the same way. I would personally see a more natural and ecological balance in Britain but that is a Dodo hope while we are encouraged to overpopulate, overproduce and overconsume. Such deer have very often to be put out of their misery. Others less ill may need to be tranquillised before treatment can be begun; this is not a problem with an incapacitated animal, but with a moving target a dart-gun may be needed and there are few vets licensed to use one. There is, moreover, always the risk – in the event of a loose shot – of the highly potent dart being lost.

Antlers cased in 'velvet' are live and vulnerable to damage; at other times they are not and may be removed, preferably by a vet using an embryotomy wire, to reduce the dangers to handlers and attendants if long-stay treatment is envisaged. The simple spikes of Muntjac deer and the 'first-heads' of other antlered species can be made less dangerous by wrapping and tying sacking around them or pushing a section of hosepipe onto each. Velveted antlers must be carefully protected by liberal padding and wooden splints.

One way of emphasising the potential dangers of attempting to handle deer would be to imagine taking similar liberties with horses or even ponies, which do not possess the headgear of deer or seek to butt in any way. I would like to think that the domestic horse is so familiar that anyone finding an injured or sick 'wild' pony or indeed colliding with one, would know automatically what to do – summon veterinary

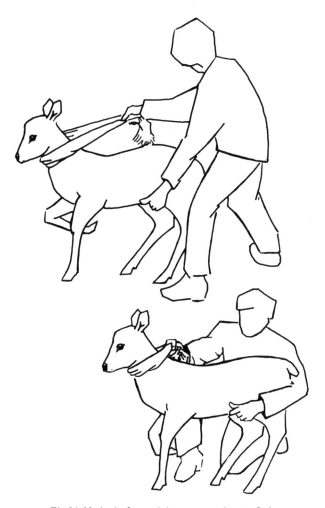

Fig 24 Method of restraining a young deer or foal

or stable assistance immediately. They also ought to know that under provocation a horse's hooves are terrible weapons, a wild pony's are not much less so. Additionally, because ponies are not really wild, the layperson is, hopefully, less likely to become flustered by one in difficulties and more likely to respect it and know something of its basic requirements.

Until professional help arrives, pony or deer road victims should be kept as quiet as possible, so prevent a surrounding audience. It is not usually practicable to attempt to hold a wild pony but if, for example, a mare is injured, its foal can be restrained by using something like a scarf or belt around the neck with one hand, the other arm securing the buttocks (Fig 24). Avoid coming between mother and young; keeping on the far side of the foal (or fawn) will minimise maternal distress and the arousal of protective instincts.

The likelihood of being bitten by many of the smaller mammals has already been mentioned. Biters include virtually all rodents, mustelids, leporids (hares and the Rabbit), bats and insectivores. One of the latter, the popular Hedgehog, is supposed not to bite, feeling more than secure within its prickly armour. However, one I once found on a road near my home, and took inside before moving to a safer place, broke off from its circuits of the kitchen walls and made a beeline towards my wife as we sat in the centre of the not small room watching it. We both peered down indulgently as it approached but without pausing or thinking twice, it sank its teeth into one of Mij's exposed toes and went on its way to the opposite wall. My amusement and suggestion that it probably thought it had seen a slug was somewhat spoilt by her remonstrations about the stupidity of letting 'ridiculous flea-ridden carnivores' loose in the house.

Hedgehogs certainly do have healthy populations of parasites – maybe no more than many another animal but rather more easily seen and accessible. It is a mistake to conclude that they are necessarily harming or irritating the host for usually such partnerships are in equilibrium, and these parasites do not stay on humans. But ticks are not so much commensal partners as dangerous predators.

Despite the incident of Mij's toe, it is usually true that the Hedgehog does not try to bite when handled; and handling is not always as difficult as it sounds or as one is led to believe. My hands do not seem the least leathery, and yet I seldom experience difficulty in cradling a rolled-up Hedgehog onto one palm. With gloves of any sort there is no problem whatsoever. The knack lies not in trying to grasp or grip it, nor in trying to pick it up gingerly, but in exposing the largest area possible of both your hands to the spines low down on either side, taking the weight of the beast and tipping it gently onto one slightly cupped palm. I must admit that some Hedgehogs do seem to have sharper spines than others, but if any difficulty is experienced the animal can be easily rolled onto a large handkerchief or coat and picked up suspended in a bundle. However, if as often happens, a Hedgehog is seen running along beside a road, or indeed lying curled up on one in the charming but naïve assumption that its prickles will protect it, there may well be no time for such niceties if its body is not to become an aggregate of the tarmac – one of a long succession.

Some bats will not hesitate to bite given half a chance, but on account of their aerial specialisation are not difficult to catch hold of whilst grounded or roosting. However, the following extract from Stebbings' and Jefferies' useful booklet *Focus on bats: their conservation and the law* (1982), published by the Nature Conservancy Council, ought to be noted carefully:

> Under the Wildlife and Countryside Act 1981 it is illegal for anyone without a licence intentionally to kill, injure or handle a wild bat of any species in Great Britain; to possess a bat, whether alive or dead; or to disturb a bat when roosting ... The only exception is for bats in the *living area* [my italics] of a house ... To summarise, do not ... disturb them when roosting, or block entrances to their roosts; and only handle them to remove them carefully from the living area of your house or to feed and tend them if this is essential.

I would recommend picking them up by the method shown in Fig 23 but, except for young inexperienced bats entering a house through an open window, becoming disorientated and landing or clinging to a curtain, it is unusual for a human being, except now illegally (see Chapter 11), ever to come into contact with a live bat. They can be transported in a box where they will cling to a piece of bark or similar wedged firmly, or carried in a cloth bundle.

Rabbits and hares care nothing for their popular image, and a stricken animal may bite heartily if picked up carelessly. The long ears of both types are a perfectly appropriate 'handle' but must never be employed to lift the animal unless some of the weight is taken by a hand placed beneath the rump in such a position that the forearm cannot be scratched by the claws on the powerful hindlegs as the animal kicks convulsively in an effort to escape (Fig 25). It is safer to enclose the animal in a thick towel, rug or sack which, with a string tie, can be a useful emergency carrier. Exaggerated slowness and methodical handling is always necessary with these timid creatures; even so, a distressing shriek or scream is always likely.

Road and snare casualties and myxomatosis are the most likely hazards though hares are not susceptible to the disease and are much rarer these days (see page 42). Also on that page, the bites of rodents in the context of a young squirrel were mentioned. Whenever I have seen a Grey squirrel in a cage-trap, I have always been struck (not literally, fortunately) by its venomosity. I confess I have never

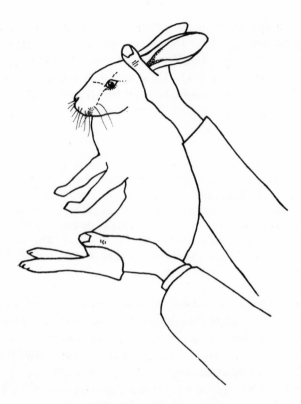

Fig 25 Method of picking up a leporid

attempted to handle directly such a fury and, following experiences with wounded chipmunks – a considerably smaller species – do not regret it. I would not, furthermore, rely on even the strongest gauntlets as protection against a squirrel's deep and painful bites. Human jaws could no doubt make some impression through such gloves, and they are feeble compared to the combination of honed chisel-sharp teeth and mighty jaws designed to carve open nuts and chew wood. A mobile squirrel will invariably evade capture, and I have never seen one badly injured though they are occasionally killed on roads, frequently shot or poisoned by warfarin-type rodenticides – the most likely cause of one reluctant to move. A net (Fig 19) or coat could be used to gather up a partially mobile specimen, and the tail may be used to swing one gently into a container. Nets and coats are indeed the best allies of potential trappers of small mammals, from squirrel-size downwards.

Cold-blooded Fauna

Human body heat, mentioned before with regard to sick birds, is appreciated still more by the reptiles. I find it hard to resist handling Slow-worms, not just for the feel of the smooth, shiny, supple and strong bodies of these legless lizards but more for the pleasure they so evidently derive from the heat of which I, as a mammal, am blessed with a surplus. Very soon they stop struggling and literally bask in the warmth: the coldness of their touch slowly abating as they sate their craving. Snakes likewise, though it is best not to handle them at all, especially if unable to distinguish the poisonous Adder or Viper (Fig 18). The Grass snake is said to eject an evil-smelling secretion from the anal glands; I have never experienced this, but they do sham death most effectively at times of severe danger.

To be small and cold-blooded is a helpless existence – at the mercy of the whim of nature, dependent utterly on forces over which there is no exercisable control and under which there is precious little room to manoeuvre. Hibernation during winter and a precarious endless migration between available shelter and available heat are the only options of these poikilothermic animals. Like one of those Swiss weather clocks, small reptiles come out and go in as the elements dictate. Is it any wonder that a reptile – a British reptile at that – accepts the gift of warmth from a human hand and asks no questions?

4 Accommodation and Nutrition

It should be appreciated from the outset that the caging of wild animals creates a fundamental contradiction and poses a dilemma to which there is no really satisfactory answer. An humane compromise must acknowledge the anxiety and bodily deprivation imposed by *physical* control on a creature which has hitherto blindly obeyed only *biological* restrictions. On the other hand, we have to recognise the necessity of such restraint if the casualty is to be helped despite itself.

The physiological stress caused by what we might term 'psychical imprisonment' begins the moment we gather in a wild creature. Physical imprisonment, if we think about it, began before, with the injury or disease which caused the incapacity. In collecting the casualty, we are superimposing one form of imprisonment on top of another.

In assuming responsibility for the destiny of a wild animal we are, in a sense, playing at God. More than assuming we know what is best, we also imply that we can do a better job than anyone else. If this is not our intention it is the effect. And before making these assumptions we would do well to question our motives if we truly wish to care for wildlife.

Modern scientific midwifery urges mothers to have their babies in hospitals because these are considered to be the safest, not necessarily the most pleasant, places for the physical wellbeing. That they may not be the safest for psychical health, suggests it is a compromise that can yet be improved on. Likewise, some sick animals, especially if of fairly specialist species, may fare better at a professional collection or with someone experienced in their peculiarities. Deer, birds-of-prey and marine animals immediately come to mind and one could lengthen the list considerably. Potentially dangerous ones could also be included. Local circumstances will greatly influence and often control such questions but it is important at the outset to consider them. Selfish pleasure must not be allowed to displace the sad necessity of caring for sick animals; any pleasure there is to be had must come in by the back door as we cope with the anxiety through the front.

If, after initial critical assessment (see beginning of next chapter), we consider closer examination necessary, there are one or two points worth extra consideration before that critical step is taken of catching and gathering in a wild creature. These can be set out in a positive and negative way:

+ removal to safe site
− removal from home environment

+ observation and examination under optimum conditions
− observation in original position, stress of catching

+ access to specialised care and techniques
− possibility of poor adaptation to captivity and loss of will to live

Difficult as it has been so far to offer generalised advice, the same applies to accommodation. Maybe we would do better to consider the possible phases: temporary or short-term caging, which can include the in-transit stage; intensive care, which can include the diagnostic and pre-operative periods; medium-stay care including the post-operative and convalescent stages; and long-term, possibly indefinite, accommodation for the chronically sick or permanently disabled (see Chapter 10). There are shades in between and, of course, no single patient will require all options; many once at home will need, or be given, no more than one.

Unless forewarned, getting a creature home often demands a certain amount of ingenuity, innovation and imagination. Desperation can help to inspire all three! Never, for example, be afraid to seek help at a nearby dwelling; as we discovered right at the beginning of this book, the sight of a helpless wild creature can soften the hardest heart. There I mentioned one or two examples: particularly relevant here are the collections of waterfowl begun by hunters who winged or injured birds and found themselves − like the sportsman confronted by a juvenile Pheasant − unable to shoot the sitting duck or, more often, the grounded goose.

Mercy at this critical juncture often spawns a deeper interest. Some wildfowlers have admitted to me that they gain more pleasure from breeding Mallards in summer than they do from shooting them in winter. (The spectacular mental acrobatics that enable them to do so is

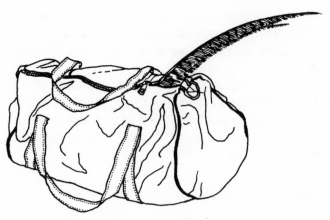

Fig 26 A zip bag such as this, or similar, makes an excellent carrier for long-tailed birds

quite another matter.) And a pest control officer I knew who day in, day out waged war against the Woodpigeon, jealously guarded and watched expectantly over a pair of that selfsame species which had the temerity (or shrewdness) to build its nest in his own backgarden. Such delightful inconsistencies perhaps offer evidence for measured optimism over the future of our own species. The story of the Belstone Fox (rescued by a gamekeeper and brought up with hounds) could encourage me, were there no alternative, even to take an injured or orphaned Fox cub to the gate of a gamekeeper. But I would watch very closely his face.

Getting birds home, excepting the dangerous ones (see Chapter 3) and the extra large – of which only the Mute swan is commonly encountered – presents few real problems.

A bird other than one totally inconsolable is better off being carried correctly than rolling around in a cardboard box. I have carried birds quite long distances in just my hand, and many have remained more passive than they do in containers. If this method is not possible for some reason like having to drive a car or ride a bicycle, a pocket – preferably one with fastenings – also offers security as does the inside of a shirt where a casualty will also derive benefit from subdued lighting and one's body heat. A cloth bag, sports-bag or satchel must be preferable to a cold hard box, but best and cheapest of all for medium-large birds (eg oiled auks) is the disposable plastic carrier-bag if left unsealed. It softly cradles the bird in a natural position and even if sharp-billed birds puncture the plastic, they cannot escape. Long-tailed birds like pheasants can be trammelled comfortably in a cloth to

86

Plate 12 The delicate feet of water-orientated birds kept in dry conditions may need attention to prevent drying and cracking of the skin. Here, a Black-headed gull (not in breeding plumage) is treated with cod-liver oil *(Les Stocker/The Wildlife Hospitals Trust)*

Plate 13 Dribbling glucose solution as an anti-shock measure down the underside of a hen Blackbird's upper mandible to avoid all risk of choking *(Les Stocker/The Wildlife Hospitals Trust)*

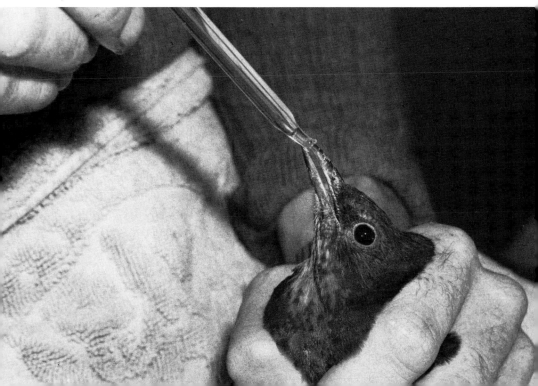

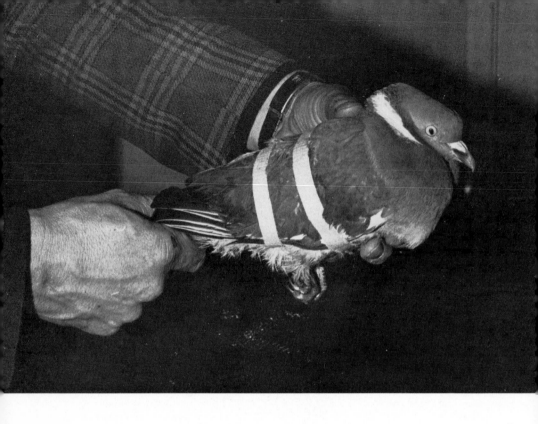

Plate 14 Fractured humerus in a Woodpigeon: *(top)* temporary strapping of affected wing – leaving free good wing – with good alignment of simple fractures no other fixation is needed; *(bottom left)* adhesive tape removed shows classic and telltale droop; *(bottom right)* appearance and position of the compound fracture *(sequence: author)*

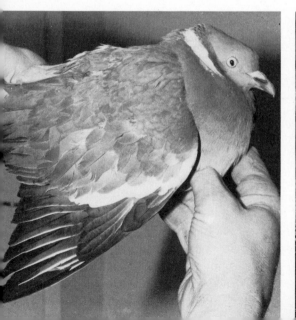
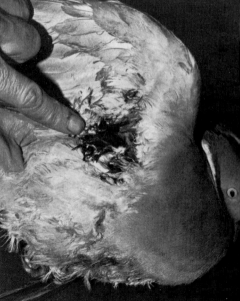

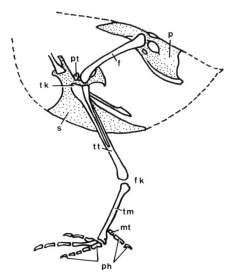

Fig 27 Skeleton of a bird's leg, showing both the false knee (heel) and true knee (stifle joint): **f** femur; **fk** false knee; **mt** metatarsus; **p** pelvis; **ph** phalanges (digits); **pt** patella; **s** sternum; **tk** true knee; **tm** tarsometatarsus; **tt** tibiotarsus *(after Ede)*. See also *Figs 1* and *49*

prevent turning, and placed in a style of bag that allows the tail to protrude (Fig 26). But beware of gamekeepers and landowners laying claim to the bird. In emergencies, the tail feathers may be plucked out; they will regrow and in the meantime their absence will not inconvenience the bird.

If a box or pet-carrier is used, I prefer to make a deep soft nest out of whatever non-dusty material is available: dry grass, leaves, cloth, crumpled or shredded soft paper, short lengths of the packaging material known as 'wood-straw' etc, though not musty straw or hay. Usually all one sees as bedding is a sheet of newspaper, which is neither use nor ornament. Human casualties, while still alive, are conveyed in hammock-like stretchers not coffins. The oiled seabird requires warmth, and that is hardly likely to be gained floundering around in a bleak empty box or, for that matter, in rubbing shoulders with equally contaminated and bedraggled brethren. The wicker basket, so useful for mammals, can be dangerous to birds on account of the hard sharp projections on the wickerwork.

A complication can arise with the long legs of wading birds such as herons if forced to 'sit' for too long on the ankle joint or 'false knee' (Fig 27). Such paralysis can be prevented by allowing able-legged specimens their 'liberty' when hooded (see Chapter 3). Alternatively, if crating is necessary and a tall crate is not available, a short one can be effectively heightened by replacing the top with a very loose hessian cover. The birds can also be transported in slings; or trussed up and laid on their sides with their legs free – but not over long distances.

Notwithstanding my misgivings about the inhospitality of the cardboard box as a carrier for small birds, it does have certain advantages mainly to do with the seclusion and therefore security it bestows upon timid subjects including small mammals. It is especially valuable for the pre-diagnostic period back home, when usually a period of about twenty-four hours should elapse before the patient is examined or disturbed (see next chapter). Ventilation holes, also allowing diffused light, are best set low down if the killer draughts can be avoided, or screened with gauze so that the inmate is not harmfully stimulated.

Mice and small voles can be caught in jamjars and transported neatly if a piece of card is slipped underneath and the jar then turned right way up and 'fed' with shredded paper or dry grass in which the rodent can conceal itself. The top can then be secured with a piece of cloth tied around the neck, or the conventional lid perforated with airholes.

Shrews, even uninjured ones, are difficult to keep by the inexperienced for they required *ad lib* feeding due to their exceptionally high metabolic rate, and alternate peaks of eating and sleeping about every three hours. In the wild, they live for only about fifteen months. Archibald Thorburn wrote in his *British Mammals* published in 1920–1 about the smallest British mammal of all, the Lesser or Pygmy shrew: 'Its hold on life is so slight that it soon dies in confinement even when caught by hand and uninjured. One brought to me ... at first appeared quite lively and readily took the flies I provided while making the sketches ... but soon a gradual change began and it was dead in a few hours.' I think the 'few hours' is quite significant, and Thorburn would not have been aware of the fatal consequences of stress. To have been caught in the first place could indicate an already poor condition. In a satisfactory, warm environment – such as decent vivarium furnished with loose earth, dried leaves and a small retreat – and fed correctly, shrews can even be bred. In less than a year, one pair is known to have produced no fewer than sixty-six young.

Bats tame quickly, and are not difficult to keep if need be. Some, like the Pipistrelle, are 'crevice-creepers'; others prefer to hang free.

Larger mammals present different sorts of problems, clearly most forcefully appreciated by ill-equipped or inexperienced handlers. Some of the hazards involved in the capture and conveyance of the Badger, Fox, Otter, deer etc, have already been considered, and their follow-up penning is covered more fully in the penultimate two chapters. The dustbin (see page 73) can actually be much more than just a sort of heavy-duty pet-carrier, perfect for short-hauls between two people or longer car journeys. The galvanised metal type is less suitable here, for once the motion of the vehicle stops, the internee may well become active, so much so that as you return to your car after a quiet cup of tea it sounds as if you are approaching a West Indian steel band struggling with its instruments. Dustbins also make adequate overnight accommodation, preferable to release into a garage if, like mine, this is a depository for useless junk and half-used paintcans which necessitates a stressful recatching next morning. And most if not all households possess a dustbin which can be emptied and washed out. As Phil Hunt says: 'I would happily go to bed for a few hours with a Badger in my dustbin, knowing it will come to no harm.' The only danger is a build-up of carbon dioxide (CO_2) in the base, but this can be overcome by removing the lid every couple of hours to exchange the air, or by piercing airholes in the lid. Even so a build-up could be possible around an inactive animal.

We are left with the volatile medium-small species which are also certainly more than a handful in their way. Squirrels detest being confined and will, given time, chew their way out of most, save metal, containers; even smooth-sided heavy-duty plastic ones will not deter them indefinitely. The mustelids are both less inclined and less able to escape provided there are no holes large enough for the head to pass through, and can be contained successfully in a sack or wooden box, maybe even in a stout cardboard one over short distances. At home, the pungent odour exuded by their characteristic musk glands will likely determine their accommodation in some outhouse.

Transfer to a larger cage always follows when appropriate (see page 114). A simple boxcage (Fig 28) such as can be knocked up by even a poor handyman or converted from an old drawer or cupboard, has many uses for the smaller varieties of birds and mammals owing to the seclusion it affords. It is without doubt the most useful general-purpose cage. If its open front is then directed towards a quiet position, the inmate should gradually settle down. So much the better if it can be placed so that we can observe it from a discreet distance, ideally through a window. Hospital-cages and the provision of heat for

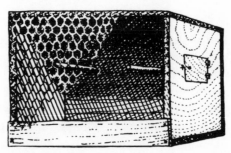

Fig 28 Boxcage made from an 'orange-box' and chicken wire; note the perches screwed into the back

new arrivals are referred to in the next chapter.

Larger animals generally have to make do with whatever is available, so do active ground birds. This could be garage, garden-shed, chicken-house, outhouse, greenhouse, stable etc. Best of all perhaps, except for strong active animals or those associated with water, is an unwanted room in a non-houseproud home, for it is secure from predators and can have its lighting and heating controlled precisely. Windows need to be screened in some way to provide diffused lighting, security and safety. A spare room or outhouse can, if more than passing interest is discovered, be partitioned off into several compartments by a framework of 4cm (1½in) square timber, clad in small-gauge wirenetting.

The actual structure, so long as it is secure, is rather less important than the way in which it is fitted out. Imagination and a sympathy with, and knowledge of, an animal's natural existence must be brought into play. Again, in the early stages, the emphasis must be on seclusion and an absence of harmful stimulation. We have all been ill and we know how we feel; there is no reason to suppose that we are any different to any other animal except that we are able to rationalise our predicament. Shock, fear, terror, stress and consequent panic can all befall a wild animal plucked by fate out of the only environment it knows and the one it has been conditioned to. Such conditions are not assuaged by curious humans, peering children's faces and the domestic clamour that may seem normal to us. On the other hand, birds more than mammals need to be subtly stimulated, hence our need to distinguish between harmful and beneficial stimulation. It will repay us to consider briefly why this should be.

Of these two higher groups of animals, mammals are generally more amenable to captivity than birds. Their 'intelligence', hitherto a source of mischief, serves them and us rather better once presented with a *fait accompli*. Birds, crows apart, are slaves of 'fixed action patterns' – dependent on rather inflexible routines – relieved, enlivened and rescued only by a marvellous mobility which originally helped to rescue them from the yoke of the Reptilia. A 'thinking' flock-bird for instance could well be 'too clever for its own good' because it would lose all the benefits provided by its social tendency. For example, the anonymity it finds within a flock helps protect it from predators, and there are considerable advantages in co-operative food-finding. And a bird, for all its mobility or perhaps because of it, would be ill-equipped to capitalise on the benefits of 'insight-learning' (what we think of as intelligence). The power of flight, as we saw in Chapter 2, controls and shapes a bird, and is thus a two-edged sword – simultaneously freeing and confining.

Modern placental mammals from bats to whales, and taking in all ground types, not only exist in a far greater diversity of form but have the singular advantage of a lengthy learning adolescence, plus a longevity sufficient to enable them to practise, perfect and pass on their skills and experience. So while birds conquered the air and discovered fresh and inviting pastures, their success largely depends on this one facility: as an order, they are specialists, incredibly successful but with some unyielding limitations. We have already discovered that specialists are less suited to the rigours of captivity and, in a general sense, birds deprived of their flight – as they are in captivity – become poor 'mammals'.

This is not to say that mammals accept captivity without question! But the problems they present are more to do with the quality of existence rather than basic survival. The mammal keeper has to be conscious of, and cannot ignore, the strength and considerable insight and learning ability of his or her charges, while the aviculturist working with wild species wrestles more with problems of fixed action patterns, and releasing stimuli (releasors) and responses. Mammals of many kinds will try purposefully to escape while birds may fly repeatedly at wirenetting or, as in the case of most gamebirds, patrol endlessly around the perimeters of their runs, presumably in the hope that a hole will miraculously appear.

We have seen that a bird to be collected has probably already been rendered flightless, and that this is effective physical imprisonment. But all the while it remains *in situ*, the grounded bird remains cognisant of its physical situation and retains a certain comprehension of it. The moment we intervene and impose psychical alienation, the bird becomes confused and disorientated; and liable to deteriorate for want of charged instinct. In other words, its environment is suddenly impoverished and the bird patient is deprived of essential and beneficial stimulation. This is why breeders of undomesticated birds require flair, particularly concerning the attractive presentation of quality food and the stimulus for exercise once the prime natural source, ie appetitive, is removed.

At least a mammal may move about its accommodation, however small, in a natural way. If immobile, at least it is so in a natural position. Most perching-birds, though, are rarely inactive while awake: they fly, flit, hop, run, clamber and engage in a wide variety of other movements, mostly to do with food-finding. All call upon different motor-responses as they react to a succession of enormously varied stimuli: their bodies are animated, their toes and wings forever flexing.

A perching-bird in a hospital-cage must stand continually on the same bit of wood, staring blankly at the same meaningless walls; the only stimulation it is likely to get will excite a flight response – the one of all it cannot obey. Even birds-of-prey, which may appear to stand for long periods doing nothing, are actually passively hunting. In view of this, it is not surprising that the most successful birds in captivity are waterfowl, pheasants and the true parrots (ie not parakeets), all of which are either unreliant on flight or able to concentrate on another equally valid dimension to their existences. Enforced inactivity on top of everything else hits a perching-bird hard. Such a bird prevented even from perching normally is a wretched spectacle indeed.

A bird suffering from a physical injury probably feels its incapacitation more acutely than one under the effects of a debilitating disease. In the same way, we are frustrated by a sprained ankle but resigned and apathetic under the influence of influenza. For reasons such as this I am rather inclined against the amateur treatment of traumatic injury in birds by people who do not appreciate the psychological estrangement special to them in this predicament. I mention this here only because of the attitude so prevalent, or so it seems, that a 'simple' fracture only requires organic reunification.

Maybe the question of accommodation now has a better chance of receiving the priority it deserves. There may not be much we can do to provide qualitative space for an incapacitated animal but our very awareness of such things inevitably alters and refines not only our actions and therefore our decisions about bricks and mortar, but also our attitude, and we are then more likely to pay greater attention to its ecology etc. It is furthermore my belief that emissions of the subconscious are, to some extent, comprehended by their object.

So the actual quarters are less important than their fixtures and fittings, and the ambience and indeed actual position in which they are sited. For birds which habitually perch in trees, for instance, the flight distance (see page 59) reduces significantly when in a plane elevated from that horizontal with human eye level. So place their cages high above floor level in rooms where there is likely to be frequent human disturbance, and their perches high in the corner of their aviaries. Heavier birds, like pheasants, prefer firm perches but most passerines are often happier on a springy one providing it is not insecurely fixed. Size of caging is plainly determined by more exoteric considerations, such as that of the animal in question, the equipment and space at our disposal, and the phases of accommodation likely to be needed.

Before moving on to other aspects and nutrition, I want to reiterate the nub of the preceding chapter because it is as applicable here as it was there. The immediate pre-capture planning can be broken down into what Jill Nute calls 'the 4 Cs'. *Consider* the casualty's age, condition and predicament. 'Consideration' also affects the remaining three: *calmness* – although it is probably true that stress risk decreases as size increases, it will always be present and it is therefore even more important not to transmit one's own nervousness to the animal; *competence* in approach and handling avoids aggravating injuries, and injury to onself; and *confidence* in our ability and knowledge promotes a gentle but firm and unflustered manner.

Consideration should also be given to the equipment needed immediately following capture and, in the event of a dangerous or awkward customer, necessary to effect it. While handled-nets (Fig 19) are always useful, they are seldom near at hand when needed. In the absence of any kind (see page 66), improvisation is necessary with small mammals and, very often, partially mobile birds: towels, cardigans, scarves, travelling rugs etc can all be employed for the larger types, with lighter cotton items safer for small birds. If these items are thrown over with the edges held down, biters can be scooped up and held restrained for treatment prior to release, or deposited in a suitable receptacle. These include picnic-hampers and containers with flap or slide openings on the topside in which the patient can be placed and lie contained in its trammel while the lid is closed. A portion of cloth remaining outside will allow the wrapping to be eased out.

Paper bags with perforations will often suffice for small birds but cloth bags with a drawstring are far superior. They are warmer and escape-proof; can be suspended to preclude squashing; present no risk of suffocation; and can also be used for small rodents, bats (under licence) etc. I once flew all the way from Kenya with an Elephant shrew tucked up happily in a little muslin bag, inside my shirt for warmth. For larger subjects, shopping bags, sports bags, rucksacks and boxes and tins of all kinds such as plastic lunchboxes and biscuit tins are useful, though they have to be sacrificed by holes being punched through the lids. Above this size, sacks, teachests, crates and dustbins can all be requisitioned. Teachests, crates and hutches can be modified to provide semi-dark, clean, quiet holding quarters for small mammals. All holding facilities need to be as stress-free as possible to promote rapid recovery.

The cheaper forms of absorbent newsprint make first-rate fairly sterile emergency bedding either laid as a thick bed or torn and crumpled and compressed in imitation of a nest which will give support to disabled or young animals. Over-cautious as it undoubtedly is in the majority of circumstances, it should however be appreciated that printers' ink can contain lead and is poisonous.

The function of bedding is to provide warmth, 'nest' material for a sense of security, insulation from cold flooring, and to absorb urine and other discharges. It must not be allowed to contaminate wounds and abrasions, nor the atmosphere with dust or pathogenic organisms (qv aspergillosis), nor must it impede movement of an animal with, say, its legs in a cast. It ought to be cheaply available so that it can be replaced at regular intervals. Hay and straw must be fresh and dry, particularly when near birds. Sawdust and wood-shavings are an excellent traditional floor-covering, and can be obtained cheaply or for nothing from sawmills, carpenters and timber merchants; but it must be checked very carefully for splinters and metal fragments, and make sure that it is not from wood treated with preservatives. Perhaps best of all, as general-purpose bedding, is a liberal supply of short lengths of shredded paper which can be obtained in large amounts from larger offices – a friend who directs The Zoological Trust of Guernsey, claims that it is the only thing he gets out of his accountant for free.

Heavier mammals held in unheated quarters with concrete floors will appreciate a raised wooden pallet, slatted for hygiene, on which to sleep and on which bedding can be placed. Given that all terrestrial animals including birds such as waders appreciate secluded retreats, a most useful way of providing this and simultaneously a valuable acclimatisatory link between the conveyance (which, after even a fairly short journey, may well have come to represent security) and the 'permanent' quarters, is to leave the container as a retreat. With the opening partly screened or turned to the wall, the nervous patient can take refuge in a familiar place whenever feeling vulnerable. And when the time comes for catching-up, it does the job for you.

Predatory birds and others with good cause to fear mankind must also be given safe retreats. Highly excitable species or individuals should be kept in very dim conditions, well screened until habituated, with no exposed wirenetting on which a bird-of-prey would certainly damage itself persistently. On no account should aviaries or holding pens be entered for routine purposes while there is visual contact. Since owls – the nocturnal ones – hide away in daylight they are much the easier of the two groups to manage and house successfully. The all-wire budgie cage and similar might just pass for domesticated birds deprived of most natural instincts, but are anathema to most wildings. Only certain finches (eg the Goldfinch and Greenfinch) can in emergencies be adequately accommodated in this way; even so the cage should be sited high in a corner and well draped. A boxcage (Fig 28) is always better, preferably with a nestbox or screened-off corner in which the birds can hide.

The heavier birds are prone to foot conditions such as bumblefoot (see page 146) which, in birds-of-prey, can be caused by perches of insufficient diameter to prevent the sharp talons puncturing the underside of the foot. Perches need special attention because of the quite inordinate lengths of time cagebound birds are forced to spend on them in the same position: they need to be kept scrupulously clean and exchanged frequently with ones of slightly different size and texture.

Ground birds in captivity suffer from associated environmental defects such as excessive exposure to concrete kept either too wet or too dry for the species in question. A few sods of turf, or sawdust, shavings, gravel, sand, newsprint, kitchen towels (excellent but expensive) and earth all help to alleviate the harshness of this type of flooring. All, though, will require frequent changing if souring and contamination is to be avoided. Once its natural habitat is understood, one of these will be found suitable for the bird in question.

Aquatic birds are not really the problem they may seem, for the simple reason that if they need large areas of water they do not need to be in captivity at all. Most, especially those convalescing, will require a daily 'splash' in a pool, and some prefer to take their food from water – which will quickly foul it in warm weather. Seabirds inevitably contaminate an artificial environment due to the composition of their excrement and the force, necessary when swimming, with which it is expelled.

Concrete outdoor pens, tiered or strewn with large rocks, and which can be hosed and scrubbed down are the only really practicable long-term enclosures for birds which, when not at sea, inhabit rocky cliffs. Freshwater birds and those tending to brackish water, like many waterfowl and grebes, are liable to foot sores if kept incessantly on even smooth concrete. A grass paddock is preferable and, because long-term accommodation should not be necessary for seabirds re-cuperating from external oiling (but see Nutrition) all types can be kept in pens or arks, preferably with opaque sides, which can be moved daily to fresh ground or placed on concrete, deeply littered with sawdust etc, for freshwater birds. Seabirds pending release should have continuous access to clean bathing water. Waders have the most delicate feet of all and should be kept on a surface that imitates a mudflat, marsh or tideline: moist newspaper, sand, peat, sawdust etc. Such birds are very nervous and must be given a screen behind which they can retire. Birds may be temporarily grounded by taping together the primary (outer/flight) feathers on one wing (see Fig 34).

Nutrition (see also Chapter 9)

This is a vexed and confused subject, often unnecessarily so. Fundamentally I believe it to be a topic about which we do not need to worry unduly; and perfectly legitimate reports of deer enjoying pilchards in tomato sauce, kingfishers being reared on fishfingers, and woodpeckers on bread and honey reinforce this opinion. Avicultural and zoological diets can be a very different matter because they have to bring into condition and maintain adult specimens often from exotic countries, and moreover nurture their young. Here we are concerned with native species spending hopefully no more than about three weeks as our guests.

Bird-table feeding shows just how eclectic even birds which seem fairly specialised can be. As I write this, for instance, I look up and see a Nuthatch carrying off large beakfuls of mashed potato in preference to shelled peanuts, which would seem to be a more natural food; and this in late autumn when there must be an abundance of natural food available. No resident British bird, with the possible exception of certain fisheaters suffering from thiamine deficiency (see Chapter 8), is going to come to grief in a few weeks whatever vitamin or trace-element its diet lacks, and anyway these can be easily supplied with powdered and liquid supplements. Note though that this statement excludes insectivorous summer visitors which, as pointed out in Chapter 2, are never ideal subjects, and oiled seabirds which, if poisoning has occurred or if in heavy moult, may require a rather longer period of rehabilitation.

It is a curious thing but 'experts', in my experience, and I tell this against myself too, often have less success in feeding wild animals than interested amateurs who have fewer prejudices about what they should and should not eat. For example, bread soaked in milk – an excellent food, and not a million miles from what professional Canary breeders rear their pedigree stock on – is often derided instead of being appreciated as a very useful standby for a whole host of species, into which an infinite number and variety of additives can be mixed. However, cows' milk can cause diarrhoea and other disorders (see page 207) and is safest diluted 2:1 with water for smaller subjects, or replaced by something like Lactol.

Perhaps the most useful general advice, bearing in mind the hundreds of species of mammals and birds concerned, is to provide small quantities of the widest variety of foods one possibly can, no matter how eccentric they may seem. A variety of presentations can also be tried on wary subjects: different dishes, stimuli, techniques etc (see below). Once food is sampled, the worry is half over; once it is accepted, it is fully over because if inadequate for any reason it may be surreptitiously enhanced or phased out.

Funnily enough, mammals can be more infuriating than birds to begin with: their suspiciousness and increased sensitivity to human proximity can deter them from approaching food containers let alone sampling their contents. Hunger usually overcomes this but some ultra-sensitive specimens with certain conditions may perish first. Generally, though, their 'insight-learning' aptitude serves them well. As discussed in Chapter 5 a good case can be made for offering no food at all, except with small insectivores, for the first 24–48 hours. To sum up, while some animals set to with gusto, others seem to contemplate the prospect of eating with abject horror as though they never have, and never will if they have any say in the matter.

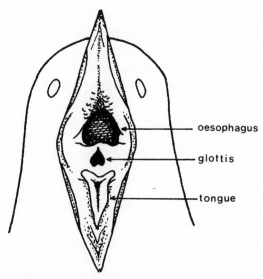

Fig 29 Interior of a bird's beak, showing the tongue, the opening to the oesophagus, and the glottis – the opening to the trachea, which opens and closes as the bird breathes

Sadly, if this condition is suspected and the patient shows every sign of remaining utterly implacable, forcefeeding has to be considered a priority. Plainly it is generally impracticable with all small mammals, and with most dangerous ones save possibly under anaesthesia. Deer, notwithstanding the dangers involved in handling, are an exception, and though it is a fairly long-winded and time-consuming business, can be fed a porridge-like consistency of cereals squeezed or otherwise introduced into the side of the mouth: as much as 600ml (1pt) twice or thrice daily for the larger species. However, a deer reluctant to feed has a less than good chance of making a full recovery and successful rehabilitation.

Birds, in contrast to most mammals, are simple to forcefeed, but it is a very subjective matter – not so much in methods and recipes but in timing and quantities. There are two principal ways of doing it. The primary and simplest involves inserting suitable items into the throat (the opening to the oesophagus) or towards the back of the tongue avoiding the glottis (opening to the trachea) which will be seen opening and closing rhythmically as the bird breathes (Fig 29). Small items can be helped down with a finger, 'feeding-stick' such as a lollipop stick with a blunt end, or rubber-tipped forceps. Once in the throat, the beak may be closed and the food gently massaged down.

The majority of beaks can be prised open by applying pressure near

100

the base, never at the tip. The size of bird has little effect on the practicality though clearly the dexterity needed to forcefeed a small insectivore, should this extremely unlikely necessity ever arise, would be beyond even the most nimble-fingered; and the dangers to the inexperienced of doing so single-handed with a Gannet were indicated in Chapter 3. This is preferably a task for two or even three people: one to hold the bird, one with leather gloves ready to hold the mandibles apart, and one to insert the fish (headfirst) and massage it down the throat the farther the better to avoid regurgitation to which many carnivores (piscivores and raptors, though with the latter forcefeeding is seldom if ever necessary) are prone.

Distracting the bird for a short while following forcefeeding may help to prevent disgorging, as may holding the oesophagus low down for a minute or two. Gulls are particularly likely to disgorge their last meal and are best left to the pangs of hunger; tablets, if necessary, being forced down on their own rather than via a small slit in the abdominal cavity of a small fish which is the usual way. If retained there forcibly for a while, as Fitchie (1983) points out, gulls drink as soon as possible after human contact and, once they relax, can be released near a bowl of water so that the medication is washed down voluntarily.

Gulls are pretty omnivorous, but auks, herons, grebes, divers and diving-ducks will prefer fresh fish such as whitebait, sprats, Herrings, Sand-eels, Cod, Whiting, Sole or Mackerel. Sprats are most popular being the cheapest and most conveniently sized but larger types may be cut into appropriate, say finger-sized, strips (see also page 176). Two or three appropriately sized fish a day ought to be sufficient although a few more should be left in reach to encourage the bird to start feeding itself. A half-starved bird though will eat considerably more at first. On Christmas morning during the harsh winter of 1962/3, Dr Maurice Burton encountered a one-legged Slavonian grebe weak and exhausted. Placed in a bath of lukewarm water it eventually bathed energetically and efficiently with its one leg. It ignored strips of red meat and live mealworms but after some live small fish and freshwater shrimps had been caught and placed in the bath, consumed sixty immediately. The grebe tamed down quickly and proceeded to take dead whitebait from the hand, consuming about 200 daily!

Freshwater ducks and other waterfowl will invariably take food voluntarily; I have never known them not do so but scoters always seem to need forcefeeding and are tricky.

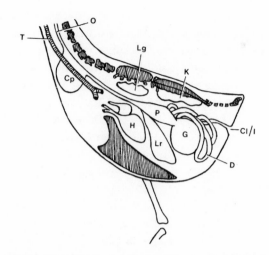

Fig 30 Digestive system of a bird: **O** oesophagus; **Cp** crop; **P** proventriculus; **G** gizzard (muscular stomach); **D** duodenum; **Cl/I** cloaca from intestine; **K** kidney; **Lr** liver; **T** trachea; **Lg** lung; **H** heart *(after Ede)*

Waders can be as problematical and, of course, their diet is substantially more refined. Should all else fail or if food is retained in the crop and not passed into the proventriculus (Fig 30), feeding via an oesophageal- or stomach-tube (Fig 31) can be attempted though the chances of ultimate success in this eventuality, certainly with waders, is small. The tube, made of rubber (boiled to sterilise) and lubricated with liquid paraffin, is eased down the oesophagus. Depending on the species, use a purée consisting of fish, meat or baby cereal similar in consistency to that recommended for deer, ie sufficiently moist to allow it to be drawn up into a syringe. For large birds, tubing of about 12mm (½in) diameter can be used and fitted to the nozzle of a thoroughly cleaned washing-up liquid bottle.

While the species of birds generally encountered away from aquatic environments can be forcefed in much the same way as outlined for piscivores, an appropriate substitute food has to be found and this is not quite so straightforward as it is with confirmed fisheaters. Jordan and Hughes in their book *Care of the Wild* (1982) are quite right when they say that 'a bird which normally eats flies might quite easily enjoy a portion of plum-pudding'. Even so it must be remembered that the plum-pudding was chosen voluntarily; if we are going to forcefeed an animal we have to be as certain as can be that the food we introduce into it is suitable. In the absence of natural items, try something like a

102

bland yet nutritious substitute similar to the eggfood used by aviculturists. It can be made up at home from readily available ingredients:
one egg boiled for at least half an hour to make it digestible, finely
grated and mixed with four times as much sweet biscuit such as
digestive; add a pinch of salt, and mix to a moist friability with cold
water. Softfood is the name given to the same or a similar mixture to
which egg has not (yet) been added.

Small regular quantities of eggfood should be made up since it soon
goes stale even when stored in a refrigerator, and it must not be fed
chilled. Such foods are suitable for a great many birds, young and
adults alike. Alternatives include moistened turkey starter-crumbs/
rearing-pellets, various baby and invalid foods, plain yogurt and
scrambled egg. When forcefeeding by hand, aim for a consistency

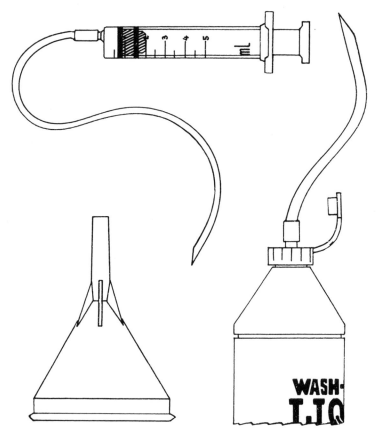

Fig 31 Apparatus for forcefeeding: a washing-up liquid bottle can be utilised in the absence of a
funnel; for smaller subjects, a 5ml syringe is ideal

which permits forming into fairly small pellets.

With guile, resource, imagination and flair, forcefeeding should be consistently necessary only in rare circumstances. When a day or so of peace and quiet urged on by hunger are insufficient in themselves, the wild-bird custodian can resort to certain tricks of the trapper, dealer and aviculturist such as lacing a commercial softbill or insectivorous food obtainable from petshops with live insects. Larvae such as small maggots, grubs and mealworms bring such inert food to life and to the attention of birds used only to taking animate items. Sprinkling a choice seed like niger onto old teazle-heads will tempt reluctant Goldfinches, then mix the same into a bowl of standard seed-mix such as Haith's of Cleethorpes 'British Finch Mixture'. Dispensing with dishes altogether and scattering the food on the ground will entice many slow kinds. Try bowls of different colours, and place some inside and some outside where possible. Lawn-mowings or duckpond weed (*Lemna minor*) can be floated on water for ducks and swans. A small amount of an expensive or natural food can be mixed into a more readily obtainable substitute.

Before concluding this chapter with a list of animals alongside suggested or favoured foods, a few general observations may be found useful by novices.

Passerines tend to fall into one of two categories called, not unreasonably, by aviculturists 'hardbills' and 'softbills' – more descriptive of the nature of their food than their beaks. 'Hardbills' is applied chiefly to finches but can be usefully extended to incorporate other seed-eaters such as gamebirds and columbids even though these do not crack open the seeds but swallow them whole to be ground down by grit – essential to all these birds – in the gizzard, where a certain amount of protein digestion will also occur. Softbills feed on soft-bodied omnivorous and insectivorous fare, and include many familiar garden-birds (Blackbird, Song thrush, Robin, Dunnock, titmice, Starling, crows including the Jackdaw and Magpie, and so on) and slightly less common or allied groups (such as the wagtails, Nuthatch, Treecreeper, woodpeckers, chats, warblers, flycatchers and Kingfisher). Perceptive readers may already have noted some of the ambiguities inevitable whenever we try to categorise nature. For instance, why is the Nuthatch a softbill and not a hardbill given its diet high in seeds (nuts)? And, more to the point, what about the equivocation caused by all finches, which become exclusively softbilled when feeding their young on insects and greenfood? These and similar points are partly resolved if we think about my mashed potato observation (page 98) and our discussion on the omnivorous inclinations of most animals in Chapter 2. Fledgling diets *per se* are covered more fully in Chapter 9.

Drinking water must always be available, preferably in shallow nonspillable dishes or, for some mammals, suspended fountains (Fig 32). Long-billed birds such as herons will require a deeper container. Even birds-of-prey, which drink little or never naturally, must be permitted to bathe, and this is essential to most birds in the maintenance of their plumage. Tap water is usually adequate for all save maritime birds under severe stress, which excrete salt from the nares and may therefore suffer from salt-depletion. However I have little doubt that rainwater is superior and occasionally essential for some individuals. For those suffering from shock, water can be replaced by a glucose saline solution obtainable from veterinarians. Animals reluctant or unable to drink (and this necessarily includes nestlings) can or will obtain their fluid intake from their food, and this can be artificially enhanced accordingly. Healthy mustelids maintained on a near natural diet, ie whole small animals, have no need for water as such at all; indeed its provision only speeds cage fouling. Many animals foul their drinking water, it thus needs frequent replacement even though it may look untouched. Mammals often need to have standing drinking vessels fixed in some way.

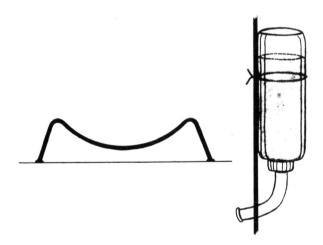

Fig 32 Section of a non-tilt dish – plastic or stainless steel – and a water-bottle suitable for small mammals

105

Simplified Nutrition Chart

BIRDS	BASIC DIET
piscivores (see also Kingfisher)	preferably whole fish (see page 101) except after ingesting oil (see Chapter 8)
carnivores: falcons, hawks, owls, corvids, shrikes and occasionally herons (but see above)	any available raw red meat or animal corpses (road casualties etc) though do not feed if risk of being poisoned, and beware of transmitting disease (avoid pigeons–see page 120). Sex-linked day-old chicks from commercial hatcheries (the unwanted cockerels) and 'pinkies' (baby laboratory rodents) are cheap and unsurpassable due to their being a complete natural meal providing all any raptor requires (roughage, protein, soft and hard parts etc); fish will be taken by some. If only red meat such as shin-beef is available, no harm will befall birds of prey if denied roughage for a day or two but this can be easily supplied by mixing in rabbit fur, chicken feathers, dog hair, pulverised bone or even shredded paper etc. Additives should not be necessary. Some, notably the smaller shrikes, Little owl, and various falcons like the Hobby, Merlin and Kestrel take, to varying degrees, large insects and invertebrates
waterfowl excluding fisheaters	poultry-food (grain, cracked maize, proprietary pellets etc). Supplements: wholemeal bread, greenfood, puppy-meal. All should be soaked or fed in water
gamebirds	poultry-food as for waterfowl, supplemented with appropriate tablescraps etc
hardbills	appropriately-sized seed (millet, hemp, canary-seed, rape, niger etc). Supplements: greenfood (eg Chickweed, Groundsel, Shepherd's purse, Dandelion, sow-thistles and various grasses), softfood (see page 103 and Chapter 9). As softbills when rearing young
columbids	pigeon-mix from petshops, poultry food
softbills (see also corvids on next page)	base of insectivorous food either homemade or proprietary (eg Sluis Universal) mixed with grated hard-boiled egg. Nuts of many sorts, shelled or whole (eg *unsalted* peanuts, acorns) for some spp. (Not over-ripe fruit of almost any kind: diced, mixed with insectivorous food, or laid open and impaled near a perch. Livefood: cultivated larvae such as maggots ('gentles') and mealworms, also locally collected grubs, aphids, caterpillars (*of common spp*), ant-cocoons ('ants-eggs), flies, spiders and other insects and invertebrates; home-cultured adult insects (eg flies from maggots), locusts, stick-insects, crickets and fish fry; daphnia, fruitflies and tubifex for tiniest spp; refer to avicultural handbook

specialist insectivores: flycatchers, hirundines, Swift, Nightjar	usually require handfeeding due to aerial habits: live insects; slivers of, or minced, lean meat. In emergency, try dried flies from pet or angling shop, and nectar (see below) from dish or pipette
woodpeckers, Treecreeper	fit out cage with upright bark-covered timber, scatter grubs (larvae) and other insects around. Jordan and Hughes recommend smearing or plastering same with a mixture of meat and insectivorous food – I would agree (and add peanut-butter) but timber would need replacing *frequently*. Try a little fruit. American spp known to take 'nectar' (invert sugar syrup or honey dissolved in water)
Kingfisher	highly individualistic in manner of acceptance: try minnows etc, in bowl of water, waving or wiggling one in front of bird, placing in beak, forcefeeding in that order; earthworms, mealworms, strips of larger fish etc
corvids including Jay, Magpie, Chough	as softbills, paying special attention to variety: nuts, large livefood, fruit and a coarse-grade insectivorous food. Meat, preferably day-old chicks (see carnivores), is essential in longer term care if cannibalism and unnatural aggression is to be deterred. Supplements: tablescraps, poultry-pellets etc

MAMMALS AND OTHERS

insectivores including shrews, Hedgehog, Mole, bats, reptiles and amphibians	locally collected livefood such as young slugs, snails, woodlice, earthworms (for the Mole, fed on ground or in bath of loam); cultivated (bought varieties (see softbills). Tinned pet meat appreciated by most, especially the omnivorous Hedgehog. *Ad lib* feeding necessary due to fast metabolism. Cottage cheese is extremely useful as is chopped or grated hard-boiled egg, and bread and milk is a good standby for some; but meat in some acceptable form is essential ultimately for ALL; raw egg
leporids (hares and the Rabbit)	petshop substitutes and hay readily available. In emergency, bread and milk may be accepted, but in summer months when local vegetation is abundant nothing other than natural food required. Offer unsprayed clover, grass, weeds, cultivated lettuce, vegetables or offcuts etc (see page 198)
small rodents: chiefly voles and mice	as above but more omnivorous, requiring some animal protein as insectivores, and nuts and grain (chicken-food)
large rodents: chiefly squirrels	nuts in their shells favoured above all else; poultry-food, fruit, vegetables, tablescraps etc. The Red squirrel does not have a good captive history

107

carnivores: Fox, Badger, Otter, mustelids etc	tinned pet meat mixed with biscuits exactly as for dogs (Fox and Badger) or neat (Otter and mustelids) or day-old chicks (see bird carnivores). Supplements/alternatives: raw egg, milk, road casualties, fish, eel, raw meat, crustaceans, earthworms etc
seals	whole raw fish either thrown within reach or skilfully handfed – about 2¼kg (5lb) daily divided into two feeds, although more than twice this may be taken after fasting. Additives usually unnecessary
cetaceans	do not feed while stranded
ungulates: chiefly deer	natural herbivorous fodder; if paddock is available, supplement with leaves especially ivy and trees – evergreen oak traditional winter fodder (hay for ponies), cattle-cake or nuts, peanuts (shelled and unsalted), tablescraps

NB: All perishable food and water to be given in clean containers and renewed every day.

Feeding Times

Fish- and meat-eaters (at correct weight) are usually fed once, sometimes twice, daily. Longer term care for larger species may require one 'starve-day' a week.

Insectivorous mammals and all softbilled and hardbilled birds require *ad lib* feeding, but beware of bats overfeeding.

Waterfowl and gamebirds are fed morning and evening, scattered on the ground for the latter.

5 First Aid and Parasites

In a sense, as I tried to make clear in the preceding two chapters, first aid in its original sense begins the moment we apprehend the casualty. Here, we are mostly concerned with elementary diagnosis and treatment, in other words alleviation of distress and suffering such as can be accomplished by the amateur at home replacing, alongside or prior to professional veterinary treatment. But it will be seen that the following diagnostic information often refers also to initial observation *before* capture.

Occasionally, sufficient and adequate treatment can be undertaken on site, as with our hypothetical snared Badger in Chapter 3. Some animals escape with a snare-wire tight around limb or body. In general, if able to catch the animal, avoiding injury to oneself, apply restraint to victim before releasing encumbrance so that injury can be examined and treated (see also Chapter 6).

It will be necessary to establish whether the circulation has been permanently damaged, resulting in necrosis followed by gangrene. This process can also result from frostbite and malnutrition, and is recognised in advanced stages by the dead or necrotic appearance and odour of the affected tissue: hard, dry, leathery and shrunken pieces of skin will hang off, and the area will be black, cold and have no sensation. There is no cure other than amputation or excision and cleaning, followed by sparing daily treatment of the affected part with antibiotics or sulphonamide powder, or euthanasia (see Chapter 11). In earlier stages, the first few hours of constriction, the circulation may not have been irretrievably damaged; the affected part will be swollen, feel cold compared to rest of the body, and pain may or may not be evident. Remove encumbrance and use hot bathing and/or massage in an attempt to restore circulation. Sepsis (putrefaction) is generally less common in birds than mammals.

Adult victims of concussion following collision with windows or

First Aid Chart

	INITIAL EXAMINATION AND ASSESSMENT	
CONSCIOUS CASUALTIES — **NO OBVIOUS INJURY** — **FULLY MOBILE**	Probably best left alone or persuaded to a nearby safe place and ideally kept under observation. If extremely apathetic to external stimuli, a poor general body condition (unhealthy integument, severe ectoparasitic infestation, dull eyes/snout etc) suggests disease or some other internal problem. Ease of capture is a good indicator to seriousness of condition but clearly pathogens are most effectively controlled in the early stages. Note distressed respiration, overgrown claws, and dental or beak disorders etc	
NO OBVIOUS INJURY — **PARTLY MOBILE**	Take time to assess fully; could be debilitated due to old age or inexperience, dazed, exhausted or suffering an intercurrent disease condition. If able to catch easily, examine for body condition and any hidden injury; if necessary put in semi-dark, warm place, offer suitable food and water, and reassess after 24hr. Brain damage can be indicated by dysfunction such as circling, fluttering or staggering, but such apparent convulsions and fits can also be the result of poisoning (see Chapter 7)	
OBVIOUS INJURY — **FULLY MOBILE**	Often the one likely to cause most trouble. Depending on the injury it may well be left or persuaded to a safe place to rely on time and natural healing, but if capture is necessary, do not aggravate the situation and make sure animal is well restrained before closer examination (see Chapter 3)	LOOK: is limb touching ground? Is wing trailing? Are joint angles normal, comparing sides? Colour of mucous membranes of eyes (glazed?) and mouth: if blueish or pale, internal injury or shock is indicated. Is nictitating membrane functioning normally or sluggishly? Any obvious swelling? Presence of wound: is there any foreign material contaminating, eg snare, shotgun pellets, wire, elastic band, broken glass or other trash? Shining bright torch through wings shows up pellets. Are parasites visible — a sign that host is losing bodyheat due to shock or imminent death? Blow up feathers of birds to inspect skin LISTEN: do broken ends of bones grate (crepitus)? Does skin crackle to the touch (see below)? Respiratory noises
OBVIOUS INJURY — **PARTLY MOBILE**	Probably the easiest to assess as animal is showing how it is coping with its injury. Is recovery likely without intervention? If not, note prior to capture: (1) loss of which function? (2) abnormal posture: remember which side is affected — often difficult to tell under restraint	FEEL: weight, general body condition, size of bird's pectoral muscles. Dehydration prevents skin sliding easily over body. Entry of air beneath skin results in a crackling feel. Presence of heat, cold, especially to distal parts (indicative of shock), matted integument, swelling, pain — more evident in mammals than birds, abnormal bone alignment — compare with normal side, any foreign material? Examination of specific areas (see below)

| UNCONSCIOUS | CASUALTIES | NO OBVIOUS INJURY | First check whether still alive: breathing? Response to stimuli: touch animal (with foot if dangerous), pinch webbing between toes etc. Consider surroundings for possible cause, eg roadside, beneath overhead cables, under window, cat or dog attack. May only be dazed and/or exhausted, in which case remove to safe place and/or return later; or remove to semi-darkness and warmth and keep assessing condition. If no improvement over several hours probably hopeless: seek professional help or consider euthanasia (see Chapter 11) |
| | | OBVIOUS INJURY | Probably the easiest case to approach and handle but one of the most difficult to assess due to unknown factors: how well will the animal be able to accommodate its obvious incapacity? Is there other less obvious damage? Proceed as for conscious obvious damage |

Fundamentally one seeks to establish, in the absence of obvious injury, whether the trouble — often accompanied by below average bodyweight — is due to disease, starvation or poisoning and whether human intervention is desirable or likely to be detrimental

slow-moving vehicles, or cat-maulings etc, which may only be dazed, should not be removed other than to a *nearby* place of safety; there may be a young dependent family which will perish if deprived of parental care. Concussion (the equivalent of a boxer's knock-out) may be discernible from position of animal – in birds, limpness, wings spread out and eyes closed; respiration is obvious; examine for signs of head or neck injury (see chart).

The natural powers of recovery of a wild animal should not be underestimated. Dr Archie McDiarmid, a leading authority on deer, told me the remarkable story of a fawn run over by a grass-cutter; the distraught operator, on finding two little hooves, organised a search-party but the fawn was never found. Some years later, during a cull, a buck was shot which looked to be standing low at the shoulder. On inspection, he was found to be in excellent condition but missing his two front hooves, in their place were two healthy stumps, grown over and calloused. The inference is that the fawn survived a literally shocking loss of blood and the invasion of pathogenic organisms particularly from contact with the ground, not to mention the considerable distress he must have had to endure.

Dr McDiarmid also cites several cases where deer hit by loose shots or motor vehicles have made off, clearing fences higher than they normally would and covering many miles before being overtaken by a stalker. Invariably they are found to have suffered severe fractures of the limbs. Incidentally, ill-advised head shots frequently result in a smashed jaw – an abominable wound and one of the hardest to follow up.

Poisoning of wildlife, usually from chemicals, is covered in Chapters 1 and 7. To quote Rentokil company: 'None of the rodenticides produced by Rentokil is corrosive to the alimentary tract. If an animal has recently taken bait, emesis [vomiting] followed by gastric lavage [washing out] of the stomach is an appropriate first course of action in all cases.' Nearly always, prompt professional aid is essential to a successful outcome.

Other than with the smallest creatures (insectivores, small rodents, finches etc), all collected patients require peace, warmth and an absolute lack of visual stimulation. With mammals it ought to be remembered, no matter how little we can do about it, that they live as much in a world of scent as of sight – some more than others of course. A state of shock will exist in many waifs, and this state will be further aggravated by chasing, catching, handling and transportation. Recuperation for one or two days will allow some adjustment and a return to more natural functions so that a better diagnosis can be made and treatment begun. The smallest and most ill specimens will not be able to withstand such a period of limbo.

An associated kind of ambivalence (I hesitate to say hypocrisy) to that which allows vehement animal lovers happily to eat meat, can also be found with cat lovers who are often, it seems to me, among the most passionate and sentimental of all. And here I am thinking more of the casual pet than the working cat. The same people who are understandably indignant of small boys throwing stones at birds, hare coursing and fox hunting, tend to smile benevolently when their cat (or cats, as is more often the case) comes home day after day with some

112

wretched corpse or small animal in a state of severe physiological and organic stress (shock). Without being drawn into the ethics of pet owning, it should be appreciated by everyone who allows their cat to range freely, that they are unleashing on their local wildlife not a cuddly pet but a mean predator which kills for fun. Nevertheless, I do not doubt that many cat owners are distressed by the spectacle, even if not to the extent of dispensing with the cat, and wish to do whatever they can for still living victims of their actions. Bear in mind also that some victims will certainly have a family dependent on them, so a cure is not only desirable but extremely urgent if the crime is not to be compounded by another greater one.

Shock, induced by chase/capture or injury can cause a 'flight or fight' response by releasing adrenalin which makes available extra reserves to help prey animals escape or face danger and dulls the pain response which may help to release many victims at least from the agony of their demise. In its unnatural pampered world the domestic cat, which does not actually need its prey as food, will play with its victim or bring it home for our delight. Thus shock ceases to protect and begins actually to endanger life. Prolonged stimulation of the flight or fight response can produce severe stress and exhaustion, and such depleted energy resources can be helped by oral doses of glucose solution to a base strength of 15 ml: 600 ml (1tbsp: 1pt) water. Where blood loss has been significant and the victim is of suitable size, commercial 'blood-replacer' fluids are available for injection by veterinarians. These therapies should run consecutively with a gradual rise in ambient temperature, and seclusion as outlined below. It is, moreover, important also to bear in mind that the effects of shock can be delayed for as long as thirty-six hours after the incident.

Stress and shock are frequently confused. Stress, induced by social, climatical and other environmental factors (stressors), is a natural population control and part of a wild animal's existence. Clinical signs only appear when an individual is unable to cope with the extent of its stressors, and this can lead to 'death from stress'. Young birds not fully capable of self thermo-regulation are particularly prone to clinical signs of lethargy and ultimately death when affected by unduly lowered body temperature — even in the summer months.

At the beginning of the book I mentioned here and there the plight of birds caught in severe winter conditions, and other casualties arising from natural causes. I intimated that, being natural, however distressing, we should ask ourselves whether by intervening we are performing a useful and ecologically justifiable action or a misguidedly harmful one. Having said that, and owning that either way our decision is probably inconsequential, I must say that few people, myself included, could walk past an animal in difficulties and coldly assess its fate in those terms.

Many species are pushed to the limit during winter, but of course we tend to notice only the larger ones – other than at birdtables and when mass mortality occurs such as with shrews in autumn – and the larger the body volume, the better suited an animal is to cope with severe conditions. Those dependent on open water for food and shelter, including protection from predators (eg waterfowl) are perhaps the most at risk. The Grey heron is particularly susceptible to prolonged freeze-ups, and is a frequent visitor to bird hospitals. One found in poor condition should be taken into warm, quiet quarters to relieve the stress of capture, and encouraged to feed, staying as a guest until its condition and the weather have improved.

Damp or wet integument should be dried by swaddling in absorbent material to minimise the risk of chilling. Once dry, warmth should be increased gently (to preclude the risk of haemorrhaging) up to a temperature of about 30°C (86°F), in diffused lighting. After an initial period of twenty-four hours, a cursory inspection may reveal a slightly more lively patient; the lighting can be brightened a little and some appetising food offered if not already available. As soon as possible, and no more than an equivalent period later, diagnosis and treatment must begin. If the patient has still shown no signs of feeding, forcefeeding (see Chapter 4) must, regrettably, be regarded as urgent due to the fasting which more than likely preceded the capture.

Warmth can be supplied in a variety of ways. Although the cardboard box and airing cupboard is a frequent and, for the first twenty-four hours useful, combination, the hospital-cage, standard equipment of all aviculturists, is not difficult to make and ideal for most small animals. One can be fashioned from a boxcage (see Fig 28) by inserting a false floor over one 60W or two 40W lightbulbs, sealing the wire-netting with transparent polythene or replacing it with glass, and providing ventilation holes (Fig 33). Heatpads can also be usefully employed.

For larger subjects, heatlamps (dull-emitter are best) may be suspended at a height appropriate for the heat required; if hung at one end or in a corner of the pen, a temperature gradient is established in which the subject can choose its own most comfortable position.

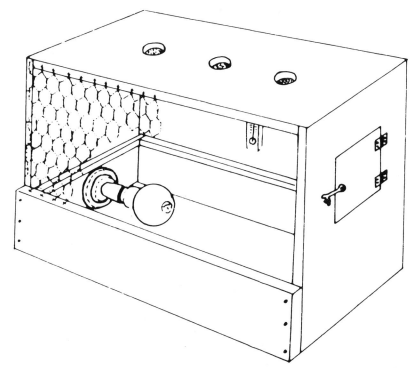

Fig 33 Homemade hospital cage. Note the supports for the false floor (which will cover the heat source, eg 60W bulb); polythene tacked over wirenetting will increase the temperature as required (the aim is usually for c28°C); the gauze-covered ventilation holes on top

Electric wiring has to be protected from mammalian teeth by metal conduiting, or fixed out of reach. Ordinary hotwater-bottles or make-do substitutes such as plastic detergent bottles with screw-on tops can be useful in an emergency if well wrapped in paper or an old blanket to obviate burning and puncturing by birds' beaks and claws. Such hotwater-bottles are however altogether too risky for mammals unless the stone variety is available; if not, glass jars do well. For smaller subjects, use two jars, one on either side, or one ordinary rubber bottle underneath. Don't forget that all hotwater-bottles will need periodic refilling.

Physical examination must be thorough and yet as rapid as possible noting – as well as the points listed in the chart – infections and growths, eye injury and/or infections, ear infections, any discharges,

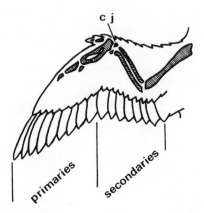

Fig 34 Wing of a bird, showing the wrist or carpal joint (**cj**) and flight feathers *(after Ede)*. See also *Fig 1*

soiling of vent or anal region (noting colour, consistency etc). Examination of the limbs should follow if necessary. With birds, flex each wing and palpate in turn, holding at the carpal joint (Fig 34), and inspect for damage to feathers; fractures and dislocations are revealed, if not already apparent, by abnormal movement, swelling and bruising. Each leg and foot is then examined. Remember that a bird walks on its toes (digitigrade) and therefore has an extra 'cannon-bone' (the tarsometatarsus) caused by a transformation of the metatarsals (Fig 27). The toes clench automatically as the bird's weight folds the false knee and flexes the tendons; this mechanism saves muscular energy and ensures that sleeping birds do not fall from their perches.

In the absence of noticeable deformity, abnormality in a limb is likely to be the result of internal injury or a disease affecting the central nervous system. The feet of mammals and birds are prone to injury on account of hefty general wear and tear and their almost incessant contact with foreign and sometimes dangerous surfaces. Specific conditions are dealt with in the next chapter, but it is very unlikely that an animal suffering only from lameness or even from one useless foot will allow itself to be caught by a human: three-legged mammals and one-legged birds, otherwise apparently healthy, are a not altogether uncommon sight.

Similarly with beak and claw disorders, although these are usually incidental or the result of poor captive accommodation (overgrowth). A bird with a badly damaged beak should be referred to a veterinarian (see Chapter 6).

So far, these examinations have been concerned with formulating a working hypothesis – is the patient treatable? If we decide so, what can we learn of its condition; is specialist treatment desirable? Is rehabilitation to the wild possible? If not, can the patient perform any useful function, for instance to science, education or conservation? If the answer is negative, is lifelong accommodation feasible and, if so, where and by whom? Plainly, these questions have to be resolved after the physical examination, but resolved they must be for the answers if favourable, may well modify or influence our prognosis. If unfavourable, we may, of course, elect for a second or professional opinion before contemplating the distressing yet sometimes merciful option of euthanasia (see Chapter 11).

From the decision to treat onwards, we embark on a programme of qualitative housing, observation, diagnosis, veterinary treatment and, hopefully, convalescence and rehabilitation. There are few accolades and no gratitude, only a commitment.

By now, we should have decided on a course of action and sought veterinary assistance if the condition seems too severe or complex for home treatment. Either way, after its physical examination, the patient should have been reinstated in its hospital quarters.

An obvious injury not requiring palpation or immediate attention – as would a haemorrhage (see Chapter 6) or maggot infestation (see below) – need not be handled at home until after the initial 24–48 hours settling-in period when traditional first aid can be administered. This involves cleansing and anointing of wounds with a mild antiseptic or salt and water (1–2tsp: 1pt) or potassium permanganate; applying an astringent; temporarily taping damaged wings into their natural folded position (Plate 14); and splinting legs.

Parasites

In summer, the cleansing of wounds may have to take precedence over considerations of stress. Fly-strike (myiasis) is usually revealed by the fairly nauseating sight of maggots usually of *Lucilia* blowflies (greenbottles) infesting living tissue in open wounds, the eyes, ears, rectum and other orifices. Caught in the early stages, it is a condition which looks worse than it actually is. The maggots can be removed individually with blunt forceps, tweezers or, near delicate organs, by suction with a bulb-ended glass pipette. Open wounds smothered in cornflour will cause the maggots to lose traction and drop off; other

117

methods remove them and unhatched eggs by flushing with syringe-fuls of much diluted warm soapy water or hydrogen peroxide (20 or 30 volumes; 15–20ml: 600ml or 1–2tbsp: 1pt). Eggs alone may be removed by their adhesion to gauze impregnated with petroleum jelly, olive oil etc. Finally cleanse the wound and it will be seen, ironically, that the maggots have actually helped to keep the wound clean by feeding on the tissue as it dies. Eyes are the most dangerous area and will need constant applications of a mild eye-wash. Specific larvicidal/antiseptic creams and powders are obtainable from vets, and phenol-type or carbolic antiseptics such as Dettol are useful for cleansing wounds away from eyes.

Once all the maggots have been removed, regular checks must be made to prevent re-infestation and confirm that no grubs or eggs have escaped. Severe attacks should be referred to a vet even if initial cleansing seems successful, in case internal organs have been affected. Defenceless psilopaedic (naked) nestlings are also susceptible to myiasis. Flies seen near a potential victim can generally be relied on to have begun their work.

Much the same can be said for the bot-flies, *Gasterophilidae*, which are among our largest, although they parasitise mammals in a different way. The commonest is the Horse bot-fly, which also attacks other equines. Eggs are laid on the host's forequarters, and after hatching are ingested by licking. They become attached to the stomach wall, which in rare cases they may penetrate causing peritonitis, living there to 9–10 months before passing out in the faeces to pupate in the ground. Heavy infestations will cause a serious loss of condition and may promote secondary infection. It is important to include bot treatment in routine worming if feasible, and to remove eggs from hosts' coats while grooming, scraping off or using suitable preparation to kill eggs and hatching larvae.

Other flies which attack wildlife are the notorious warble-flies, *Hypoderma* spp. – a scourge of cattle, sheep, and deer in the north. Warble-flies are on the wing from late May onwards, their buzz causes irritation – the mad gallop or gadding of cattle – and can lead to animals damaging themselves on wire etc. The Cattle warble-fly lays its eggs on the body of the victim, and the larvae bore into the body, feeding as they go; they end up back just under the skin where they cause inflamed sores (warbles) before dropping out, again to pupate in the soil. The larvae, surprisingly large, can be removed with forceps or tweezers, and the wound can then be disinfected with alcohol or hydrogen peroxide via a syringe or pipette. It can have an aberrant form in the horse. Do not squeeze swelling as this can crush the larva which releases toxin into the body. Its incidence has been greatly reduced by the Warble-fly Eradication Scheme.

A relative, the Sheep nostril-fly *Oestrus*, and the Deer bot-fly are equally charming except that their larvae live in the gullets, nasal cavities, sinuses, brain-tissues etc. The hapless victim endures much agony before death brings merciful release or the full-grown larvae or hatched pupae leave. Examination of infected animals must be thorough and observation ideally maintained for a fortnight in insect-proof quarters.

Fly control is important in animal hospital stable areas. Use insecticidal strips, site dungheaps away from stables, and if necessary spray or pour on fly repellents. Fly-repellent wound dressings are also available.

Many other parasites affect wildlife but the effect is usually minimal because, for reasons of their own survival, they live commensally with their hosts – at least in healthy animals. When a host becomes debilitated for any reason and loses its natural vigour, its resistance also decreases and parasites may then multiply excessively and become pathogenic.

Parasites are broadly classified into the following groups: **ectoparasites** which live *on* the host; and **endoparasites** which live *within* the body of the host. Within these two broad groups there are parasites which are *obligatory*: spending their lives in or on a host, eg most parasitic worms; *temporary*: passing a definite phase or phases of their lives as obligatory parasites, eg bot-flies, ticks; *facultative*: existing free or as parasites, eg blowfly larvae; *permanent*: living by far the greater part of their lives as parasites, eg lice, coccidia; *occasional*: visiting hosts for a short period to obtain food, eg fleas, bloodsucking flies. The scientific name of a parasitic disease is formed by adding 'osis' or 'iasis' to the generic or collective name of the species causing the disease, eg 'fascioliasis' means disease of animals infected with *Fasciola*, a liver fluke.

Parasitic diseases, as we have seen, are seldom caused by a few specimens. The reason why parasites are widely involved in many disease processes is because of the ways in which they damage the host:

1 by taking nourishment which would otherwise belong to the host, eg intestinal worms

119

2   by obstructions, eg of air passages by gapeworms – nematode roundworms usually of *Syngamus trachea*
3   by feeding on the tissues of the host, eg all bloodsuckers
4   by producing toxins, eg warble-flies, intestinal worms
5   by traumatic damage to body tissue, eg ticks, mites, blowflies and many more
6   by facilitating entrance of pathogenic bacteria
7   by transmitting diseases for which they act as intermediate hosts, eg fleas carrying certain tapeworm cysts and myxomatosis.

Fleas (see Ectoparasites below) are highly organised species, but parasites vary in complexity down to the primitive single-celled protozoa. Most of the parasites which affect animals are animals themselves; one category which is nearer the plant kingdom than the animal is the fungi, and these are covered in Chapter 7.

Endoparasites

There are two subdivisions of protozoa which are a source of concern here: Mastigophora and Sporozoa. Organisms of the class Mastigophora move by means of whiplike processes called flagella – flagellate protozoa. One of these, *Histomonas meleagridis*, causes infectious enterohepatitis, mainly in poultry but pheasants, grouse and other birds can be affected. It is not likely to be seen in wild birds but is important in view of long-term patients and disease control. The disease is commonly called 'blackhead' due to discoloration of the skin especially in the head area but the organism, carried by a caecal nematode *Heterakis gallinae*, attacks the bowel and liver. Another is a Trichomonad, *Trichomonas gallinae*, a common inhabitant of pigeons which, if eaten by birds-of-prey, can cause a fatal outbreak of 'frounce'; for this reason, if pigeons are used as food, the head and crop should be removed first. Trichomoniasis prevents birds from feeding, and on inspection the mouth might be seen to contain caseous (cheesy) yellowish lesions.

Members of the class Sporozoa are exclusively parasitic; they do not have any particular form of locomotion, and produce spores. The organism responsible for malaria in man belongs to this group. There are two genera in the order Coccidia, members of both being fairly host-specific: *Eimeria* mainly in gallinaceous birds and rabbits, and *Isospora* which is known chiefly from finches. The organism is picked up from infected ground and can multiply rapidly in the digestive tract, causing considerable damage. It is important to be aware of this parasite so that waterfowl, pheasants etc are not infected while in temporary occupation of, for example, hen-runs. Coccidiosis can be precipitated by stress after having lain dormant for years. The most common symptom is greenish diarrhoea – possibly bloodstained, loss of weight, weakness, and staring coat or ruffled feathers. If infection is suspected in ground which has to be used, preventative treatment consisting of medicating drinking water with a suitable sulpha drug or coccidiostat from a veterinarian is desirable. Positive diagnosis can be made by microscopic examination of faeces.

There are three main classes of parasitic worms: Trematoda, the unsegmented flatworms, or flukes; Cestoda, the segmented flatworms, or tapeworms; and the less closely related Nematoda, the unsegmented roundworms. The Trematoda concern us little; flukes have complicated life-cycles which work against cross-infection in captivity, and they cause few clinical signs of disease. Occasionally the liver fluke, *Fasciola hepatica*, normally of cattle and sheep occurs in unusual or aberrant hosts such as deer particularly after a series of wet summers which favours mud-snails, the intermediate host. The following two groups are more important here, and are significant vertebrate pathogens.

Cestoidean tapeworms (Fig 35) require intermediate hosts to complete their life-cycle, usually as a tapeworm in the intestine of one host, and in cystic form in the other. In wildlife we may find the cystic forms of tapeworms of domestic animals and man, and the tapeworm stage of species which have a cystic form in, for instance, sheep and occasionally man. The most important of these is the tapeworm *Echinococcus* of dogs and the Fox, the cystic form of which is generally found in sheep but can also occur in man as an aberrant host, where it causes a very severe condition known as hydatidosis. Infection in man and sheep is by ingestion of tapeworm segments passed in the faeces of dog or Fox, or on the coat. Carnivores can be infected by eating cysts

Fig 35 Cestode (tapeworm) from a bird; those from mammals can be very much larger, up to several metres exceptionally (*after Watson & Amerson*)

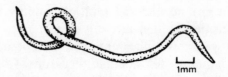

Fig 36 Nematode (roundworm) from a bird; like cestodes, they can grow much larger *(after Watson & Amerson)*

found in sheep, and it is therefore important to dispose of dead sheep and institute strict personal hygiene where there is a possibility of infection from Foxes; routine dosing of farm dogs helps limited the spread.

Different species of tapeworms can also be found in poultry and wild birds, the intermediate hosts being slugs, snails, flies, ants and earthworms. The damage done to the host by the tapeworm stage is not really significant except in heavy infestations, when a loss of condition and diarrhoea occurs. One minor exception is where horse tapeworms cause ulcers in the large intestine – a possible cause of unthriftiness in 'wild' ponies.

The indirect life-cycles of cestode worms preclude the re-infestation which is a characteristic of roundworms (see below); and in captivity the only conditions suitable for the spread of infection are unhygienic or overcrowded outside enclosures which can support crustaceans and other secondary hosts. Rigorous hygiene will break the life-cycles of most endoparasites, including the flukes and spiny-headed worms, Acanthocephala.

Nematode roundworms (Fig 36) usually have a simple, direct life-cycle in the intestine or trachea, but some inhabit other organs as well. Their eggs are either voided by the host and are swallowed or hatch and develop outside to infect the same animal (often the case in captivity) or another usually of the same species, or retained within the host's blood for the intermediate stages.

Hookworms, Ancylostomidae, belong to this group and can affect gallinaceous birds, carnivores and others possibly including deer. Roundworms are the commonest endoparasite of wild birds, but anthelmintic drugs such as Levamisole, Piperazine and Thiabendazole are effective. They also infest larger hosts like ponies, giving symptoms similar to those caused by the tapeworms above. Lungworms can also occur in larger species, commonly in Roe deer, and cause persistent coughing, emaciation and in extreme cases parasitic pneumonia. They are particularly dangerous if deer or ponies are

122

confined to paddocks previously grazed by cattle in the case of deer, or donkeys in the case of ponies, and where the parasitic larvae is left in faeces ready to infect the next season's grazers. As many deer prefer to browse rather than graze, there is a modicum of natural prevention.

An understanding of host/parasite relationships, and laboratory screening of faecal or blood samples are necessary for prevention and to instigate effective treatment.

Ectoparasites

Two main classes are involved here: Insecta and Arachnida. The Insecta are typified by a six-legged adult stage divisible into head, thorax and abdomen, and include lice, Mallophaga and Anoplura (=Siphunculata); fleas, Siphonaptera; and louse-flies, Hippoboscidae. Other flies of the order Diptera are also parasitic, the most important of which were mentioned on page 118. The Arachnida have an eight-legged adult stage divisible into cephalothorax (head and thorax combined) and abdomen. They include mites and ticks, Acarina, relatives of the spiders.

These parasites are not likely actually to cause pathogenic conditions and are often visible – with a hand-lens there is no problem at all. They, like the endoparasites, can multiply excessively on vertebrates brought to a low pitch, and during routine examination note should be taken of any parasites seen (Figs 37–40) and any abnormalities of integument which could be parasite-caused. Different bird species and individuals are parasitised to varying degrees: parasites can teem all over one specimen while another is free. Relief of such secondary conditions is bound to benefit patients and ease their distress; and may even, as definitive first aid, help to restitute complete health.

Mites and Ticks

These can be nasty vectors of disease. They are suckers of blood and tissue-fluids or, in the case of the feather-mites, feeders on feathers and skin debris – sometimes to the extent of virtual denudation. They cause anaemia, distress and various conditions of the skin. Skin-mites Sarcoptidae, are virtually microscopic and live usually on the skin (sucking-mites) or burrow into it (itch-mites). The nasal-mites, since they live in the respiratory system, are in effect endoparasites. Feather-mites are so small that they may look like dirt particles on body, wing and tailfeathers. Examine especially the undersides of

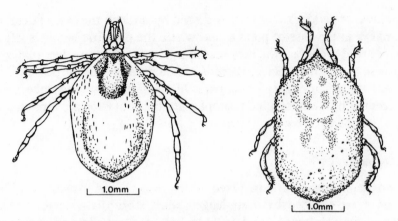

Fig 37 Hard tick *(left)* and soft tick *(right);* the engorged female looks considerably larger *(after Watson & Amerson)*

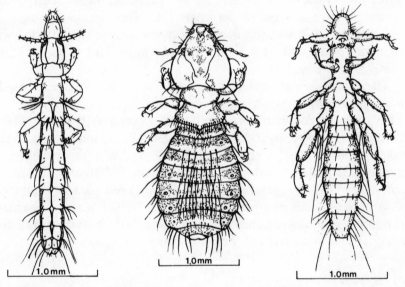

Fig 38 Biting feather lice *(left to right)*: wing type; head type; breast/back type *(after Watson & Amerson)*

wing and tail quills and between the barbs. Skin-mites are usually harder to see than other mites – the head and brood-patches of adult birds are important places to examine. On nestlings, any area devoid of feathers, such as the neck, belly and underwings, is important.

Mites cause mange and other severe skin irritations. Ear-mites in rodents and rabbits, for example, are revealed by the scratching of ears and by rubbed fur; they are barely visible to the naked eye. Vets

124

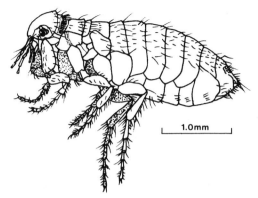

Fig 39 Bird flea *(after Watson & Amerson)*

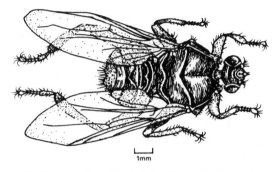

Fig 40 Louse-fly or flat-fly *(after Watson & Amerson)*

can supply ear-drops which kill mites and soothe inflamed ears etc. Mites can also affect the body when they are indicated by rubbed patches. Itch-mites, being burrowers, are even less easy to see than other skin-mites, and diagnosis is confirmed by microscopic examination of skin and hair samples. Again, wild animals can tolerate mild infestations; but take care in handling and avoid direct contact because some parasites can bite and cause skin reaction. For example *Cheyletiella*, the Rabbit fur-mite, causes small red spots especially on the arms.

The infamous sucking Red mite, *Dermanyssus gallinae*, is a well-known pest of cagebirds. Although most mites can be treated safely with insecticides, Red mites are usually nocturnal and migrate to their prey from nooks and crannies near roosting-sites in buildings or nests etc each evening. Only in heavy infestations will they remain permanently on the birds. Treatment involves removing at-risk birds from the site harbouring the scourge while it is carefully disinfected by spraying with gamma benzene hexachloride. The safest on-bird insecticide is probably pyrethrum powder, but a 10 per cent emulsion of benzyl benzoate is also recommended despite its latent toxicity. Similarly for the *Cnemidocoptes* itch-mites, well known because they are responsible for depluming in domestic birds – the irritation making them pluck out their feathers – and scaly-face and scaly-leg which appear as yellowish nodular-masses (encrustaceans). Wild birds, too, can be affected, and treatment involves removing and burning the flaky crust and applying the emulsion for ten days to the legs and three days to the facial area. But beware of possible toxicity to some species.

There are two main families of bloodsucking ticks or Ixodoidea (Fig 37): soft leather-ticks, Argasidae, and hard shield-ticks, Ixodidae, which are the more numerous and probably best known by the Common sheep-tick and Hedgehog-tick which occasionally fasten onto humans. They are much larger than the mites and easily visible when engorged although male hard-ticks can be overlooked because they do not distend. Like sucking-mites, they can spread disease and, since their saliva is poisonous, can seriously affect both birds and mammals although heavy infestations are rare. Examples of the infections ticks can spread are louping-ill (page 165) – a virus causing meningitis mainly in sheep but isolated also from wildlife, tick-borne fever (TBF) and red-water. Louping-ill is transmissible to man. The chief effect in wild species is local irritation.

An application of methylated spirit or any neat alcohol to the tick will greatly facilitate its removal by forceps or tweezers. Care must be taken that the mouth-parts are not left embedded in the host to cause infection. Geoff Nute injects ticks with local anaesthetic to allow some relaxation before removal; other techniques involve suffocating the parasite by liberal applications of any fatty substance, eg margarine, oil or Vaseline. Burning with a lighted cigarette is not to be recommended on wild animals. Heavy infestations can be treated as per mites – seabird colonies are well known for their high populations – but ticks use their hosts mainly as sources of food between meals, spending their various life stages in leaf-litter and vegetation where they can remain for up to a year. A female lays up to 8,000 eggs on the ground.

Lice

Animal lice (as opposed to booklice) fall into two main groups: the sucking-lice, Anoplura, that inhabit mammals and feed on blood; and the chewing- or biting-lice, Mallophaga, mainly found on birds though those of the family Trichodectidae infest mammals. Bird lice live mostly on feathers and skin debris, eg feather-mites, but a minority also take body fluids, notably from eyes and growing feathers which are seriously impaired. Species of one genus live in the throats of Cormorants. They will erupt on sick hosts, the consequent irritation leading to almost incessant scratching which, in turn, causes skin damage, loss of blood and the entry of pathogenic organisms, wasting and possibly death. A lacklustre, dishevelled appearance – especially in regions where the host has difficulty in grooming or preening – is symptomatic. The shape of a louse (Fig 38) depends on the part of the body to which it is adapted, eg back of the head or beneath limbs; and be sure to look along the shafts of wing-quills for the long slender species. The eggs tend to be attached to the host; Mallophaga eggs on feathers sometimes looking like small oblong scales. The hairs or feathers on which these nits are laid in rows can be simply cut off; the lice themselves can be killed by an appropriate insecticide from a spray or puffer. The life-cycle is spent entirely on the host.

Fleas

All adult fleas are bloodsuckers and may be seen scurrying through the coat as laterally compressed wingless insects with piercing and sucking mouthparts. There are at least 100 varieties of bird-flea (Fig 39) although about 95 per cent of known species parasitise mammals. Their eggs hatch off the host in a suitable place, such as a nest or lair where there is an accumulation of detritus and coagulated blood on which the larvae feed and then pupate. Controlled hatching enables them to take advantage of the proximity of a suitable host, and they are not generally host-specific. Because of this life-cycle and the extraordinary jumping ability of the adults, fleas are more difficult to control than most other parasites. However, flea infestation is seldom so bad as to be directly responsible for illness although they are important casual vectors of disease. Also they themselves can be intermediate hosts to, for example, species of tapeworms found in dogs and the Fox, and myxomatosis is spread by the Rabbit flea (see Chapter 7). The animals least likely to possess fleas are nomadic ones which do not live in permanent homes including holes, burrows, lairs, nests, crevices etc. This explains why man alone among the primates is habitually a host; why there are comparatively few bird-fleas –

mammal-fleas being able to breed all the year round; and goes some way to explain why the Sand martin is probably the most flea-ridden bird species. As bathing is often inappropriate for animals, they can be uncomfortable to handlers; but effective insecticides are readily available.

True Flies

The louse-flies and keds, together with two British species of bat parasites, Nycteribiidae, bring us full circle in this review of Arthropod parasites because they are highly modified members of the order Diptera (see also page 117). Although the name 'louse-flies' correctly suggests their parasitic habits, the synonym 'flat-flies' – from their flattened leathery bodies – is far more descriptive of their appearance (Fig 40). Like many of the foregoing they are bloodsuckers, and indeed like the lice they have well developed claws which enable them to cling tenaciously to fur and feather. They are by far the largest and most conspicuous of all ectoparasites and are reminiscent of house-flies in those species, about twelve in Britain, which have retained their wings. In some, such as the Deer-ked or Deer-fly which attacks all species of deer and some other mammals including people from time to time, the wings are shed when a suitable host is found. Others, like the Sheep-ked, are wingless, or have only vestigial wings throughout life. The Forest-fly attacks the tender skin beneath the tail, principally of horses and cattle, and is common in the New Forest.

Anyone who has handled more than a few wild birds, especially those dying or recently dead, will be familiar with the sight of these parasites scuttling sideways and quickly through the surface of the plumage preparatory to finding a warmer host. In normal numbers they do not unduly harm the host, although I doubt if the twenty of the flightless species host-specific to the Swift recorded on one specimen were welcomed. Those species which fly, do so rapidly, some flying away when danger threatens only to return later. The hirundines also seem particularly favoured – adults and young being attacked in the nest, sometimes seriously.

The life-cycle is interesting in that the female produces only one egg which hatches within her body, drops to the ground as a larva, and immediately pupates over winter. Louse-flies can transmit protozoan parasites and also transport true lice – as many as twenty-two being found on the abdomen of one fly – from host to host. The bat-flies, also wingless and pupiporous, seem to favour *Myotis* bats. Like their relatives, they are difficult to catch hold of manually if removal is considered necessary.

A convenient way of dealing with a small animal heavily infested with ectoparasites is to put the head through a slit in a piece of oil-cloth and then lower the body into a jar containing pybuthrin powder. The animal will struggle and in so doing will dislodge many of the parasites already disturbed by the insecticide. This technique is adapted from Michael Chinery (1974) who recommended chloroform; this is now not considered safe enough for use except by qualified persons.

6 Injury

Some of the mildest forms of injury have already been considered and, at this level, natural healing often occurs after first aid (see Chapter 5). Here we are mostly concerned with more than superficial lesions and abrasions, but there will inevitably be some overlap.

While it seems to go without saying that all serious injury must be referred to a veterinary surgeon, there is a grey area which will involve home doctoring. Moreover, since vets' fees are not cheap especially for home visits – and wild animals seldom tolerate surgery visits on account of handling problems and the inevitable stress and distress which can cause relapses and even new injuries – anyone in charge of sick wild animals will want to understand whatever professional treatment is taking place and to participate both during and between such visits. Even though experience is best gained direct from the vet, commonsense is also invaluable in that grey area.

Looking again at the chart on pages 110–11, reference is made to 'obvious injury'; in this chapter we try to define this more precisely.

Bleeding

First of all identify site of origin – possibly indicated by staining of fur, the amount and colour of the blood, and whether clotting has taken place. Bright red arterial blood tends to spurt out and may be less easy to stop than the darker red venous blood from smaller veins, which tends to ooze or well out. Arterial blood loss is the more serious because of the possibility of a greater volume drained. Natural defence mechanisms provide for the arrest of much venous loss; for instance the victim may be shocked (qv), one of the signs of which is a cooling of the skin which has the effect of constricting surface blood vessels.

It is sometimes possible to get an idea of the quantity of blood lost if the animal is unconscious, and then to identify the site or origin. The cause of the haemorrhage may be obvious, eg broken glass on a road etc. Where the source of a haemorrhage is a natural orifice, internal bleeding is indicated. Ear, mouth and nostril bleeding is often a consequence of head injury, ie skull or possibly even brain damage. If unconscious, keep nose down to prevent blood running back down the throat and the patient drowning in it, apply a cold pack (see below) to muzzle, and try to keep air-way open. If blood is coming from both nostrils, place a piece of wood between the jaws as animals are not natural mouth breathers. Seek professional help. Inspect mouth – taking care not to get bitten – for a cut, or bitten tongue, and cold bathe if possible.

Bleeding from the rectum, urethra or cloaca strongly suggests severe internal injury or poisoning by a warfarin-type anticoagulant rodenticide (see page 112 for appropriate first aid, and Chapter 7). Seek professional help, keeping animal as still and quiet as possible; if conditions permit, place on newspaper, and cover with some warm material to conserve body heat.

The one notable exception to the foregoing is the quite natural production of mammalian afterbirth – the discharging of foetal membranes. New mothers go to great lengths to achieve isolation and are therefore hard to find at such times, however should you happen on such a scene, retreat as quietly as possible and pry no further.

Otherwise, profuse external bleeding may in some cases be staunched by applying manual pressure to the wound, or a tourniquet above the site of the haemorrhage if the injury is on an extremity. But on wild animals a tourniquet should only be used as a last resort because it is difficult to stop the haemorrhage and still allow the blood to reach the tissue around the wound or below the tourniquet. If inexpertly applied it can lead to necrosis and gangrene. To minimise the risk of losing a limb, tourniquets should not be left in place for more than about 20 minutes. Take no chance of an animal breaking away with a tourniquet still in place (Fig 41).

Applying coldness to a haemorrhage causes a spasm or contraction of the smaller and surface blood vessels thereby slowing the blood-flow in those cut and aiding clotting. This may be achieved solely by cold running water, but the application of pressure as well is a far better way of stopping bleeding in the absence of styptic agents such as Friar's balsam which will control a seeping haemorrhage. Make a cold compress by soaking a pad of absorbent material, eg lint, surgical gauze or even a clean handkerchief, in cold water; wring out and apply tightly against the bleeding point for a short time, then repeat.

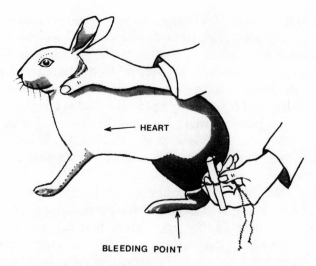

Fig 41 'Stopgap' tourniquet between the heart – pumping point – and the bleeding point. The stick is turned until the string is tight, and is slackened several times a minute to allow the blood to flow a little

Crushed ice instead of water can sometimes be used if placed between two pieces of gauze, but it is not suitable for prolonged use as it can cause tissue destruction and, in small animals, excessive heat loss and precipitate shock. Always avoid undue wetting of small animals.

The compress may be tied in place or bandaged, taking care once again not to stop the blood-flow beyond the wound. Feel the temperature of this area; if it is colder than above the wound, or if pink skin has a pale or bluish tinge, the blood-flow has been interrupted, so loosen the pressure pad accordingly.

Skin Damage/Loss of 'Integumental Integrity'
There are several types of wounds:
Abrasion or graze　not through full thickness of skin; may be localised or extensive; usually not so serious as others.
Incision　usually cut by sharp object, a clean cut with no tearing which can bleed profusely.
Laceration or torn skin (predator attack etc)　full skin thickness, often involves underlying tissue and larger blood vessels.
Puncture　a small but deep hole in skin which can introduce infection not immediately apparent, eg wounds caused by teeth penetration of predators, or gunshot.
Ulceration　removal of some surface layers of skin; usually results

132

from either (a) foreign non-animal material rubbing against skin, eg identification ring too tight; or (b) damaged part, which may be swollen, rubbing against adjacent part of same animal, ie where the skin-folds rub against each other. Wound discharges can also cause ulceration of skin, usually over a period of time and not as a result of a single short incident.

Contusion accompanied by much bruising.

Suturing or Stitching

Serious lacerations and incisions may require ligation if the flow of blood is to be arrested. Only in dire emergencies should this be attempted inexpertly with an ordinary needle and thread. Veterinary surgeons will decide or advise on the need for anaesthetics. In an emergency, prepare your equipment carefully: needle (preferably suture or small, curved upholsterer's needle); silk thread or dental floss may be substituted for catgut; sharp scissors; adhesive tape; forceps or tweezers; antiseptic salve; surgical gauze; medicine dropper or pipette – this is the bare minimum.

Sterilise instruments by boiling or steeping in a vial of disinfectant such as hydrogen peroxide or alcohol; wash hands carefully. The patient may be wrapped in a clean towel and laid in one's lap. Prepare the vicinity of the wound by using tweezers to remove foreign bodies, snipping off ragged fragments of flesh, and by light disinfection.

Pass the needle and thread through the skin on the side farthest away from the central nervous system first about ⅛in (3mm) from the edges to be sutured. To avoid tearing, gently close the wound together with finger and thumb while drawing the thread through. Stitches may be individually tied, or continuous as in simple overhand or whip-stitching – each stitch being about ⅙in (4mm) apart. Use as few as possible, and do not bring together so tightly that any discharge cannot drain away. In continuous stitching, leave a few inches of loose thread at each end to tie together. Afterwards, drop antiseptic salve over the area and apply an aseptic dressing. Sutures should be left in place for about 7–10 days and inspected every 2–3.

Haemorrhages not Requiring Suturing

Where the skin is not broken, blood is probably from grazed or bruised tissue. Superficial bruising clears up quite quickly. Clean area as indicated in Chapter 5. Do not use soaps, detergents or household disinfectants as they may be toxic and interfere with waterproofing

Fig 42 A jar containing hot or cold water – useful for bathing paws, which may be immersed
with little splashing

and scent mechanisms. Salt in water is an excellent antiseptic.
Hydrogen peroxide is poisonous but, diluted as given on page 118, can
be used as a sterilising agent for wounds. Other common antiseptics
are potassium permanganate, gentian violet and cetrimide.

If the wound is more than skin deep, underlying tissue may be
exposed. Stop haemorrhage as described earlier and clean as for
grazes. Such casualties may not be suitable for early release, in which
case plan for restraint and nursing. Repeat bathing in salt water daily,
or more often, until healing is established in 1–3 weeks. Wounds in
which the skin and muscle are torn and bone or tendons exposed must
be referred to a veterinarian because of the risk of infection which can
be controlled only by the correct use of antibiotics. Similarly, if a body
cavity or organs are exposed. Such casualties are very prone to shock.
If of recent origin – little dry blood or scabbing around edges, exposed
tissue red and moist not brown and dry – cover with clean, damp
warm pad or cloth to avoid shock (if not bleeding profusely) and seek
help.

Aftercare nursing may include saline bathing. Remember that heat
applied in the form of bathing or a poultice (see page 146) stimulates
blood-flow with its consequent cleansing and soothing action, while
cold decreases it and subdues localised inflammation (Fig 42).

Older wounds may have (semi-) healed naturally but drainage may
be needed and beware of fly-strike (see Chapter 5). On examining or

preparing the site, take care not to pull at the integument in such a way as to disturb a scab (granulation) and restart bleeding.

To sum up, each new case must be treated on its own individual considerations: (1) severity of damage, (2) facilities available, and (3) likelihood of recovery sufficient to enable a return to the wild. The main aim is to give nature the best conditions in which to promote healing. After initial cleansing and the removal of foreign material, the site must be kept clean; infection must be prevented, or treated if already present; and the patient must be given good housing, diet and nursing.

Nature has great recuperative powers, as we have already seen, and there are many specific and non-specific defence mechanisms. For example, inflammatory reaction (inflammation) with its cardinal signs of heat, swelling, pain and loss of function is a non-specific defence mechanism which attempts to repair damaged tissues, and leads in most cases to scar formation and return of function. Respiratory mucus production is also non-specific; dust particles adhere to the mucus, which is expelled thereby protecting the lungs.

Bandaging

Bandaging is very unsatisfactory in wild animals, for they chew or scratch at dressings. It is better to leave the wound uncovered and, if necessary, bathe more frequently. Once healing is established, warm bathing helps the blood to reach the affected area.

If covering the wound is unavoidable, for instance to protect stitches from self-interference, it may be necessary to resort to artifice.

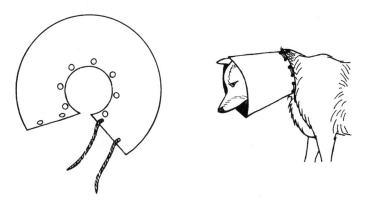

Fig 43 'Elizabethan' collar *(left)* and a bottomless bucket muzzle *(right)*

Chewing may be prevented or discouraged by putting mustard or bitter aloes on the outside of the bandage. In extreme cases a form of muzzling which allows eating and drinking may be needed. The 'Elizabethan' collar is made of strong plastic or cardboard and attaches to an ordinary dog-collar; it is quite suitable for Foxes. A variant, the 'bottomless bucket' – a plastic pail of appropriate size with bottom and handle removed and holes punched around the base – can be laced onto a dog-collar (Fig 43). Scratching can be prevented by wrapping adhesive tape around the foot after padding out claws with cotton-wool.

Materials
Dressings are applied directly to the wound and serve as protection, a vehicle for anointments, a barrier to infection, and to control a haemorrhage etc. *Surgical gauze* is used on open wounds since it is soft, non-irritating, absorbent, porous and does not disintegrate. *Cotton-wool* is extra absorbent and useful for swabbing and protection but is not usually placed on open wounds due to its disintegration, although in an emergency a wafer-thin layer placed on a haemorrhage will aid clotting. *Gamgee* solves this problem by combining the two and is a sandwich of cotton-wool between two layers of gauze. *Lint* may be used instead of gauze. *Tulle* is a fine-meshed dressing impregnated with antibiotic ointment supplied in individual sterile packs. It may be applied directly to open wounds, using sterile forceps.

Cotton open-weave bandage is the lightweight cheap all-purpose type found in all first-aid kits. *Crepe bandage* has a certain amount of elasticity, is re-usable after washing, and it is used to give more flexible support. *Adhesive tape bandage* (eg Elastoplast) is also well known and has a variety of uses from invalidating the beaks of dangerous birds (Plate 19) to its more conventional use as a fastener and protector of splints and cotton bandages. It must not be used on plaster-casts before they are thoroughly dry. Other types of useful adhesive tape are Sellotape and Scotch tape, insulation tape, masking tape and brown gummed paper. *Plaster-casts* are made of open-weave cotton bandage impregnated with plaster of Paris. They are cut into suitable lengths and applied wet, usually to limbs as a strong support, or to immobilise lower leg bones of larger animals. The more modern plaster-cast materials are less bulky, lighter and allow air to reach skin. Synthetic materials such as Hexcelite (Hexcel Medical Products,

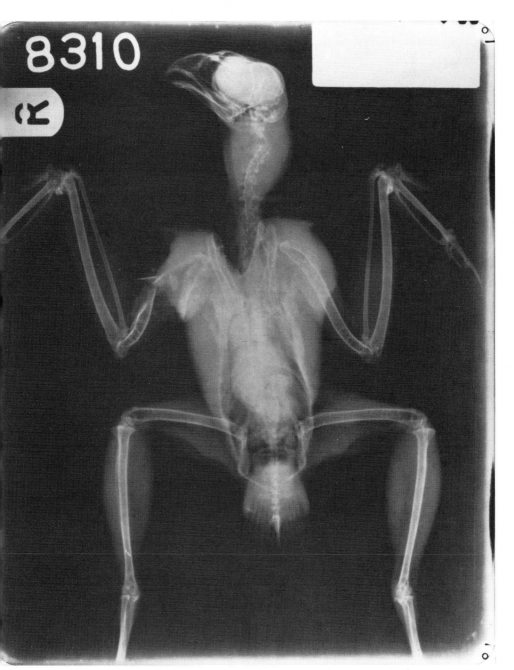

Plate 15 X-ray (radiograph) of Sparrowhawk hit by a motor vehicle; note its severely fractured right humerus (corresponding with the upper arm) *(Geoff Nute)*

Plate 16 Kestrel in hack. Its slightly misaligned left wing should not inconvenience the efficiency of this hovering hunter *(author)*

Plate 17 Compare this pathetic Kestrel with the one in Plate 16. Raised illegally on a wholly unsuitable diet lacking in minerals, it now suffers from osteodystrophy with spontaneous fractures in the legs *(Les Stocker/The Wildlife Hospitals Trust)*

USA) are also easier to remove when the time comes. *Tubular stockinette bandages* or *tube gauze* are quickly affixed to limbs by passing the special metal cylindrical applicator supplied by the manufacturers up and down over the dressing. They come in various sizes and are fastened by strips of adhesive tape.

A nylon stocking can sometimes be similarly used, and with holes cut in it at appropriate places makes a good body-stocking for small mammals. It is porous and lightweight but affords little protection. It may also be employed as a head bandage as worn by some criminals, but combining the attributes of a Balaclava helmet (which would appeal only to very silly criminals). For larger body-stockings, a bandage tailor-made from cotton sheeting might be necessary.

Applying Bandages to Mammals

Roll bandages can follow the contours of the body by twisting (see below), and they should be fitted reasonably tightly to prevent undue movement. Over a dressing on an unjointed part of a limb or around the abdomen, a *spiral bandage* is applied so that each circuit overlaps the preceding one by at least half its width (Fig 44a). Near a joint, a method sometimes called a *spica bandage* is used. This is begun by a spiral bandage above or below the joint, followed by a criss-cross or figure-of-eight over the joint, finishing with a normal spiral action on the other side (Fig 44b). Bandages may be fastened by adhesive strips as mentioned above or by bisecting a length at the end, twisting

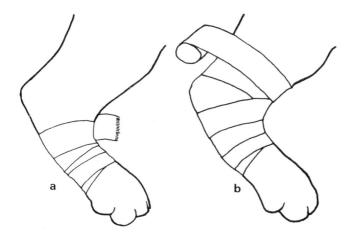

Fig 44 Spiral bandage (a), and how to bandage a joint (b)

around the limb and tying with a reef knot. If adhesive tape is used the bandaging will be more permanent if a portion of fur adjacent to the dressing is included. These are the two commonest forms of bandage, which separately or combined are suitable for most work. Where a limb thickens, a *reversed spiral bandage* in which the material is twisted 180° at each turn will be more likely to keep in place.

Any bandage around the neck region must not constrict the breathing passage; check by inserting two fingers between bandage and neck. Feet often set problems for the amateur: after cotton-wool has been placed between the toes to prevent chafing, a length of bandage is run down the lower limb, under the foot, up and down again before the spiral is begun at the foot. Ears are bandaged in a similar fashion, in this case being finished off around the head and neck (but see above). A spiral bandage is suitable for a tail, except near the base where a spica may be needed. The tip can be protected by any lightweight, rigid appropriately sized cylinder held in place by adhesive tape; the end may be left open or covered with gauze to permit 'breathing' if the material used is not porous.

Fractures and Dislocations: Skeletal Damage

The term 'fracture' includes all broken bones. Usually it is the result of traumatic or mechanical injury: birds flying into obstacles or animals being hit by moving objects such as vehicles or gunshot. There are several different classifications, sometimes given different names (Fig 45). In young birds, the areas near the joints are vulnerable. Growth in long bones occurs at the epiphyseal or growth plates (Fig 46); when adult dimensions are reached the plates close and ossify, but until then they are areas of weakness.

Fractures in limbs generally reveal themselves by a loss of function in the affected animal or a misalignment of the affected part, although dislocations can give similar signs. At the point of fracture, there is often visible swelling, local heat, bruising of skin and the broken ends may be heard or felt grating together.

There are significant differences between birds and mammals. The bones of birds, notably the wingbones, are more pneumatic and therefore lighter. They are also usually smaller insofar as the usual bird casualties – especially those suffering traumatic injury – tend to be the smaller perching-birds; equivalently sized mammals do not suffer in the same way. Birds also have a higher metabolic rate than all but the smallest mammals. These factors help their bones to mend

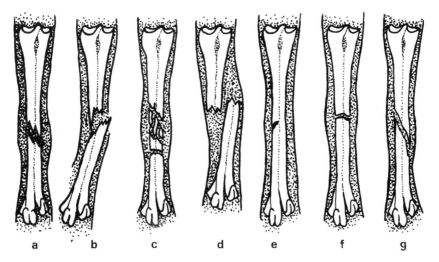

Fig 45 Classification of fracture types: (a) simple single – little displacement; (b) compound – penetrating through skin; (c) comminuted; (d) over-riding; (e) incomplete 'greenstick'; (f) transverse; (g) oblique (or in combination, eg compound oblique over-riding)

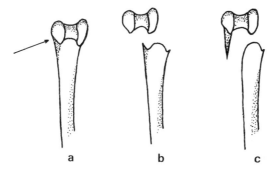

Fig 46 Epiphyseal or growth plate (a); epiphyseal separation (b); epiphyseal fracture (c)

more quickly: 10–15 days in smaller bones compared to 3–4 weeks in mammals and larger bones.

The primary aim, particularly when treating fractures in wild animals, is to return the animal to full mobility and function. We have to achieve good apposition of fracture fragments, followed by prolonged immobilisation to allow healing. This should *always* be regarded as a surgeon's job. If the bone heals incorrectly due to inexpert treatment, a permanent handicap is likely.

When attending the patient, aim to keep the fractured limb uppermost and not to move it more than necessary. In order to facilitate removing the animal for treatment elsewhere suitable restraint must be used, which may necessitate temporary splinting or some other means of immobilising the affected part. Remember that moving the injured patient can cause more pain. Splints can utilise such materials as matchsticks, cardboard, plastic, lollipop-sticks, larger pieces of wood, heavy-gauge wire etc. Cover the splint in softer material, eg cotton-wool or foam, and secure with adhesive tape. Splints are applied over the fracture, bending or adjusting as necessary to fit, and bandaged above and below – not too tightly.

If the damage is not too severe, the surgeon may consider conventional treatment in the form of splints or casts, ie *external* fixation. Compound fractures (through skin) are potentially serious and a possible source of infection which in bone is not so receptive to treatment as infection in soft tissue. Here the surgeon may consider *internal* fixation by intramedullary (along the medullary canal or cavity of long bones) stainless steel pins, or plates, screws or wire. In either case, aftercare for the necessary time using cage restraint to limit activity, and the provision of the best conditions for healing – quiet attention to hygiene and good nutrition – are important (see Chapters 4 and 10).

In yet more severe cases, where there is no hope of bone repair, there is the option of amputation of the useless part. But here we must consider the quality of life of the amputee; if this is unlikely to be satisfactory, the only remaining alternative is, sadly, euthanasia (see Chapter 11). Damage to bones such as the pelvis and the vertebral column or spinal cord can cause paralysis, ie permanently useless limbs.

Broken or Damaged Wings

We must always remember that specialist flying birds require perfect functioning of their wings if they are to thrive or even survive in the wild; and repaired wing fractures in these birds are seldom successful.

A broken wing characteristically droops (see Plate 14). Note position and mobility, and compare the two sides. Damage may occur along length of bones (Fig 34) or to joint or nerves; fractures fall into the same categories as shown in Fig 45. They usually occur at or near the elbow joint and, since the natural healing process begins immediately, it may be necessary to set about immediate repairs if proper flight is to be restituted later.

Gentle palpation of affected parts should reveal any fractures. If in doubt support the wing (see below) and seek expert aid, for the problem could be dislocation or nerve damage and repair could take anything from hours to several weeks. Ultimate prognosis is not good with dislocations as they have a habit of recurring. Affected bones need to be replaced in their correct position. Dislocation occurs most frequently to the joints of the elbow and metacarpo-phalanges (wing-tip).

Compound and comminuted fractures are certainly not cases for the layperson. Until professional treatment is available consider temporarily supporting the wing in its natural resting position by encircling body and injured wing with adhesive tape or, better still, masking tape which is less sticky, leaving the good wing free (see Plate 14) to assist balancing. Feathers adjacent to lesion may be removed to keep the site as clean as possible. Take care not to obstruct cloaca or impede leg movement when bandaging. As mentioned before, healing of wing-bones occurs relatively quickly.

Simple fractures may not need splinting provided good apposition is achieved with the wing supported as shown in Plate 14. And a fractured radius bone already has its own 'splint' in the form of the ulna. Various forms of splints are seen but are often of dubious value. If considered necessary, wing splints should always aim at strength coupled with lightness, and stout cardboard suitably affixed is often all that is necessary. Alternatively, the stiff plastic nowadays often used in visual display packaging is useful when cut to the appropriate size. Splints can be fashioned by measuring against the good part on the other side of animal.

Swollen tissue should not be forced into a 'correct' position, but folded comfortably and adjusted as swelling subsides. Broken joints seldom seem to heal satisfactorily, generally they become ankylosed (stiff) and prevent flight.

Bats' wing-membranes heal rapidly, but a torn hind edge may need suturing. The most common injury is a broken forearm, which unfortunately cannot be bound due to the membrane. Splints of wire have been successfully fixed for short periods with 'super-glue'. Carefully open wings from time to time to exercise the muscles, but do not allow flapping.

Broken or Damaged Legs

Fundamentally, the same principles apply as for broken or damaged wings. In birds the legbones are less pneumatic than those of the wing since the legs have to be very strong and muscular to absorb the shock of landing, long periods of standing, and provide lift for take-off.

The rule of allowing twenty-four hours for observation and recuperation before treatment – which with wing injuries may need to be waived – again holds good, although it may be necessary to attend to soft-tissue wounds by bathing and applying antiseptic dusting powder etc. Lacerated skin reduces blood supply and hinders healing.

Dislocation most frequently affects the tibiotarsus (hip) joint, and should be treated along the same lines as dislocated wings. Prognosis is somewhat better here. Fig 45 illustrates possible kinds of fracture, and if most of the information below seems to relate to birds it is because of their more exacting demands; techniques for repairing mammalian leg fractures are similar and generally more straightforward.

Each case must be judged on its own merits according to type and weight of bird, and injury. Small birds often seem to suffer such severe damage that the leg hangs uselessly, attached only by skin or tendon. In such cases there is little alternative but to amputate the useless part with sharp scissors. Many passerines appear to get about perfectly satisfactorily with only one leg. Only the larger birds and mammals are really capable of supporting plaster of Paris casts, and they can be tricky to remove. Splints – much more successful with leg fractures – should again aim at being light, strong and functional.

Anaesthesia may be necessary with leg fractures, remembering that birds *appear* to feel pain less intensely than mammals. Veterinary surgeons will decide on this but fractures of the femur (Fig 27), if there is not much displacement or over-riding, may be repaired by similar methods to above, ie encircling and supporting with adhesive tape. Splinting is awkward in birds due to musculature and feathering. Lower leg fractures, whether of the tibia/fibula (tibiotarsus) or metatarsus, will probably need extra support and splinting, eg lollipop-sticks or split bamboo for medium-sized birds, rigid plastic, or the cardboard which Hickman and Guy (1980) recommend, reinforced with balsa wood, for larger bones. Suitably sized quills split longitudinally are useful for the smallest subjects as are the plastic tubes from hypodermic needles. Geoff Nute finds the plastic cases from disposable syringe bodies useful when cut to appropriate size and shape.

Splints should be placed on both sides or just the outside of the limb and padded thinly with gauze, gamgee, foam or some other soft material, and held in place by adhesive tape. Size can be determined by measuring against the good leg. Hickman and Guy recommend an 'elbow splint' (Fig 47) for all leg fractures of birds, reasoning that it is

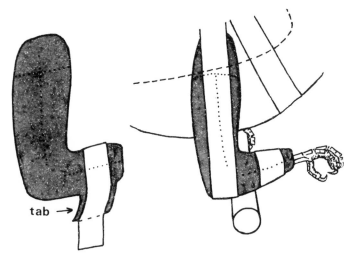

Fig 47 Elbow splint, cut from cardboard and bent to fit on the dotted line

the only kind of splint which will completely immobilise the broken leg and permit an uninterrupted healing process. They claim that it allows the bird to perch, rest on the ground and move without impediment, the patient soon learning to balance on the splint. Splinted thus but with a more acute angle at the 'elbow', they find that ankle fractures usually heal with no further support. The elbow splint is cut an inch or so longer than the overall length from ankle to the top of the femur so as to increase rigidity and protect the leg. Hickman and Guy recommend the elbow splint even for fractured femurs, it being held in place by adhesive tape applied longitudinally, and then around the body beneath the wings. On lower-leg fractures, a tab is included which is rolled round a pencil and used to cradle the leg. I confess I have not tried this method but offer it because it sounds sensible and has evidently been found successful by these American workers.

When bandaging any sort of splint or cast allow for some swelling and check daily, being prepared to adjust tension. After the initial twenty-four hours, check that the foot and distal portion of leg is not colder than the remainder of the body, or excessively swollen and discoloured which would indicate that the circulation has been damaged. A hard splint which is allowed to come in contact with the skin will cause a lesion and possible infection.

The aim of treatment is to hold the fractured segments in apposition as near as possible to the original longitudinal axis of the bone without movement of the ends. If movement does occur, healing may not take place and a false joint may form instead.

Snare or Trap Damage

Injuries resulting from self-locking traps ought to decrease as such devices become illegal. However, plenty of animals so wounded still turn up at many veterinary practices. Birds-of-prey, for instance, still have pole-traps to contend with on some estates. And despite the law which states that all snares must be visited at least once every twenty-four hours, animals with wires deeply embedded around neck, abdomen or limb are still regularly found. Such wires may not be easy to remove (see page 73), while recently caught mammalian victims will probably be enraged. Cleanse with saline solution and apply emollient antiseptic creams like Dermisol (Beechams) to keep skin supple and lift necrotic tissue. Bear in mind that internal organs may also be constricted and damaged.

Hot bathing and massage will improve circulation to the affected part and beyond. In some cases, the application of a poultice may be more convenient. A poultice is made from heat-retaining material such as kaolin spread on two pieces of lint or gauze. Heat on an inverted saucepan lid over boiling water; when sufficiently hot, ie just bearable to the back of one's hand, apply to the site and bandage in place. The effect is the same as hot bathing but less restraint is needed. Fomentations (using hot water) may wet integument excessively as well as other dressings, bed, etc, and need more frequent attention. A disadvantage of a poultice is that the patient may try to remove it. Repeat the application as and when the preparation loses heat.

Damaged Feet and Toes of Birds

A badly damaged foot can be softly padded or cushioned, then splinted and taped into a natural position (Fig 48). By using good foot as a templet for the cardboard splint an exact fit can be achieved. After the toes have been secured in their correct position, final taping should aim to cover the splint and protect it and the wound from soiling. A fractured digit can be thinly padded and 'splinted' by taping to an adjacent digit. A period of a fortnight should see healing complete.

The feet of birds kept in captivity are prone to infection by pathogenic bacteria, mainly staphylococcus. This gives rise to abcesses and the common condition called bumblefoot, which is revealed by

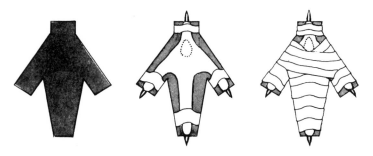

Fig 48 Foot splint cut to an ivy-leaf shape from cardboard. It is important to keep the foot dry during healing

lameness following a wound to the underside of the foot and a hot, painful, pus-filled swelling. Puncturing by a sharp object such as a thorn or a raptor's own talon (see page 97) may cause such a wound. The condition seems particularly prevalent in the heavier perching birds, eg pheasants, pigeons and the larger raptors, which suffer bruising from heavy jumps onto perches and when forced to stand for long periods of unsuitable perching. Any damage to the epithelium allows the entry of bacteria, and is encouraged by unhygienic conditions. Initial treatment, pending the prescription of antibiotics, can include bathing in a warm saline solution and the removal of necrotic tissue. Feet should be examined at every opportunity for the first signs of trouble.

Penetration of Foreign Bodies

Fish-hooks are a frequent and distressing problem, usually with the nylon line still attached. They may be embedded anywhere from the angle of the beak to gizzard, oesophagus or stomach; in such internal positions surgery will be necessary to extricate them. Where the hook can be reached, the nylon line must be removed completely, and the hook passed right through and *not* pulled back, because of its barb. Sometimes a hook will be seen encapsulated and may be left in place. If birds are seen trailing nylon line and can be caught (often impossible), the affected parts must be closely examined after the line is unravelled to ascertain the extent of the damage.

Look for other foreign objects, eg thorns, metal fragments, splinters, gunshot etc. Lead shot is frequently seen in animals X-rayed for other reasons, and may not be of any significance. It is, in fact, often difficult to find if the entry tract has healed over as, for example, in

147

intercostal muscle between ribs; and it may therefore be better to leave well alone. Puncture wounds and bites should be cleaned with saline solution and embedded hair etc, removed; infection may already have set in.

Eye Injuries

Eye injuries, as a result of traumatic accident, are not uncommon in wild birds. In mammals they are more likely to be the result of predator attack or incidental accident. All serious conditions require professional treatment, in the meantime place a clean pad or dressing over the eye. Foreign bodies – grit, seed-husks etc – can be removed by repeated flushing with a mild saline solution. Conjunctivitis, keratitis and blepharitis are inflammatory conditions which can result from injury, the presence of foreign matter and the entry of pathogenic organisms. Clinical signs are swelling, lids half-closed, inflammation and discharges; the irritation so caused is then further aggravated by the animal itself in rubbing, scratching etc. If caught early, the application of an ophthalmic ointment can be spectacularly successful, but care must be taken to ensure that it is placed directly on the cornea and not on the lid or nictitating membrane. It is easiest to place it in the corner of the eye, allowing the blink reflex to spread the ointment.

A prolapsed eye can sometimes be replaced if attended to early enough.

Damage to Birds' Beaks

This usually results from traumatic collision with windows, motor vehicles etc, but see Plates 10 and 11. Mandibles can be refashioned from modern plastic padding and fibreglass materials, formed over a stainless steel pin inserted into the remaining basal portion. A veterinary surgeon may feel inclined to enlist the support of a sympathetic dental surgeon in sufficiently worthy cases. Some severely damaged beaks will indicate euthanasia, it depends to a certain extent on the diet of the patient. Simple fractures heal satisfactorily in 2–4 weeks if immobilised; some patients may require force-feeding until then, but thereafter prognosis is good.

Accidents Resulting from Machinery and Implements

All too often agricultural machinery causes direct death or injury. Survivors of such accidents have usually lost one or more limbs, and there is likely to be much loss of blood. Even severely injured victims may try to escape (see page 112) but mercy-killing is often the only sensible and humane course. Carried out before the effects of shock have worn off, the victim may well be spared a lot of pain (see Chapter 11).

Sometimes animals become impaled on garden-fork prongs etc; these often seem to be amphibians (frogs and toads) but reptiles and even mammals like the Hedgehog can be stabbed. If the victim is alive but shows signs of stress and there is a strong possibility that vital organs have been affected, euthanasia is essential; otherwise remove to a quiet safe place and observe after having bathed wounds in salt water. Remember the natural tail-shedding of lizards mentioned in Chapter 2, and that snakes slough or shed their skin completely approximately once a month when not hibernating; this process is called 'ecdysis'.

Fits and Convulsions

Disturbances of the central nervous system can mean several things: damage to the brain (concussion); meningitis (inflammation of the meninges or membranes covering the brain); bacterial and viral encephalitides (infection of the brain); hypoglycaemia (lowering of blood sugar levels) in terminally sick animals, and other metabolic and nutritional diseases; middle ear infection which bursts through towards the brain; and poisoning including high salt intake on de-iced roads in winter. The signs are variable: lying on one side with inco-ordinate leg-paddling – rapid or slow – as if trying to escape; frothing at the mouth possibly with signs of blood from mouth and/or nose; constriction of the eye pupils; twitching eyeballs (nystagmus); dysfunction, such as is seen in birds perching normally but with the head inverted. In the absence of positive diagnosis (such conditions are symptoms rather than diseases), patients should be nursed gently – to prevent further distress to an animal which may be conscious but convulsing uncontrollably – in quiet, warm but not hot, dark quarters. Administration of the drug diazepam (intramuscular injection: 10mg/kg; intravenous injection: up to 2mg/kg) will quieten patient. Vitamin B_1, glucose and calcium may all be tried systematically.

Poisoned animals can sometimes be cured. Again destimulation is important as maintaining life is the first priority on the road to therapy and/or natural recuperation. Gastric lavage is frequently to be recommended. At the same time a simple absorbent and antidote can be administered. A formula including kaolin is the safest method of removing poison from the gut. A.G. Greenwood in Cooper and Eley (1979) gives the following formula, recommended as suitable for all birds, which includes two adsorbents: activated charcoal (10g) and kaolin (5g); light magnesium oxide (5g), an antacid; and tannic acid (5g). Water makes up the solution to 500ml. Dosage is 2–20ml depending on the size of the subject.

A strong brew of cold tea is a useful emergency source of tannin, which is a good stopgap neutraliser of many metals including copper and mercury, and vegetable poisons of an alkaloid nature, eg strychnine. Milk and egg-white are also useful and readily available, and gastro-intestinal irritation can be reduced by a mixture of eggs, sugar and milk, or an oatmeal gruel. However it cannot be stressed too strongly that professional treatment must be summoned as rapidly as possible (see Chapter 7).

An animal convulsing in the wild should be observed initially to see if it moves to a retreat, which should be carefully pinpointed and help summoned. Sometimes it is possible to move the victim to such a place oneself, but avoid getting bitten. If help is not available and the condition seems severe, it may well be kindest to put the creature out of its misery (see Chapter 11).

7 Diseases Including Poisoning

It is always important to remember that some animal diseases can be transmitted to people (zoonoses), and that until a diagnosis is made all necessary precautions must be taken to prevent such an occurrence. By their very nature, all obscure diseases require specialist veterinary techniques. The amateur can help by carefully noting symptoms, contacting a veterinarian swiftly, and isolating the patient.

A disease is broadly described as some disorder or upset affecting the normal functioning of an animal; and the simplest method of classification is according to cause: physical, chemical, nutritional, fungal or mycotic, bacterial, viral, parasitic (see page 117) and congenital.

Physical Disease

Usually termed 'injury', this is probably the most important category of disease, hence it was allotted the whole of Chapter 6 which covers most of the more likely eventualities leaving only excess heat for consideration here. Before dealing with this, it is as well to reiterate that we should be aware of the circumstances and locations where injuries are likely to occur (see Chapter 1).

Excess Heat

Excess heat resulting in burns and shock usually affects wild animals as a result of gorse fires, straw or stubble burning etc. If any fire seems out of control or illegal, such as heather or bracken burning on uplands out of season, immediately inform the appropriate authority – fire service, police etc. Afterwards, if an animal is seen suffering from burns, first restrain and examine as previously described. If treatment is indicated, immediately cool the burn site with cold water if of recent origin; keep it clean and summon professional help to control tissue damage, infection, pain and shock.

Long-term care of a burn case involves nursing, keeping the area clean, changing dressings when necessary, giving plenty of fluids and encouraging their consumption if there is dehydration, avoiding irritating or rough bedding, and if necessary preventing the animal from interfering with affected areas during healing. (see Chapter 6). In the case of abandoned young, see Chapter 9.

Chemical Disease

As we saw in Chapter 1, the chemically caused condition most likely to be encountered in wild animals is poisoning, either accidental or deliberate. There are many poisonous chemicals, but the environment can sometimes help identify the causal agent if you look around for evidence of empty containers etc, and then try to decide if the animal or animals you have found is likely to be the target, eg squirrels in commercial woodland, the Fox and crows in game and lambing regions (and seasons), the Heron near fishfarms, and so on. Many agricultural practices are seasonal and associated with particular crops, eg insecticidal spraying of corn in spring and summer to control aphids.

In general, wild animals with an unrestricted choice of food are unlikely to succumb to the common plant poisons for three main reasons: (1) animals inherit and/or acquire knowledge of what is harmful to them – avoidance; (2) specific defence mechanisms exist against certain poisons in some species, for example Deadly night-shade is a well known poisonous plant whose active poison is atropine, however the Rabbit can eat quantities with no ill effect for its liver contains a substance known as an esterase, which rapidly destroys this particular poison – immunity; and (3) poisonous plants often have a repulsive smell or contain irritant juices to deter the unwary – deterrent.

As many poisons give rise to similar signs, we can best deal with them here by considering the circumstances under which they will be seen, and their effects.

Watercourses
The obvious signs of pollution are many dead or dying fish and other sick wildlife nearby. Less obviously, long-standing pollution such as that caused by acid rain (qv) gives the appearance of crystal-clear pure water; only close examination will reveal it to be utterly dead. With

local incidents, contact the water authority. Clinical signs in wildlife are unconsciousness, apathy, immobility, nervousness, respiratory distress, and irritation such as salivation, vomiting, colic or abdominal pains which may make the victim roll around on the ground. If possible, remove from the area and summon professional help (see also Appendix 3).

As mentioned in Chapter 1, there is a possibility (probability in some areas) of finding sick and dead swans and other waterfowl following their ingestion of lead-weights, usually split-shot. All such victims should be removed; for with very modern techniques involving the insertion of endoscopes with delicate instruments down the oesophagus, it is possible to remove lead objects from the gizzard. In the long term prevention is the hope: in the short term we must strive to reduce the incidence of lead poisoning from gunshot and angling weights.

In the meantime, the swan, one of nature's most perfect and magnificent creations faces a depressing future made no easier to bear by frequent acts of stupefyingly horrific vandalism. Dozens die each week, and of the hundreds collected from all over the country and from France by the Swan Rescue Service, about 50 per cent are contaminated by lead. Mortality breakdown is discussed on page 21.

Symptoms of lead poisoning in live animals are similar to those of botulism (qv), and expert diagnosis including blood-tests may be needed to differentiate between the two. Nervous disorders and severe foetid diarrhoea are evident in acute cases, while in chronic stages there is progressive debility and weakness accompanied by bright green faeces. Stress-induced lead poisoning has also been seen in swans convalescing after successful treatment of botulism and other diseases. Alongside surgery to remove pieces of lead, therapy often includes chelation and the intravenous administration of calcium disodium versenate in a not always successful attempt to cleanse the bloodstream.

Agricultural and Domestic Areas
Chemicals play a big part in modern farming – insecticides, herbicides and fungicides are all used regularly as sprays, and two groups of poisons are used as actual bait against molluscs and rodents. Slugbait and its signs were mentioned in Chapter 1; evidence in 1982 from A.K. Cruickshank, a veterinary surgeon in New Zealand, suggests that administration of barbiturates and vitamin B_{12} (cyanocobalamin)

to fatally convulsing dogs has successfully restituted normal breathing and pink mucous membranes. The same therapy has also been successful in mild cases of paraquat poisoning.

Rodenticides require more detailed attention. It cannot be denied that rats and, to a lesser extent, mice, apart from 'parasitising' and competing directly with man, present a very real health hazard to him and his domestic beasts (see Leptospirosis), therefore rodenticides are here to stay. It is the non-target species that are a matter of concern, and for appropriate first aid see pages 112 and 149.

Most of the following information is adapted from Rentokil's useful *Treatment of domestic animals affected by rodenticides* (1982); quotations are from personal communication with A.P. Meehan, Rentokil's chief biologist. There are two major kinds of rodenticide in use today: anti-coagulants, the active ingredients of which are warfarin, difenacoum and bromadiolone; and alphachloralose. Preparations manufactured by Rentokil are colour-coded to aid identification: anticoagulants = blue; alphachloralose = light green.

To deal with the warfarin-type poisons first. 'The toxicity of anticoagulants will of course vary from species to species', a dose having no effect on one animal may kill another. The LD_{50} of warfarin for dogs is about 20mg/kg; ingestions of large quantities can cause rapid death from vascular collapse without haemorrhagic symptoms. Warfarin appears to be one of the most toxic anticoagulants to domestic mammals; difenacoum appears to be more toxic than warfarin to birds.

Symptoms are variable; the first sign is often a tenderness over bony prominences of the limbs due to internal haemorrhage. Diarrhoea and vomiting may occur with blood in the voided material. Lethargy and lowered level of prothrombin (a substance formed in the liver with the assistance of vitamin K, and essential for the clotting of blood) also occur. Treatment involves vitamin K_1 by parenteral injection daily for 3–4 days; the first dose can be repeated after 4 hours if necessary. 'Vitamin K dosages would have to be worked out according to the species' from the basic guide of 2mg/kg. In cases where severe bleeding has already started, vitamin K_1 should be slowly injected intravenously to obtain maximum therapeutic effect. If symptoms are well established, blood transfusion may be required; glucose and saline is a temporary substitute. For cases caused by bromadiolone and difenacoum, the vitamin K regime may have to be continued for longer. 'Very little work has been conducted on the effects of

154

Plate 18 Risso's dolphin *(Grampus griseus)* stranded on the north Cornish coast and mutilated by humans (lower jaw removed). This large toothed-whale, up to 3.5m (11½ft) long, resembles a very pale Pilot whale (see Fig 7) and lacks the prominent 'beak' characteristic of some better known dolphins *(Bernard White)*

Plate 19 Method of cleaning lightly oiled seabird (Razorbill – note taped mandibles): *(left)* applying detergent solution; *(right)* after all traces of oil are removed, rinsing with warm water is continued from all angles until it begins to bead off plumage - note cleaner and more fluffy texture *(author)*

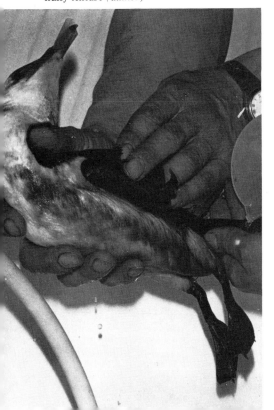

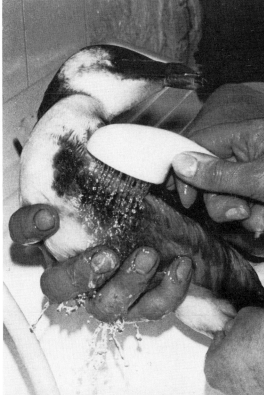

Plate 20 Orphaned Barn owls at about seven weeks old *(Jane Miller)*; inset shows a younger pair – at about four weeks – orphaned after their mother was shot *(author)*

rodenticides on wildlife and even less has been published. However in the case of the anticoagulants, symptoms of poisoning and treatment will be similar for all mammals, and I suspect vitamin K will also work for birds.'

The toxic levels of formulated alphachloralose bait fluctuate wildly for cats and dogs. The minimum effect level is 1g/kg; the LD_{50} for beagles being between 15g and 25g/kg, for cats 2.5g/kg. Initial symptoms are hyperactivity followed by inco-ordination, ataxia and sedation; hypothermia follows ingestion of large quantities. Occasionally cats show hyperactivity after consuming stupefied mice still containing alphachloralose in the gut; this condition should be treated in the same manner as direct poisoning. 'With the exception of cats, I believe the reaction of other mammals to alphachloralose will be [as above]. It will produce more severe symptoms and possible death in birds but the effects are very temperature dependent.'

If administered within thirty minutes of taking bait, emetic treatment can be effective. In most cases the animal recovers without treatment if kept warm to counter hypothermia and roused to stimulate body metabolism. If the animal enters coma, artificial respiration may be required. Sedatives should not be given, and stimulants are of doubtful value.

Contrary to some notions, 'alphachloralose has *never* been allowed for the control of squirrels. In fact its use as a rodenticide is restricted to indoors only, in order to prevent accidental poisoning of wildlife, particularly birds. To the best of my knowledge, warfarin is the only material allowed to be used for squirrel control and then only in certain circumstances.'

Another rodenticide relies on the active ingredient calciferol (colour-coded brown); those of this kind produced by Rentokil do not contain anticoagulants. Field experience is at present insufficient to indicate toxicity to domestic animals, and 'I do not know what [its] effects on wildlife would be' but the acute toxic dose of formulated bait to dogs is about 13g/kg. Some of the following symptoms may be exhibited by poisoned animals: anorexia, constipation or diarrhoea, lethargy, dull coat, spinal arching, polyuria (excessive urination), and polydipsia (excessive thirst). Treatment is symptomatic: low calcium diet, high fluid intake and high salt intake, and avoidance of exposure to sunlight.

Acids as defoliant sprays are used on potato haulms to prevent the spread of blight and these, if they make contact with animals in the potato field at or soon after spraying, can cause eye and skin burns. Flood the affected area(s) with water and get professional help.

Arsenic is used in weedkillers, insecticides, wood preservatives and fruit-tree sprays. It can be absorbed either through the skin or the digestive tract, and can accumulate in the body, being stored in bones, hoof and hair. Birds can eat affected insects. Acute poisoning causes death; more common is chronic poisoning which gives signs of intestinal irritation, watery diarrhoea, depression leading to staggering and convulsions, unthriftiness and a dry staring coat. Diagnosis is confirmed by chemical analysis. If an animal is known to have eaten or been in contact with the poison, it should be taken to a vet immediately. Chlorine in sodium chlorate weedkillers can cause death if treated plants are eaten. Organic mercury compounds are used to prevent fungal growth on seedcorn; birds may eat the dressed corn and in turn be eaten by predators. Symptoms are nervous disorders producing limb weakness. There is little hope for victims of such lethal agents, and prevention is again more important: reduction of incidence, preventing access of birds to grain stores etc. Mercury poisoning has also long been a cause of infertility in wild birds.

Herbicides are another source of poisoning. In the past, dinitro compounds such as DNOC and DNP used as contact weedkillers accounted for many losses in higher animals. Hormonal weedkillers such as 2,4,D and 2,4,5,T, dalapon and paraquat, which replaced them, have less direct effect – except in concentrated form – on animal life although they may alter the taste of poisonous plants making them more palatable. And the dangers of spray-drift, particularly from aircraft application, should never be underestimated.

With regard to insecticides, the older groups of vegetable origin are almost non-toxic to warm-blooded animals, the more modern organophosphates and organochlorines have entered the food chains and caused heavy losses (see Chapter 1). Effluent pollution was discussed in the same chapter.

Strychnine, as already mentioned, is used deliberately by landowners to kill Moles underground, and illegally to kill crows and the Fox. There is little to stop the 'wrong' animal taking the poisoned worm or egg, usually with fatal consequences. If recently taken, emesis or gastric lavage may help, but terminal signs following absorption are convulsions and spasmodic rigid paralysis. The only course of action is to get professional help, and then try to prevent such indiscriminate and malicious slaughter.

With on-going improvements in research and practice, agricultural poisoning is receding and is now only of local incidence, usually the result of careless handling, usage and disposal of containers. Industrial chemicals are powerful and a much more serious threat as they are less controlled and are causing build-ups of hazardous proportions on a worldwide scale.

Summary

We have already noted that many poisons give rise to similar symptoms; the circumstances and numbers of animals involved will give some idea of the problem.

Ingested poisons often result in irritation – salivation, vomiting, colic (abdominal pain) and diarrhoea, leading to collapse. Some affect the central nervous system causing inco-ordination, muscle tremors, convulsions, paralysis, and in extreme cases coma and death.

The first thing to do on suspecting poisoning is to make an assessment of the situation as outlined above. Action must be twofold: (1) with regard to individual care, and (2) with regard to in-contact animals. If applicable, notify appropriate authority; take note of circumstances, pollution etc; and consider the provision of a place of safety in the meantime.

The individual animal's diagnosis and treatment must be the responsibility of a veterinarian; the finder's help is needed to supply an accurate case history. Note the following:

1 where found
2 respiration – fast, slow or depressed
3 eyes – nystagmus (rapid movement of eyeballs) and size of pupils, whether large or small
4 presence of odour on breath or vomit
5 pattern of urination and/or defaecation including colour, odour and consistency
6 any other symptoms.

General rules of treatment, where possible, and hints may be summarised thus:

1 prevent the absorption and ingestion of more poison; give 'safe' food and water; using *water only* wash off skin and integument (soaps and detergents may precipitate further absorption where chemical is unknown)
2 administer gastric lavage under direction from qualified vet, and

159

specific antidote if possible; deal with any residual poison by rendering inert or neutralising (see page 150)

3 symptomatic and supportive therapy.

Post mortem examination may be undertaken by a veterinary surgeon who may involve the Ministry of Agriculture, Fisheries and Food (MAFF) and other official bodies if pollution is suspected and where other livestock or the public are at risk. He or she may also remove samples for analysis.

Nutritional Disease

This is not generally seen in British wild animals since they will either adapt or attempt to move to a more suitable environment if conditions deteriorate to such an extent. It is more likely in animals whose food supply or range is restricted by unnatural means such as in African game parks. But when hospitalising wild animals suspected of suffering from dietary deficiencies, ensure that they have a suitable diet with a satisfactory vitamin, mineral and trace-element intake. These substances may have to be administered as additives (see pages 99 and 179).

Fungal/Mycotic Disease

Mycotic infections in British wild mammals are mainly those causing the disease known as ringworm even though no animal parasite is involved. Clinical signs of the disease may or may not be present. Where hairy sites are affected, the ringworm fungus (there are about twenty species involved) attacks the hair follicles, causing the hairs to die and fall out, usually in a characteristic ring shape. Round bald patches with crusty and damaged skin are therefore fairly typical of the disease. This can be transmitted to man, and there is clearly a risk when handling such patients if severely lesioned; although it can be cured, several weeks may be needed, and permanent scarring can remain.

Quite a large percentage of voles, mice and shrews are infected, and Morris and English (1969) found 20–25 per cent of Hedgehogs carrying the fungus; urban Hedgehogs were more infected than country-dwellers, possibly due to their higher density. Ringworm does not seem to be contracted by Hedgehogs under a year old, and seems not to harm the host greatly although chronic infection can cause skin changes and disfiguration.

Prevent the spread of disease to in-contact animals and those using the same cage areas by disinfecting these thoroughly between use.

Aspergillosis is a disease of the upper respiratory tract, lungs and air sacs of birds caused by the mycotic organism *Aspergillus fumigatus*. Young birds are most endangered and can contract the disease from nesting material harbouring the spores; there is some evidence indicating that eggs are also at risk. However, all birds can succumb; the infection is airborne and can also be spread by damp and mouldy food and litter. Seabirds are particularly susceptible due to their normal alienation from vegetation. It can exist in latent form in many birds to be triggered off by a lowering of condition or stress such as results from capture and being brought into confinement.

Clinical signs are few, a difficulty in breathing being the most obvious and reliable; but by that time a cure is generally not possible. Prevention is by far the best hope of avoiding this disease.

Bacterial Disease

Bacteria are microscopic organisms and, though many are harmless and even beneficial to higher animals, some cause disease under certain conditions. These are referred to as 'pathogenic', and the remainder as 'non-pathogenic'.

One is unlikely to identify a bacterial infection in a wild animal on first encounter. It is more important to be aware that they do occur, and of the ways in which infection is caused so as to prevent spread to other individuals and species, and indeed to oneself. This is important when establishing standards of hygiene. The common and most important pathogenic bacteria affecting British wildlife are of the genera *Clostridium*, *Leptospira*, *Pasteurella*, *Yersinia*, *Mycobacterium* and those forming the group Enterobacteriaceae.

Until a diagnosis is made, it is wise to regard a sick animal as if it were infected with a zoonotic disease. If possible do not touch in the absence of hand-washing facilities, and avoid contact with saliva, urine, faeces and other discharges; use rubber gloves to change potentially contaminated bedding; observe strict personal hygiene; and employ a suitable disinfectant.

Clostridium

This group of bacteria causes several diseases including tetanus in domestic animals; however the main type to affect wildlife is *Cl. botuli-*

161

num – botulism – which is a scourge of birds under certain conditions. Typically, the bacteria are taken in by birds in late summer after heavy rain has raised the water-table thus forming large areas of shallow stagnant water around the margins of lakes, and from infected soil such as can 'turn up' when ditches or ponds are dug out. In both instances, infected soil is brought to the surface and made accessible, particularly to waterfowl, but also to other creatures, as softened mud and local vegetation. The usual signs are dead and dying birds around the site. The bacterium releases a toxin which causes respiratory paralysis, so the cause of death is in fact suffocation. However, as pointed out on page 153, the presenting symptoms are very similar to those of lead poisoning. The following have been noted in swans infected by as few as three or four contaminated maggots: neck weakness, ataxia, inability to swim, wing weakness, dyspnoea (difficulty of breathing) with a build up of frothy mucus in the beak, and green foetid diarrhoea. A characteristic wet patch in the middle of the bird's back between the wings can be seen where the beak rested. The disease can then be spread to other waterfowl and insectivorous birds which feed on maggots from infected carcasses, or on those contaminated at source and used as angling bait, which have themselves accumulated the toxins.

As we have seen, other animals are also at risk although the incidence is fairly low. Mink have died in captivity from botulism, so they and other carnivores must from time to time succumb in the wild.

Leptospira

The most important thing to remember about these organisms is that one, *L. icterohaemorrhagiae*, is responsible for Leptospiral jaundice – a sometimes fatal disease in man – commonly called Weil's disease. The zoonosis is carried in the kidney tubules of many wild mammals but rodents are the chief vectors. The bacteria are passed out in the urine and contaminate the surrounding area – bedding, food, watercourses etc. It is communicated to man and other animals when infected material comes into contact with broken skin thus allowing the bacteria to enter the body, or by crossing mucous membranes such as the mouth.

Pasteurella

Pasteurellosis appears to be most commonly spread by the bites of affected predators, including dogs and cats. The predators will hitherto have presumably fed on resistant rodent carriers, which makes cats the most likely vectors. Thus birds admitted into care showing simple bite wounds, or known to have been caught by a predator, might have had their conditions complicated by *Pasteurella* infection and therefore should be segregated from other patients. Of one series of casualties taken alive from the mouths of cats, 40 per cent died from the direct effects of the bites, and 60 per cent from *Pasteurella* (*multocida*) infection. Antibiotic therapy could presumably have saved a proportion of the latter. Incidentally, between 1975 and 1979, most of the 1,234 *P. multocida* cases in humans resulted from dog and cat bites.

Avian or fowl cholera, caused by the pathogen *P. aviseptica*, accounts for high mortality during periodic outbreaks, particularly among waterfowl, gallinaceous birds and their predators. Diagnosis is usually only possible post mortem.

Yersinia

Pseudotuberculosis is caused by the pathogen *Y.* (formerly *Pasteurella*) *pseudotuberculosis* found commonly in birds and also in mammals such as the Coypu, Fox, Brown hare, Rabbit and Short-tailed vole. Infection is spread mainly by birds and rodents during the winter months – when animals are in sub-optimum condition and exposed to the stress of damp, cold and shortages – either directly for example to predators eating infected prey, or indirectly by contaminating food. Domestic pets more than wild animals seem responsible for its zoonotic appearance.

Mycobacterium

True tuberculosis is caused by the organism *M. tuberculosis*, and this bacillus has been isolated from the Short-tailed vole, Bank vole, Wood mouse and Common shrew. Over the last decade or so, Badgers in south-west England have been found to be infected by *M. bovis*, which is responsible for TB in cattle. The incidence has been as high as 22 per cent in the Badgers examined, but it is likely that Badger infection is concentrated in isolated pockets. The Badger/TB controversy is very complex and beyond the scope of the present work.

In birds, the disease appears to be on the increase. Accurate diagnosis is very difficult and, since infected birds excrete the bacilli in profusion and since the latter are extremely resistant organisms readily communicable to other species and man, suspect cases are usually isolated pending elimination. Scrupulous hygiene will help prevent any outbreak in captivity.

163

Enterobacteriaceae

These form a group of bacteria which inhabit the digestive tract and include *Salmonella, Escherischia (E.) coli* (page 178), *Yersinia enterocolitica and Shigella*. The last three have been isolated from Bank voles and Wood mice; and *Salmonella* from Foxes, Hedgehogs and birds, also rodents *following* contact with infected cattle (they are not the reservoirs for salmonellosis they are frequently thought to be). These organisms can all cause gastro-intestinal diseases in man: *Salmonella* is frequently associated with outbreaks of food-poisoning; *Y. enterocolitica* has been associated with a number of human illnesses; and *Shigella* with dysentery.

The importance of this group is not its effect on wildlife but the spread of infection to other species, and the possibility of introducing the organisms into hospital and convalescent quarters.

Other Bacterial Infections

Of these, anthrax must be mentioned. It is caused by *Bacillus anthracis*, and can occur in all domestic animals and man; in wild animals it has been isolated from the Fox, Rabbit and various rodents, probably after contact with infected carcasses or from unsterilised bone flour, used as a garden fertiliser. Birds possess a considerable degree of immunity.

Anthrax is uncommon, but because of its possibility and frequently fatal consequences, **no unqualified person should ever attempt to make a post mortem examination of a wild animal**. The bacterial spores, which are formed on exposure to air – for instance where blood is spilt from an infected carcass – are extremely resistant to the strongest disinfectants and can withstand boiling for half an hour. It is a notifiable disease.

Abscesses are caused when harmful bacteria are localised and attacked by the body's defences, producing pus. Many different bacteria may be involved in the same abscess, and when treating these (by hot bathing/poultices or by lancing followed by antisepsis and the correct antibiotic) suitable hygiene precautions should be taken: including the use of disposable gloves and the incineration of infected dressings and bedding (see also page 146).

Viral Disease

Although not currently present in Britain, the most serious viral disease which could affect wildlife is rabies. Once the virus enters a warm-blooded animal, usually via a bite or scratch from an infected case, it is generally fatal. It is cosmopolitan and so far the present quarantine regulations seem to have been effective in preventing its re-entry into the UK. Nevertheless, if an infected animal evades quarantine and associates with wildlife, the disease could spread rapidly. Apart from the dangers presented to man if rabies ever becomes endemic, the control measures likely to be unleashed following media whipped-up panic, will mean massive slaughter of much wildlife, restricted access to the countryside, and inevitably a change in attitude to sick and injured wild animals (see also Chapter 11).

The symptoms of the disease are largely due to the effects of the virus on the central nervous system; the classic fear of water, hydrophobia, is caused by paralysis of the pharyngeal or swallowing muscles.

Another virus disease which produces nervous symptoms is louping-ill; it is usually spread by the Common sheep-tick, and has a wide host-range involving mainly cattle and sheep. In wild animals it has been isolated from shrews, rodents, hares and grouse; and about 40 per cent of Scottish Red deer show a high antibody rate, which indicates that they live in equilibrium with the virus. Death is preceded by depression, a high fever and peculiar gait.

Viral Diseases Producing Generalised Infections
Canine distemper mainly affects dogs but Foxes and Mink among other carnivores are also susceptible, as are omnivores. Clearly, infected dogs must be isolated, but unvaccinated strays are a source of widespread infection. The course of the disease runs as high temperature, watery discharges from eyes and nose, then sickness and diarrhoea; pneumonia may follow. Death is usually the result of effects on the central nervous system. No treatment is indicated in wild animals; remove and eliminate to prevent further spread.

Infectious canine hepatitis, like distemper, mainly affects dogs; but infected dogs can spread the virus either by their saliva or urine, and the Fox is susceptible. Symptoms and course are similar to distemper. Again, do not take sick pets for walks, wild populations can be highly vulnerable to domestic diseases.

Feline infectious enteritis is highly contagious and causes high mortality among domestic cats; all felines are susceptible and possibly also mustelids. The course: fever for first twenty-four hours, listlessness, anorexia, possible crouching; fever drops then rises again, death usually occurs during the second temperature rise. Watery diarrhoea and vomiting may also feature. Source of infection is from blood, secretions and excretions of infected animals; it is probably also transmitted by fleas.

Newcastle disease (fowl pest) generally affects domestic poultry but its incidence has been greatly reduced since effective vaccination. However, other birds can be affected during natural outbreaks: geese, ducks, pigeons, gamebirds, crows, sparrows and martins have been found infected. Young birds exhibit nervous symptoms or stupor; adults show respiratory distress and their reproduction may be affected. It is spread by infected excretions, often contaminating food and water, and the authorities must be notified of its occurrence.

Paramyxovirus Infection in Pigeons

In June 1983 paramyxovirus was found in racing pigeons in Cornwall. Since then the disease has infected wild columbids and has spread to other parts of Britain. This is a virus disease in the same family as that which causes Newcastle disease (qv fowl pest) in domestic poultry. Symptoms vary but dullness, green watery diarrhoea and depressed appetite are common signs followed by tremors, leg paralysis and wing droop. Predators and scavengers too are affected. There is no treatment.

An inactivated vaccine has been licensed for use in pigeons under strict control of the Ministry (MAFF) and is available through veterinary surgeons. Good protection follows a two-dose vaccination programme. The vaccination scheme is voluntary, but it is in the interests of all pigeon owners to vaccinate their pigeons, and they are urged to do so by the Ministry. Only healthy birds should be vaccinated, and the manufacturer's recommendations must be followed closely.

Viruses Affecting the Skin

Foot and mouth disease (FMD) is generally thought of in connexion with domestic animals, but all cloven-footed (hooved) animals are susceptible, including deer. Oddly enough the Hedgehog and other small mammals can also be infected. FMD is another notifiable disease. Signs of infection are characteristic drooling of saliva, and vesicles (fluid filled blister-like sacs) on the tongue, mouth and feet.

Affected animals do not eat, lose weight and become lame. The virus is spread in all secretions and excretions.

Pox viruses cause disease which is shown by the formation of pustules on the skin; in birds lesions are proliferative and tumour-like rather than pustular. All bird pox viruses are closely related but host modified. Mouse pox or ectromelia is rapidly fatal in acute cases; chronic cases show pustules particularly on the head and feet. It is highly contagious, but more likely to be spread by pet mice than wild ones.

Myxomatosis is a highly contagious disease of the Rabbit, infrequently hares are also affected. During the outbreaks, it is the single most common cause of the public seeing sick wildlife in rural areas. Early infection is indicated by inflammation around the eyes, the eyelids swell and a watery discharge rapidly becomes purulent, gumming the eyelids together; there is a nasal discharge and swellings appear on the face and ears, later on other parts of the body. Death usually occurs in 1–2 weeks after the first signs. Myxomatosis is spread by the Rabbit flea and, less importantly, by other biting insects such as mosquitos. Rabbit survivors are either more resistant, or the virus becomes less potent.

Its virulence is demonstrated by the story of the French physician who, in 1952, imported the virus and released some infected Rabbits hoping to destroy the wild Rabbits on his estate. He not only got rid of these but within eighteen months the disease had spread through most of France, Belgium, Germany, Holland and, via human agency, across the Channel to England. As a little boy in the mid-fifties, the sight of so many of these wretched, miserable and bemused creatures, robbed of their keen senses, made an indelible impression on me.

Ornithosis

Called psittacosis when in a member of the parrot family, this is a viral-type disease transmissible from bird to man, in whom it can cause severe pneumonia and death. The causative organism is *Chlamydia psittaci* of uncertain status. It is cosmopolitan and endemic in the British Isles, feral pigeons being a major reservoir. Normally, in adults, it exists in a latent form; clinical cases show varying symptoms, generally more severe in young birds: anorexia, depression, nasal and eye discharges, dehydration and emaciation leading ultimately to death. Chronic cases occur showing anorexia, conjunctivitis, nasal discharges and diarrhoea. Infection is by way of the inhalation of the organism in aerosol discharges from in-contact birds. The disease responds readily to the tetracyclines and chloramphenicol, but can leave carrier-state birds; clinicians should wear protective masks because of the zoonotic dangers.

Congenital Disease

Diseases in which the conditions are present at birth or inherited are not normally seen in adult wild animals since the survival of the fittest regime tends to their elimination. A number of infections, both bacterial and viral, can be congenitally caused, and maybe not apparent until sometime after the animal is born; deformities such as a cleft palate will of course be present at birth.

Their recognition is important if, for instance, an animal produces such young while in care; when a decision will have to be taken regarding their survival.

8 Strandings and Oil-pollution Casualties

On page 23, I mentioned the biological frontier along the tideline and affirmed that to sea creatures it represents the very edge of their world. But we cannot know how many land birds fly – either voluntarily or involuntarily – out to sea, and are lost. Many thousands must perish thus each year while on migration; and it was not unusual, when I used to ring waders on the Wash coast under moonlight, to catch in our mist-nets – set way out on the mudflats over the incoming tide – species of owls, thrushes and other varieties more associated with woods and hedgerows. And, leaving aside the famous Lemming, many other terrestrial mammals have been found swimming strongly, at goodly distances from land, heading apparently nowhere in particular.

Deer and other prey-species will take to water in a bid to escape their pursuers. Colonisation of offshore islands certainly occurs due to overcrowding on the mainland, and casual stowaways on driftwood for example are responsible for introductions to any number of oceanic islands. The Lemming, in common with other species of small rodents, typically the voles, has cyclic rises in numbers, incurring the well-known 'plague years' and sometimes desperate emigration. Their ability to swim and their waterproofing amply sustains them in calm conditions over reasonable distances, but a choppy sea soon induces severe stress and exhaustion.

By its definition though, 'strandings' implies erstwhile specialist sea-creatures, and this chapter reflects that. Were we dolphins constructing an equivalent narrative, we might head this chapter 'Castaways'. Coastal strandings may occur with mammals, birds, fish and even amphibians, though that may sound improbable. Mammals are omitted here because of the special considerations already mentioned in Chapters 2 and 3. The only exceptions would be orphaned seal pups (see Chapter 9). Littoral creatures too, whether of amphibious ability such as crabs and whelks, or permanent sea denizens like the starfish, need not delay us either, for as was also mentioned they are as specialised as whales and lack the charisma of our beloved fellow mammals.

Sea-going birds alone remain; and so diverse are their species and so precarious their design in striving for the best possible compromise between the three opposed media of air, water and land, that we will not, sadly, have to search too hard for subjects. Some species – penguins are the most notable – 'found' that only by relinquishing the air were they able to capitalise thoroughly on the benefits of water; other birds would seem to be on that course. However, no example has existed in British waters since the tragic demise of the Great auk in 1844.

The remaining auks, our most likely clients, can fly well enough, if unimaginatively. Their wings, by almost flipper-like shortening, aptly demonstrate evolution's compromise. Next to the Guillemot and Razorbill, the most frequent victims of oil pollution – and though the trend is in the right direction, strandings are still going to be mostly so caused – are the Puffin (another auk), Fulmar, seaducks (scoters, scaup, eiders and goldeneyes), Gannet, cormorants, grebes, divers and gulls. The general decline in the populations of auks and others may well be largely due to oil pollution, if so it leaves the above mentioned trend open to serious misinterpretation.

Even more than birds suffering from fractured wings and legs, those suffering from contaminated plumage seem to inspire confidence in would-be rescuers. Unless the oiling is extremely slight – no more than a patch on the breast of one or two birds – the chances of inexpert success are slim. Birds appearing to be very lightly oiled are, in fact, probably suffering from some other or related complaint if they allow themselves to be caught; the most likely is oil poisoning.

On page 176 there is a review of what is now, by general consent, considered to be *the* correct procedure for de-oiling and re-waterproofing, and which supersedes all other theories and practices. It is a technique, brilliant in its simplicity, developed during the late sixties and seventies by the Research Unit on the Rehabilitation of Oiled Seabirds at the Zoology Department of the University of Newcastle-upon-Tyne, and we are indebted to J.P. Croxall, now at the British Antarctic Survey, Cambridge, for his and his colleagues' work and writings on this vexed subject. Moreover, I strongly urge anyone with more than a passing interest in this subject to study his article 'Birds and oil pollution' in Cooper and Eley (1979) and the unit's 'Recommended Treatment of Oiled Seabirds' (1972) from which I have freely adapted the advice.

But before we come to the actual procedures for de-oiling or cleaning, there are two vital issues to understand: one concerns the practicalities – the equipment and facilities necessary to cleanse plumage successfully and properly; the other, the effects of oiling besides the obvious contamination of plumage.

A mass oiling disaster requires a co-operative operation, even so it may well be necessary to select those individuals with the best chance of recovery. Either way, the extent of external contamination is, as we have just seen, by no means the only sign to look for. Conversely, however, a bird can have been so rapidly handicapped by a single severe oiling that it has been unable to preen much; depending on other factors, the prospects of this case could be much better. Signs to look for giving a poor prognosis during preliminary examination are: *general bodily condition* – emaciated birds with wasted breast muscles, ie a Guillemot weighing less than 600g (21oz), and a Razorbill less than 425g (15oz); *faeces* – traces of oil indicate ingestion, confirmed by traces in the mouth; *eyes* – either glazed or with a sluggish movement of the nictitating membrane (third eyelid); *posture* – unable to stand, and slumped forward with a pronounced arching of the lower back; *behaviour* – disinclination to move, and apathy to capture, handling and caging. The weight criterion is the most telling, but whereas one either has (access to) or has not the following facilities, the effects of oiling on individual birds is neither obvious nor clearcut.

The facilities and equipment one must have, or have access to, for cleaning are as follows. The first listed is vital, and lack of it is liable to render the others irrelevant.

1 an abundant supply of piped hot water – a copper cylinder with immersion heater is *not* sufficient
2 a piped cold water supply with good pressure
3 a warm indoor shelter (see Chapter 4)
4 an outdoor pen with bathing facilities as discussed in Chapter 4
5 for more than the occasional patient, a reliable source of food; and a freezer.

An abundant hot water supply means in effect a central-heating system with a hot water facility, or a shower with an electrical self-heating device. This must be stressed because it is imperative not to be interrupted by cooling water. An ordinary-sized domestic cylinder will scarcely supply enough hot water to thoroughly clean a single lightly oiled bird, and the time taken to reheat a cold cylinder can chill the patient and increases stress.

Stress is probably the single most lethal factor on account of its many ramifications. Physiological stress, as we saw in Chapters 3 and 4, begins at the moment of disability. It steadily increases as organic stress takes hold, on becoming stranded and during the whole momentous business of approach by humans, chase, capture, handling, crating, transportation, artificial accommodation and the treatment itself. Little wonder that if a weakened victim survives all this, additional stress at such a critical juncture as mid-cleaning, when handling is at its most intolerable level, can prove fatal. The only thing working in our favour is that seabirds show little inherent fear of mankind.

The effects of crude oil on refined plumage, and its toxicity when ingested should be understood. Clearly, it has immediate dire consequences. Very heavy contamination can actually drown birds, but the levels more usually seen result in derangement leading to a loss of waterproofing and insulation. This puts an extra cost on energy as the metabolism attempts to maintain optimum body temperature and leads to a greatly decreased or curtailed ability to feed, making it impossible for the bird ever to repay that debt. So, while the sufferer misguidedly preens its feathers in a futile attempt to solve its problem, and begins to ingest the evil contaminant, its resistance to bacterial and fungal infections simultaneously lessens, the pectoral muscles recede, and emaciation and dehydration set in.

Ingestion of crude oil causes various clinical signs and pathological lesions. Croxall lists them thus:

1 decline in white blood cell numbers, reducing resistance to infection
2 disruption of general fluid and electrolyte balance leading to dehydration and metabolic disorders
3 disturbance of endocrine balance, often associated with enlarged adrenal glands
4 fatty degeneration of the liver which, among other things, reduces ability to break down toxins
5 secondary kidney changes restricting elimination of waste products
6 necrosis and/or oedema in major organs.

Plate 21 Hares (unlike rabbits) are born highly developed: *(top)* Brown hares as found at two days old; *(centre)* bringing in for feeding at three days; *(bottom)* three-day-old leveret receiving food from a Catac feeder – see also Fig 53 *(sequence: E. Jane Ratcliffe)*

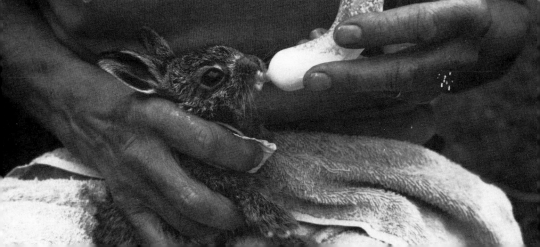

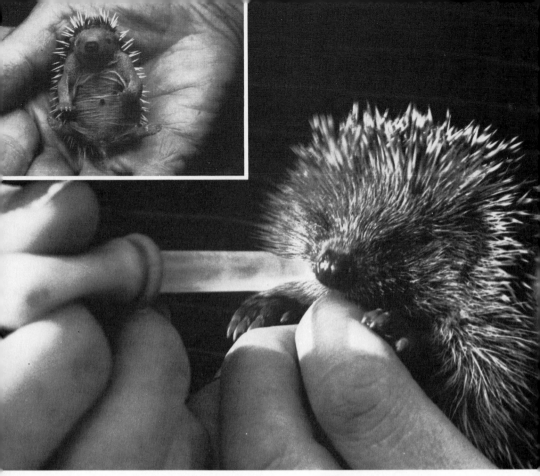

Plate 22 Feeding a young Hedgehog on Lactol – a medicine dropper may be used as here, or a 5ml syringe or Catac feeder *(Les Stocker/The Wildlife Hospitals Trust)*. Inset, an ink-dropper (see Fig 55) makes a useful emergency feeder at a very young age *(E. Jane Ratcliffe)*

Plate 23 Bottle-feeding baby Red fox vixen at about four weeks of age on Lactol and Farex *(Les Stocker/The Wildlife Hospitals Trust)*

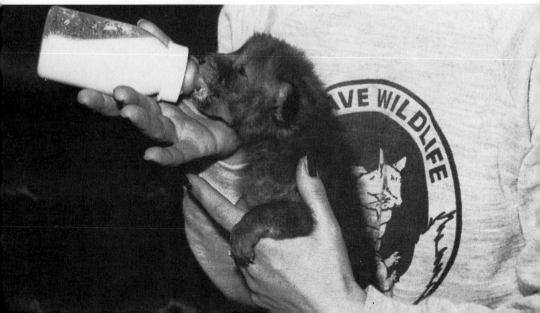

He goes on to point out that the toxicity of oils varies with the amount of refining that has taken place; for instance the fuel oils have a greater proportion of volatile aromatic substances than crude oil, and therefore greater toxic effects. Many processed oils are also much more stubborn to remove from plumage, and may require a double treatment. Furthermore, the toxicity of detergents and other emulsifying agents used to disperse oil slicks should not be underestimated even though modern ones are less dangerous. Remember then, that while contamination by heavy oil looks more serious, it may be less so than that of the lighter refined oils.

Cleaning

There are three phases to the treatment; the actual cleansing being sandwiched between the equally important pre-cleaning and post-cleaning stages. The latter includes rehabilitation prior to release; the pre-cleaning phase begins immediately after capture (see Chapter 3) with the bill wiped clean and transit arrangements.

Jordan and Hughes offer convincing evidence for dispensing with the 'poncho' and tubular bandage or body-stocking which are recommended by Croxall and frequently also by others as a means of preventing birds from preening and thereby ingesting more oil, and of sustaining bodyheat. They contend after considerable experience that auks do not preen much out of sight of water; that should a bird overbalance, its trammel impedes or prevents recovery resulting in it getting trampled on by its fellows, and bringing them down too; that a body-stocking, far from keeping a bird warm, actually lowers body temperature. They cite over 20 per cent in-transit mortality of birds so trammelled compared to less than 5 per cent when free of encumbrances.

Oiled birds travel well if kept in dark, warm, well ventilated containers, and not stimulated. Two to four individuals may be transported together, and Guillemots and Razorbills can be mixed. Boxes should be amply padded with crumpled newsprint or rags, but not vegetation owing to the vulnerability of ocean-going birds to aspergillosis (qv). Home quarters must be warm with some source of direct heat.

Contrary to advice given for most other medium to large birds, an early feed might well be advantageous for seabirds which have ingested oil. Whole fish are dangerous because the sharp bones and fins can cause massive haemorrhaging and aggravation of oil-induced intestinal problems. Bland strips of filleted white fish are far better and will actually help to remove oil. This diet should be maintained for 24–48 hours or until no trace of oil is visible in the faeces whereupon, if forcefeeding has also ceased, the birds should be ready for cleaning.

Medication depends on condition and is best left to the judgement of an experienced worker or veterinarian, but a broad-spectrum antibiotic and steroid base will help control enteritis. Mild emetics can be used with strong birds, and vitamin and mineral supplements can be given in gelatine capsule form to increase resistance to infection. An early pre-wash of heavily oiled cases may be necessary if they insist on preening.

Plumage achieves its remarkable waterproof quality by its construction much more than by the existence of an oil- or wax-producing preen gland, and the sole purpose of cleaning is to remove every last trace of alien oil and detergent. Done properly, and this is the acid test, birds other than the cormorants will immediately appear dry or at least in good feather, and regain their buoyancy. The method, after Croxall, is as follows:

1   Make up a 1–2 per cent solution of one of the cheaper washing-up detergents in a bowl (Fairy Liquid is more a soap than a detergent and does not give such consistently good results). Quantity is approximately ½cup to a large washing-up bowl of hot water – as hot as the hands can comfortably stand (40–45°C; 104–113°F). For lightly oiled subjects, a smaller quantity can be used from a jug, as seen in Plate 19, and stages 2 and 3 omitted. Concentration and temperature are fairly critical for optimum effect.

2   Immerse the bird up to its neck in the solution and hold there for about ten seconds to allow penetration into the fouled plumage. Tape the mandibles together to facilitate handling and for the sake of safety.

3   Two people are usually needed to carry out the washing: one to hold the bird, the other to work the solution into the feathers. The oiled parts should be rubbed vigorously and the feathers separated to allow the solvent to reach all the oil. The head and orbital region can be cleaned by gentle use of a toothbrush, repeatedly dipped in the solution.

4   Transfer the bird to a fresh preparation exactly as before, and complete washing until no visible traces of oil are left. A third

preparation may be necessary if a bird is exceptionally heavily oiled.

5   The patient must be very thoroughly rinsed with water of similar temperature; this stage is of vital importance. A shower attachment which mixes hot and cold water to the correct temperature is almost indispensable, and the water should be strongly jetted into the plumage, working against the grain so that it penetrates to the skin. Methodically spray all parts of the plumage – head, neck, upperparts, underparts and wings – until the appearance changes from being utterly waterlogged to regaining some of its former fluffiness. When this stage is reached, the water being played onto the plumage should begin to bead or pearl off from all parts. Rinsing must continue until this is achieved for only then can we be sure that all residues are removed, thereafter the bird should be virtually dry.

6   Do not dry or wrap the bird up but place in a warm quiet room with some fish in reach, and allow it to occupy itself by preening and rearranging its plumage. Absorbent paper towels on the floor are ideal.

7   The following day, the bird should be completely buoyant, and may be able to be released but see below.

Post-cleaning

The aim is complete rehabilitation to the wild in the shortest possible time. It depends, assuming there are no secondary problems, on the absolute re-attainment of a waterproof plumage following a buoyancy test of at least twenty minutes, and the complete lack of fetid or abnormal faeces; if these persist, the patient should be returned to a bland whitefish diet. Waterproofing can be almost instantaneous, experience can tell, but a period of 7–10 days is the average. Regular bathing stimulates preening which greatly speeds the process. During buoyancy testing, a bird which is spreading its wings and flapping is endeavouring to correct flotation and has been improperly cleaned, even a small patch can have this effect, which in a wild situation spells death.

Convalescing auks and other sea-cliff birds do best in an outside concrete pen with a ramp leading into a pool and a raised ledge overlooking the water, both of which need to be cleaned regularly if the plumage is not to be contaminated anew. Treated birds should be weatherproof, but a shelter with a heat point is beneficial for the first night or two. Salt water is not necessary. Except possibly in severely distressed specimens, which compulsively secrete a saline solution from nasal glands, salt depletion should not be a problem. If it is, sodium chloride tablets (1g a day) can be administered, concealed in a fish.

Close observation will reveal below par birds, and indicate those ready for final buoyancy testing. Release of seabirds should occur on a relatively quiet and clean stretch of suitable coast in non-stormy weather, though a brisk sea breeze helps provide lift. Preferably they should be released in groups, and their progress monitored until it is certain that none is in difficulties – any which are, usually return to land.

Seabirds under rehabilitation, subjected as they are to unnatural levels of stress, are prone to various conditions not directly attributable to oil pollution. Some of these are covered elsewhere, and others require veterinary diagnosis and treatment, but a list of the more probable ailments may help all those involved in this area of care.

Aspergillosis (see page 161) A fungal/mycotic disease dangerous to all captive birds; assumes catastrophic proportions in seabirds under stress.

Enteritis May be due to ingested oil or stress, and is characterised by watery diarrhoea, often tinged green. Prophylactic therapy with an oral broad-spectrum antibiotic such as oxytetracycline can be instigated as a routine measure, but since *Escherichia coli* is normal bacterial gut-flora in many species, it may be preferable to wait for clinical signs before attempting to control a pathological infection. Such a therapy can then be useful while assessing antibiotic sensitivity.

Staphylococcus Infections of the legs and joints by organisms of this genus of bacteria are characteristic of auks, seaducks and other wild birds forced to spend unnatural lengths of time on hardstanding; pressure sores similarly. The same antibiotic as mentioned above will cure non-established conditions. Birds kept on a membrane of foam rubber covered by much newsprint or turf are much less likely to develop these problems. Now that cleansing programmes have become more efficient, and consequently telescoped, it is a declining hazard.

The heavy-bodied eiders are particularly vulnerable to swollen joints, cracked feet and pressure sores about the breastbone. Grebes, divers and Fulmars are lighter but so refined for an aquatic existence that they cannot stand or move about much on land without also flopping down. Scrupulous hygiene plus uncrowded conditions have to obtain if fouling and deterioration of the ventral plumage is not seriously to retard rehabilitation.

Constipation Again grebes and divers are affected. They seem especially prone to cloacal impactions of urates, which are revealed by palpation of the distended abdomen and generally require professional treatment. Such sufferers may need to be stimulated to defaecate by being caught and lifted up once or twice a day; at the same time they can have their tailparts placed in water, and be encouraged to drink – which they should do at least twice daily – by having their beaks dipped in water.

Eye irritation May occur due to prolonged periods out of water, or from the effects of oil; antibiotic-corticosteroid ointments seem effective.

Thiamine deficiency A deficiency of vitamin B_1 can occur in birds fed on a diet high in fish possessing the enzyme thiaminase (eg Smelt, Carp, Chub, Turbot, White bass) which destroys it. This can lead to polyneuritis and rapid death. Symptoms are eye-pupil constriction and loss of appetite. Prevention and cure can be effected by modifying the diet and supplementing it with thiamine (eg Benerva, manufactured by Roche Products).

In conclusion, just occasionally young seabirds fall or plane down into the sea, and are stranded locally and abandoned. Usually they are able to live off their reserves of fat until independent but, if they seem particularly young or weak, can be taken in until strong.

9 Orphans

Little short of death would induce a wild animal to desert its young. None would do so voluntarily, save one which naturally abandons them or its eggs, as do many reptiles or some maritime birds at a later stage in their offspring's development, as we saw at the end of the last chapter. But these are not the subject of this chapter, nor are the nest-parasitic cuckoos. The vast majority of higher animals care for their young with more unquestioning and unbegrudged devotion than many human parents. Clearly, the care invested in young mammals and birds is fundamental to their survival, and there would be rather fewer species around today were they as careless in their parental duties as the number of 'rescued orphans' each year supposes.

At the outset, it must be stated that the chances of coming upon a youngster truly orphaned by natural or accidental means is exceedingly remote. Even the fledgling commonly found sitting disconsolately on the ground, with no apparent nest nearby, has probably not been deserted. True, it is more vulnerable to predators, but all that is usually required is to find its nest (but see page 230), or place it in a makeshift one sited in an appropriate spot where its parents can find it. Any youngster found helpless, though not sick, on the ground will almost certainly be of a species which nests in an elevated position – in a tree or bank, or on a cliff etc. Withdrawal to a discreet distance should soon disclose the presence of an anxious parent; if it does not and if after, say, two hours, the youngster is still unattended, we can legitimately begin to wonder whether we really do have an orphan on our hands. But only after such a lapse of time. And it is more than unfortunate that, despite perennial appeals by the RSPB, RSPCA and others, anyone with any kind of local reputation as a naturalist tends to become the depository for the results of others' misguided acts of kindness. These are orphans by default, kidnapped by ignorance, and by the time they reach the hapless human foster who is saddled with the difficult tasks of replacing the natural parent(s), rearing and rehabilitation, they have become orphans indeed. Even if it were possible to relocate the exact position of the original finding, the time lost would probably be too long to permit a reunion, unless there were siblings still in the nest or vicinity.

Nestling birds, mainly of the commoner passerine species and those nesting actually on human habitations such as hirundines, the Jackdaw etc, are collected in countless numbers each breeding season. That the population dynamics of the more populous species are well able to compensate for this wastage, does little to alleviate the anxiety of the elected human recipient of the demanding mouth. Just how demanding depends chiefly on the species involved, its age and, needless to say, our efficiency.

This chapter, at least, can be divided into birds and mammals with no risk of repetition. Notwithstanding basic nutrition, the problems presented by the babies are quite different – in stimulation, presentation and administration. Because of their greater complexity, and because of the greater probability of their appearance, orphan birds are considered first.

Birds

Until now, we have been considering the single fledgling, too adventurous for its own good, which has either fallen from its nest or endeavoured to leave it before properly able to fly. These are the most common of all incidents and doubly frustrating because not only is their removal seldom necessary but because they are also the most difficult cases to rear, if perhaps the easiest to rehabilitate. Rather paradoxically, easier to rear are a clutch of small naked (psilopaedic) nestlings orphaned by the death of parents or the destruction of their nest-site, such as regularly happens when trees are felled, scrub cleared, and old buildings renovated or demolished. The fundamental difference leaving aside for the time being precocial and nidifugous young which 'fly' the nest soon after hatching, is age.

Chilled altricial and semi-altricial nidicolous (nest-confined) nestlings (Fig 49) will need immediate warmth – easily given when sandwiched between two cupped hands. They should, if healthy, gape for food at the slightest provocation, in the wild usually the sound of a parent's approach or its call, and 'only' need feeding much and often with an adequate diet (see below). The older fledgling is able to discriminate visually, and while fear of man *per se*, except possibly in

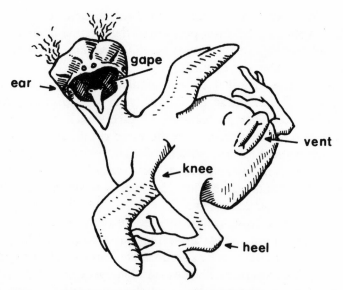

Fig 49 Altricial nestling – naked and helpless

particularly persecuted species or races, is probably not innate, it is certainly true that most fledglings learn at a certain age to recognise their parents and thereafter regard man, wisely, as dangerous. Thus the inconsistencies of our species, ranging through all shades from wholly 'good' to wholly 'bad', baffling as they are to human observing human, are incomprehensible to wild animals. And, unless the appropriated fledgling is a genius, it can have no comprehension of human individuality, much less altruism. It is bound to panic when approached by this huge and fearful form, and a panic-stricken animal will not calmly feed.

Forcefeeding, already discussed in Chapter 4, and which is so often the answer with hunger-strikers of all kinds, is not designed to win confidence. Rather it affirms the bird in its opinion of humans and prolongs its torment, though often not long enough for vindication. Younger non-imprinted birds though, after a few feeding sessions done as gently as possible – the beak being opened by a little pressure at both sides of its base – may well come to associate the human with food rather than fear. Again we encounter the dilemma of interference with biological processes. The precocious altricial chick – undoubtedly a natural phenomenon – has to take its chance between continued parental support on the one hand and benefiting some predator, as likely as not with young of its own, on the other. But again it seems unlikely that many of us could so coolly assess the situation. What really cannot be repeated too often is the foolishness, usually, of removing such a foundling to a human dwelling where the chances are that no one will benefit, least of all the orphan.

In dealing with young birds, the virtues of patience and sympathy show their true values. Having such little faith in the forcefeeding of fledglings, my preference almost every time would be to endeavour to gain its trust and confidence, even though rehabilitation then becomes much more problematical. It can be done, maybe not with all individuals of all species, but for these there is little hope anyway. Time, a gentle manner, a soothing voice and calm movements may habituate a bird to your nearness, which can slowly be increased until it not only accepts your presence and its situation but, more importantly, the food you bring. The question and timing of rehabilitation back to the wild and a healthy fear of man, have to be left until later; you cannot rehabilitate a corpse. Top of the agenda is survival, and elimination of the conflict of fear versus hunger. After all, a lame duck is better than a dead principle, and the worst that can happen is that it is recycled by nature. Perhaps the fact that it is possible to win round seasoned adults, with more cause to fear, offers encouragement in both directions.

Fledged (Fig 50) and young precocial birds clad in feathers or dense down (ptilopaedic, see Fig 51) will already be able to achieve a degree of thermo-regulation, what they require more than the steady 25–32°C (77–90°F) suitable for naked chicks is positive stimulation, beginning

Fig 50 Fledgling just out of the nest; note the gape flange still showing

as already indicated, as subtly as possible. Assuming the bird calms down and survives, it should, if it is to take its true place in nature, be exposed with care to as many different stimuli and learning experiences as possible (see Chapter 10). The same goes for birds bred in captivity which it is intended to hack off (as falconers say) to the wild.

Diets for Young Birds

The question of diet appears at first glance confusing, but is less so if, as in Chapter 4, we ignore particulars as far as possible, and concentrate on basic nutrition. The cases of kingfishers being reared on fish-fingers and woodpeckers on bread and honey (see Chapter 4), gives us confidence. For while one could not recommend such audacity, it is easy to improve on such basic diets without destroying their lovely simplicity or incurring stress and tension.

Altricial Young It can be regarded almost as an inviolate rule that all common or garden birds except the columbids (see later) rear their young on a basically softbilled and mainly insectivorous diet; and this includes finches for the simple reason that tiny stomachs cannot begin to digest an adult-type diet of seeds. It is also pretty obvious that a human cannot hope to gather the variety or quantity of small animal life that would be necessary were one to attempt to imitate a natural diet. The challenge lies in finding an acceptable, adequate, cheap, reliable and easily prepared substitute. There are many claimed, and no doubt many which work, indicating (a) it is not such a terrible problem and (b) we are correct by and large to ignore the particularities of most species.

Reference to other published and proved methods; the insectivorous food recipes such as those prepared by Sluis, Orlux and Haith; the exceptionally useful starter-crumbs manufactured for commercial poultry producers; the eggfood and alternatives described on page 103; and the following, which is adapted from a successful American recipe for the rearing of insectivorous nestlings, will convince that there is no single correct method. Also that the essential elements of all can be combined or, if necessary, adapted to suit local conditions, and substituted to give as much scope as could possibly be needed. Valuable extra stimuli can be provided in the form of whatever live edible insects can be obtained – personally I prefer to avoid most molluscs in this connexion.

```
*100g (3½oz)    strained beef heart
 30ml (2tbsp)   mashed potato (unsalted)
 15ml (1tbsp)   strained carrots
 30ml (2tbsp)   butter (unsalted)
  5ml (1tsp)    honey or invert sugar-syrup
   4 drops      liquid vitamin concentrate
```
* or similar such as very lean raw ground meat, low-fat pet meat, or tinned infant-food.

Helpless nestlings can be given the food moistened or dipped in water (to supply the only fluid intake necessary) and rolled into small blobs. Feed by means of blunt forceps, an artist's small fine-haired brush, or a round-ended feeding-stick.

It is impossible to overfeed nestlings, not because they have wholly insatiable appetites though it may seem so, but because when replete they will simply cease to gape or beg. There is, therefore, no risk of the smallest or most backward not receiving enough. As a general rule, the youngest nestlings will require feeding at least once an hour from dawn to dusk – as often as possible in fact. Very weak chicks may require quarter-hourly feeding until stronger, then half-hourly, and then hourly. The feeds can begin with diluted warm milk plus a little dissolved glucose, given via a glass pipette (medicine-dropper) to introduce the idea of feeding and liquid in case of dehydration and to provide warmth and nourishment. I would suggest progression to a fledgling diet via natural yogurt, scrambled egg and baby-foods, with supplements of vitamins/minerals.

Considering the long hours of daylight throughout which such a task will need to be performed, the dedication it requires is not to be sniffed at. Late feeding by artificial light can postpone the dawn feed for an hour or so, and it is most important that nestlings settle down for the night on a full stomach because their energy and protein requirements are prodigious. To ensure a correct growth rate and the necessary high body temperature, rearing-food should contain at least 50 per cent protein. The pleasure, indeed joy, arising from the responsibility of this toil and the giving of life, is ultimately usually reward enough. Should life fail, the disappointment is great.

Provided care is taken to ensure a comfortable temperature in the nest, usually achieved (except with hole-nesting species, see below) by suspending a (heat) lamp at a height – as a rough guide, a 40W bulb at 70cm (28in) – at which the chicks are neither too hot nor too cold, they will require little attention other than feeding. Temperature stress is indicated by panting, raised feathers and extended neck if too hot; and torpidity, neck withdrawn and chilly feel if too cold. After a meal the nestlings' droppings, each enclosed in a neat little viscid envelope, must be collected; this is most easily accomplished with tweezers. One such package is voided by each nestling directly after one feeding during most meals, always beginning each morning with a large one of the previous night's waste. As they grow, the nestlings are able to move about the nest, and develop the ability to void their droppings out over its rim.

A certain amount of care must be given to the question of substitute nests. You may read elsewhere suggestions advising the use of old natural nests, but this is a hazardous practice (qv parasites) unless they are thoroughly sterilised, and serves no real purpose. As a substitute, a round cup-shaped nest is best and most natural for, if of correct size, it provides warmth and support as the bodies are bunched together. Depending on the size of the species and clutch – although it may be as well to divide large clutches into groups of three to reduce competition – an appropriately sized flowerpot, the base of a plastic bottle, or a margarine tub, all make excellent supports if perforated to allow an airflow, shaped inside with crumpled newsprint and lined with paper tissues or kitchen towels. Cotton-wool or cloth can also be used as padding provided it is prevented from coming into contact with the birds by a layer of tissue. Never let a nestling sprawl around unsupported.

Nestlings of hole-nesting species such as woodpeckers, titmice etc, should not be exposed to direct light; their substitute nests can be heated by an ambient source or dull-emitter heatlamps. It is a mistake to wrap birds up so that they cannot move, but a tissue may be spread over nestlings to simulate the brooding of a parent.

As and when the young fledglings become more venturesome, a secure cage will be needed around the nest to ensure safety in surroundings with which they are familiar. By now the heat should have been gradually reduced until it is merely available to guard against cold snaps. Fledglings finding their wings need access to a bowl of food so that they are encouraged to begin to feed themselves, and a shallow dish of water (see Fig 32).

Although healthy nestlings grow and fledge quickly in the commoner species (see Appendix 2), most require hand-feeding several times a day until fully grown and independent. This may be anything from a few days to as long as a month or more with crows which, even though they are capable of flying immediately on vacating the nest, are not fully grown until this length of time. Nor can they abandon the advantages and security of (foster-) parental feeding: they are the nearest things to mammal-birds. At least crows, being the good omnivores they are, are not fussy about their diet. Poultry-rearing food is ideal provided it contains sufficient protein, preferably with some of it animal.

Much the same degree of dependency goes for baby raptors including herons and owls, which are semi-altricial (ie nidicolous but ptilopaedic) and therefore more able to skip meals than naked nestlings. If fed to repletion each time, four or five meals a day are generally sufficient. Their diet is exactly as an adult's (page 106) but in rather smaller pieces – though not as small as might be imagined after the first few days, when only very small morsels are required. A feeding response can be elicited by moving the food item in front of the beak, or by touching the tactile bristles at the base of it. By the time they are a week old, raptor chicks are well able to assimilate whole small vertebrates and from then on, for several weeks, each chick will consume more food than an adult of the same species reaching a peak at 2–3 weeks when about double is taken. In emergencies, raw red meat can be offered, indeed nothing more is required for the first few days of life; after this it should be supplemented with a little bone meal and roughage material. Remember that beetles and other invertebrates always form part of the diet of smaller birds of prey, almost exclusively so with the Little owl.

A major problem when hand-rearing these more intelligent birds which have lengthy periods of immaturity, is imprinting. So whereas with adult animals we sometimes have to strive to ingratiate ourselves, and win their trust and confidence, with young birds we have to maintain a distance – neither stroking nor speaking to them – if they are to stand any chance at all in the wild later (see Chapter 10).

Young pigeons and doves (squabs) differ from other altricial chicks and, like those of raptors, can be satisfied with no more than half a dozen feeds per day. This is on account of the extremely rich and nutritious quality of 'pigeon-milk', which we need to imitate, and the large quantities consumed at each feed. A squab gets its food by thrusting its beak far down either of its parents' throats, whereupon they regurgitate to it the curd-like soup produced in the crop. Most columbids produce only two squabs per clutch. If an obliging fan-tail or domestic pigeon is not available for fostering – which is by far the best possible option – the following, based on a diet designed specifically for young pigeons in America, is suitable:

> 1 mashed egg yolk, boiled for 30 minutes
> 45ml (3tbsp) mixed baby cereal
> 45ml (3tbsp) oatmeal
> 45ml (3tbsp) cornmeal

This should be mixed with milk diluted 2:1 with cold water to a consistency which can be rolled into pellets, dunked in water, and gently introduced into the fledgling's mouth. Pre-fledged squabs require it to be further diluted so that it can pass through a pipette. The mixture should not be squirted down the throat but released a few drops at a time, and swallowed naturally. When the fledgling is seen to be taking the pellets of mash with no problem, 2tbsp of small seed (eg millet and canary seed) can be introduced into the recipe, together with a teaspoon of fine grit about once a week. Columbid squabs circle and flutter their wings when seeking food, and need to be gently restrained so that the dropper or pellets can be given.

The dunking of food in water prior to feeding as an aid to ingestion, together with the liquid already in the mixture, supplies a certain amount of the water necessary; but it may be insufficient for these strange birds. What is more, adults do not drink in the same way as other species, ie by taking a beakful of water and raising the head so that it runs down the throat. Columbids drink by continual draughts in just the same way as a hoofed mammal. Squabs being hand-reared may require extra water; but if their beaks are dipped into a water dish but not held there after each feed, they will soon get the idea.

We must conclude our summary of nest-bound babies by considering those of the perplexing hirundines and Swift: always likely to appear due to the predilection of some – the Swallow, House martin and Swift – for buildings and therefore human proximity. There are, I know, decent God-fearing countryfolk who will not tolerate the delightful nests of these beautiful insect-destroying birds under their eaves on the pretext that they 'cause a mess'. We at one time, before the 1981 Wildlife and Countryside Act protected nests in use or under construction, lived opposite such a couple. Each year the nests were knocked off, and each year the martins tried again oblivious of human conservatism. And it still happens that people who would feel privileged to share their home with visitors from as far away as Africa, are forced to look on helplessly each year as the faithful birds seek out inhospitable hosts not the least interested in their welfare. The RSPB produce a very useful leaflet on how to attract (and deter) them.

Swift nestlings are hyperactive and more of a handful than those of the martins and Swallow. The parents will often continue to feed and care for strays if they are placed in a safe substitute nest or box sited near the colony. If not, hand-rearing has to be tackled. Regarding their diets, it should be borne in mind that their prey is always caught on the wing, and so any cellulose arrives by a very indirect and second- or third-hand manner – in the guts of prey animals. This results in a very high protein diet which is probably best substituted in captivity by feeding cultured and wild-caught insects and/or lean red meat either scraped or cut into small slivers and dunked in water. Scrambled egg is probably the best emergency ration. A minute amount of calcium should be given regularly. Though I have never tried it, I could be persuaded to experiment with a nectar mixture (page 107), and though I have never encountered one, I guess that Nightjar chicks – semi-altricial as they are – would present similar problems since they accept insects from the bill of the parent.

Precocial Young (Fig 51)   Hatchlings covered in down and nidifugous (soon active) are – with the exception of the semi-precocial (ie staying at or near nest although able to walk) gulls and terns, some of which coexist with humans – much less likely to be found at a young age due of course to their very precocity. Later though as they become yet more adventurous they begin to turn up: ones and twos due to true

Fig 51 Precocial chick (gull) – active soon after hatching

Fig 52 Any crudely fashioned gull beak with a red spot elicits a feeding response from Herring and Lesser black-backed gull chicks. Similar devices imitating parental beak design can be attempted with other praecoces

straying, and entire clutches often as a result of some calamity befalling the parents.

These birds fall into two principal groups: those largely able to feed themselves, eg gamebirds, waterfowl and plovers including the Lapwing; and those fed by their parents, eg grebes, divers, rails including the Moorhen and Coot, terns and gulls. Of the two, the former are, as one would expect, the least troublesome; but both require housing in a brooder which can provide a temperature gradient similar to that given poultry chicks in arks or pens. Here, beneath a centrally suspended heatlamp, they can select the temperature which suits them best at any particular age or time. Smaller rectangular enclosures should have the radiant heat source at one end. Such arrangements allow for exercise and a more natural variety of temperature than those with ambient heating. Heating should be progressively reduced until, by the time the pin-feathers sprout, it is available only at night and in cold spells. At this age, weaning onto a more adult diet begins. Less trouble will be encountered with precocial young if they can be reared

Plate 24 Badger rescued from illegal and poor accommodation shows the evidence: fur on snout and nape, and claws worn away *(Les Stocker/The Wildlife Hospitals Trust)*

Plate 25 When releasing foxes, especially those that are hand-reared, it is imperative that they are *fully* capable of hunting and scavenging *(Les Stocker/The Wildlife Hospitals Trust)*

Plate 26 Power cables across the sky might have been designed as bird death-traps. A swan in flight is a miracle of nature – here is the end of one such miracle *(Paul Scheller/Swan Rescue Service)*

Plate 27 Badgers follow traditional pathways – where fences etc are erected obstructing these, badger-gates save damage and afford unimpeded passage while preventing access to the Rabbit and other unwanted visitors *(Forestry Commission, Edinburgh)*

in groups, even if of mixed species.

Chick or turkey starter-crumbs are a godsend to these birds, as they are to many others, mashed and hard-boiled egg and live pupae, vital for waders, can be added to tempt reluctant or wary chicks. Most of the breeders of exotic pheasant and waterfowl I know of rely on starter-crumbs with only very few additives, most important of which is greenfood in one form or another (see Chapter 4).

Of the second group the terns, gulls and the Moorhen may, like the waders and gamebirds, require some encouragement to begin feeding. Natural parents elicit this response in their brood by dropping food items in front of them, by peck-scratching, and by attracting their attention with special calls – all or some of which may need to be simulated. In the case of gulls, terns and skuas, the chicks stimulate their parents to disgorge semi-processed food by pecking at the tip of the parent's beak, and forcefeeding may seldom be necessary since even a crudely fashioned imitation (Fig 52) can elicit the desired response. Any nutritious vaguely fishy mash, probably the more repulsive the better, would be a suitable diet.

Plovers, in my experience, rarely fail to be tempted by animate items. The baby Coot is claimed by some to feed itself, perhaps with some encouragement; others say it requires food to be dangled in front of it as do grebes and divers. Without the benefit of firsthand experience, I feel sure that one could soon be taught to feed itself, leaving the last named as probably the most troublesome of all British birds to hand-rear.

All precocial birds should have a shallow dish of water near their food. Those of aquatic species will soon want to get thoroughly wet, which is no problem provided there is a source of radiant heat continually available where they can go to bask dry, for they will lack a measure of the natural waterproofing available to their cousins in the wild.

Though their appearance is unlikely, an opening comment in this chapter, and the last in the preceding, ought to be elaborated. The seabirds referred to were the Gannet, petrels (including the Fulmar) and shearwaters, because they goad their young into independence by abandoning them either in or on the nest. Healthy youngsters live off accumulated fat until hunger spurs their wings. Here is a classic example of cruelty fostering kindness, for were they not deserted they would probably succumb to obesity. Young of other species incidentally will also, given the chance, crave food from human fosters, and take the easy option rather than their chance in the world. With some it takes a firm resolve tempered with a sound knowledge of the species' biology to choose the correct time for insisting on independence. Doves and pigeons can be remarkably reluctant to relinquish their pampered existences and so, as we have seen, can the crows – but from rather higher motives, and it would be wrong to abandon them prematurely. Observing a rookery at the end of our wild 'garden', I am always surprised by how long the young 'branchers' hang about, and how vulnerable they are away from the nest before becoming confidently active, even though they can fly or, rather, flap, from branch to branch.

Remote as the chances are of ocean-going orphans turning up, occasionally one or two cliff-bred youngsters, most likely Fulmars, are forced by the harassment of gulls from their precarious ledges into the sea, and are washed ashore elsewhere, where they are even more liable to attack. Such foundlings should not require feeding, and once fully fledged – adjudged by primaries extending beyond the tail – should be released at a suitable spot. Shearwaters breed in burrows and chambers, emerging at night, and are therefore less likely to be forced into premature nest evacuation. Gulls, it must be appreciated are not only formidable predators but also cannibals, and for this reason chicks which become lost in a colony will not last long enough to become orphans. As Tinbergen and Falkus (1970) succinctly put it in their classic *Signals for Survival*: 'Only a chick's parents are its friends.'

Mammals

Of far less common occurrence than birds, baby mammals present very different problems, due in the main to their greater sophistication. They tend to be less tolerant of deficient procedures, techniques, diets and conditions, and rely heavily on what may be termed 'the placental connection' and, later, the breast.

Given their infrequent and irregular appearance, coupled with the wide diversity and individuality of relatively few forms, it is neither possible nor helpful, as it was with birds, to construct groupings beyond those discussed in Chapter 2. Nevertheless, many common-sense rules apply to all. These mainly concern the need for dry warmth; a lack of draughts; no bathing or washing; fresh food, warmed to blood temperature; thorough cleaning of utensils; regular changing of bedding; the stimulation of faecal production (see leverets); and so on.

194

Why are orphaned mammals less common? Certainly, numbers of species and populations are generally smaller and while they are not only, to coin a phrase, thinner on the ground, it is this very terrestrialism that hides them well. And as regards their nests, it is more a matter of subterrestrialism, resulting in much more efficient concealment than with tree-nesting birds. Premature nest evacuation, certainly the dire consequences of it, is much less likely to occur or be witnessed by us. The increased sensitivity of mammals and, bats apart, their inability to escape from danger by flight, make them altogether more timid and furtive. You would be unlikely, for instance, to find a mammal setting up home and giving birth in such exposed positions as ground-nesting birds like plovers, larks and swans have to use. Even a mammal like the Fox can live in a garden and not be noticed and, of course, their increased nocturnalism also greatly assists their furtiveness.

Batlings are sometimes orphaned during the summer. If not much larger than a bumble bee and naked, intensive care is necessary including warmth, a furry mother substitute and milk, such as a very dilute SMA baby food given with a pipette. Cradled in one hand, a feeding response may be elicited when some of the warm liquid touches the mouth. Offer a little and very often to begin with, gradually increasing the amount. Older furred infants may have been lost, and if hung up in the evening near the home roost may be collected by morning. If not, take into care during the day, and keep trying each evening. They should take mealworms etc, but these may need to be gently eased down the throat at first. After a few weeks a young bat, if kept acquainted with its natural range, may take its place in the wild. Given their declining numbers, this is important.

The mammals which are more numerous, the smaller rodents and true insectivores, have an extraordinary ability to conceal evidence of their presence – an ability which is capitalised on when breeding. It is no coincidence that their nests are usually only discovered by accident, for example on moving a paving-stone. Since natural mortality is high in these tiny infant mammals (as indeed it is in adults), and since they form an essential link in many, many food chains, the chances of coming upon a naturally occurring orphan is extremely remote. Furthermore, the parents are very diligent and will not desert their young even if the nest is disturbed or destroyed.

Squirrels

Orphans of larger rodents are sometimes encountered but again seldom without human agency, as my own experience with Humpty – the Grey squirrel – recounted in Chapter 2, showed. It is interesting to note that squirrel infants come about in very similar ways to nestling birds, that is by tree-felling, and the optimistic precocity of some. The latter, as with fledglings, should be left for the natural parents to deal with, which they often do bodily by the scruff of the neck; even at this tender age a squirrel's bite can be severe (see page 82). Younger infants, even newly born ones, can be reared on the bottle, but before taking charge of a Grey squirrel it must be understood and repeated here that in Britain it is illegal to keep or release one except under licence. No doubt a blind eye is often turned toward the small boy keeping a pet squirrel, and the crime is not considered as serious, except to foresters, as aiding and abetting a Coypu. Lest I am accused of complicity, I point out hurriedly that the following notes are equally applicable to our native and cherished Red squirrel, although it is far less vigorous.

A squirrel's eyes open at about 20 days, and this provides a positive age guide to any found at about that age or younger. Blind and naked squirrels must be kept in a constant warm temperature of about 25°C (77°F) and handled as little as possible, preferably only at each of the 5 or 6 feeds at regular 3 hourly intervals per day. All this is better achieved if the squirrel is kept in a nest fashioned from finely shredded paper or tissues (but not newspaper) in a deep, draughtproof box heated ambiently or by a dull-emitter lamp, as for hole-nesting birds. Use nothing dusty as nest material. Sawdust may seem natural but is not; shavings from *untreated* timber on the other hand are perfectly appropriate.

From birth to week 4 or 5, feeding is best achieved via a medicine-dropper (pipette) or a 5ml plastic syringe (see under Hedgehog below). The following perfectly adequate and simple diet will take the infants through eye-opening at about week 3 to weaning which begins about a week later, ie week 4, and can go on to week 8.

Feeding Formula for Young Squirrels and Rabbits

50/50 water/milk, pinch of glucose; 1–2 5ml syringefuls per feed 5–6 times a day (no need for night feeding between, say, 2300 and 0500 hrs).

A shallow dish with a layer of bread soaked in the same mixture at blood temperature is used to tempt the weaner onto solid food. At this stage, before giving the usual bottle, offer the dish to the infant (or each in turn), gently placing its mouth against the bread. When it tastes the milk it will sooner or later begin to suck, and will then soon begin to take the bread. There should be no abrupt cessation of the bottle, which can be offered until the infant no longer requires it – at about week 8. Male babies in mixed litters kept together can suffer to such an extent from 'penis-suckling' that their segregation is advisable. The same trouble has also been recorded in other species, including the Badger.

Baby squirrels are messy and greedy feeders. In the early stages, care must be taken to ensure that they do not choke. A carefully regulated flow of milk avoids bubbling from the nostrils, the risk of inhalation pneumonia and continued feeding after the mouth is full, which is an indication that the baby is sated. Later on, the bread slows down the business. Unassisted meals, later still, are best provided in a separate box or chamber to minimise soiling of the bedding. Under no circumstances bathe any baby animal, chilling and pneumonia is a very real danger; excess splashing can be towelled off. Excessive soiling can be removed by gentle grooming, simulating the mother's licking, with a tissue and baby oil. The babies derive benefit from such attention, and it promotes correct bowel functioning.

As the growing infant begins to venture away from the nest, transfer it to a larger but still draught-proof enclosure, discontinue heating and provide a branch or two to encourage natural exercise. Along with the rearing-food, offer a wider variety – pieces of fruit, shelled nuts, poultry grain and pellets and other seeds – also a permanent dish of water. When completely independent, it can be moved to an outdoor cage provided it has dry sleeping quarters with bedding. Legal release to take place a month later if early enough in the season (see Chapter 10).

Leporids (Hares and the Rabbit)
Due to convergent evolution, adults of these species require basically the same care and nutrition as the rodents, taking into account their dissimilar habits (which have prevented competition). For young ones too there are some important differences. Most obviously, a long box replaces the deep one; and the temperature at the nest-site can be reduced by 5°C (9°F) and maintained for only two weeks. The two genera (*Lepus* and *Oryctolagus*) differ most importantly in their reproduction, and it is at birth that these differences are unmistakable and most evident.

Rabbit kittens are born blind, deaf and nearly naked below ground after only twenty-nine days gestation. Hares do not burrow, they have a longer gestation – nearly 40 days – and their leverets are born in a 'form', fully furred with their eyes open; because of this, they scarcely need artificial heat at all. Leverets disperse soon after birth to their own forms, their mother visiting each in turn only once every day, to minimise the risk of predation. This renders them very highly dependent on the doe's first milk (colostrum), and leverets deprived of this are much more likely to contract infection.

E. Jane Ratcliffe, better known for her work with the Badger, has a deep knowledge of wildlife and sent me the following account of the rearing of three leverets (see Plate 21), which I reproduce here with her very kind permission.

Received fully furred, eyes open and active.
Weights 4oz (113g), 4oz (113g), 3½oz (99g).

General Notes
1 During daytime, keep in large pen in garden on grass. Provide covered area to protect from rain.
2 For first few weeks take into outhouse at night. Put in large cardboard box with clean old sheet on box floor to enable droppings to be checked. Change sheet when soiled.
3 After each feed, for first 2 weeks, stimulate defaecation by gently stroking the rectum with warm, wet cotton-wool.
4 If after any 2 days no signs of faeces are found, give ½tsp medicinal paraffin and slightly diluted milk mixture.
5 On receiving any young mammal, give a 3-day course of Berkmycen syrup [Hoechst; a tetracycline obtainable from vet]. With leverets, give ⅓cc 3 times daily. Leave without for 4 days, then another course for 3 days. Most young are very susceptible to infection at the early stage and such a treatment is a wise precaution.
6 The amount of milk mixture taken varies slightly from one feed to another during the day.
7 Always remove stale food of any sort and sterilise bottles, teats etc, after each feed.
8 Do not handle the animals more than necessary.

Feeding

Basic food	Welpi milk powder (obtained from vet).
2 days old	Dose per feed for 3 leverets: 3 tsp milk powder + ½ tsp glucose/9tsp boiled water. Feed from kitten bottle – Catac [Fig 53]. Feed 0500hr and every 4hr until last feed late at night.
1 week old	4tsp milk powder + 1tsp glucose/12tsp water, 4 times daily. Leverets begin to feed on vegetation in pen, so from now on collect dandelion leaves, hogweed, plantain, lettuce, sow-thistles etc.
2 weeks	Leave out in pen at night with plenty of fresh greenfood. Milk feeds as per 1st week.

3 weeks	Omit late bottle but put milk out in flat dishes in pen. If slow to lap, offer on tsp to suck edge. Other feeds as usual. Increase fresh greens.
4 weeks	Introduce Farlene and milk mixture in shallow dishes (milk with little Farlene to slightly thicken). Bottlefeed at 0800hr; Farlene feed 1500 and 2230hrs, leaving dishes under cover for night.
5 weeks	Discontinue bottle. Farlene and milk at 0800, 1500 and 2230hrs; 6tsp milk powder/18tsp water with Farlene added to slightly thicken. This, as usual, divided between each dish so each animal gets its share. Always have plenty of fresh greens in pen.
5 weeks + 3 days	Farlene and milk mixture at 0900 and 2100hrs: 7tsp milk powder/24tsp water with Farlene etc as before.
6 weeks	0900hr feed only, as above; omit 2nd feed; water available in shallow dish. Fresh greens as before.
6 weeks + 4 days	0900hr feed increased to 10tsp milk powder/30tsp water. Fresh greens.

Continue with morning feed and plenty of greens in larger pen (as large as possible with netted top as they have a powerful jump). Keep to this regime until weight is c1½lb (680g) each, by which time they are old enough for release.

Release
At dusk in safe fields away from roads and railways, preferably in co-operation with a helpful farmer.

The growth rate of a Rabbit kitten (see page 196 for feeding formula) is quite spectacular, and by a week old it has doubled its birth weight of 50–60g (2oz). Grazing begins in week 3 – clover is favoured by both Rabbit and leverets – and bottle-feeds are then reduced, as is the bread and milk given to weaners. Grass etc can be given 2–3 times a day including some in late evening. Rabbit pellets, hay, oats, fruit portions and other vegetation can soon be substituted. A dish of milk may be left if needed, but certainly by the end of week 5 lactation will have ended. As soon as possible the kittens should be transferred to a secure outside run with 25mm (1in) gauge wire-netting – for they can squeeze through apertures not much bigger – and which can be moved twice a day to fresh grass. Weatherproof sleeping quarters with dry bedding must remain available until release. At younger ages, bedding may have to be replaced daily.

Deer
Since I began with vegetarians, though some squirrels are keen predators of eggs and nestlings, it seems logical to complete them before moving on to the predators and the omnivores. So this is how deer come to be wedged in between the Rabbit and the Hedgehog.

199

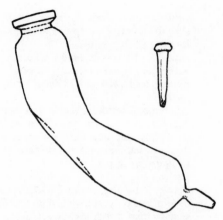

Fig 53 Catac feeder (Catac Products, Bedford) with a small teat (see also *Figs 31* and *55*)

If ever the fact that mothers do not abandon their offspring other than in exceptional circumstances needed repeating, it is here. Young deer found lying doggo in cover must not be assumed to be orphaned unless it is known for sure that the mother has been killed or is unable to continue her duties. Roe deer kids will 'freeze' if danger (for example, human approach) threatens, or lie up in cover whilst the mother feeds nearby; we may not be able to see her but that does not mean she will not be watching us.

Anyone stumbling on such a find must not succumb to the temptation to approach or touch it. Helpless young of any species found in an obviously unsuitable place, such as on a road or exposed to danger of some tangible sort, should if possible be persuaded to nearby shelter or partially covered with natural vegetation. Handle only as a last resort for human scent will taint the animal and may cause rejection by its parents. If carrying is unavoidable, rub hands well with earth or cover them with foliage, grass or a clean sack. When in doubt, the correct procedure is to leave the vicinity altogether, returning an hour or two later whereupon young deer at least will likely have vanished without trace. If not, and should the infant be making distressed 'peeping' noises, there is a very good chance that some tragedy has befallen the mother. She may have been shot by a poacher or vandal, or killed on a road, or become ensnared – and then you do have a young deer on your hands. On reflection, it will be seen that there is just as much chance of finding a partly grown youngster, unweaned and seriously ill, later in the summer for the same sort of reasons (see Chapter 10). Professional help is then essential.

200

Even with trusting newborns, a complete novice should not take on the task single-handed. In Chapter 3, it was remarked that there is generally someone close by who can do a better job; so contact local vets, animal welfare organisations, the police or the British Deer Society, who can supply a list of area representatives. If, failing all else, you are left holding the baby, it need not, with certain provisos, be too alarming. One such is that a paddock or substantial grassed area, with some form of open-fronted shelter and enclosed by 2m (6ft) high fencing, is available for the growing youngster.

Another problem is that most deer – save the Chinese Water deer, which is unique in producing 4–5, rarely up to 7 offspring – give birth to one or sometimes two young, and it is known that deer reared in isolation are much more difficult to rehabilitate back to the wild. Generally they have to go to a deerpark or some other sheltered environment.

Imprinting is a real problem in unnatural situations. It is natural and healthy for a baby animal to become attached to its security, ie its mother, and such an attachment serves it well throughout life, and helps it establish its place in society. Unfortunately, the variety in human nature, which finds expression throughout this book and which embraces the benign and malicious alike, spells death to any animal banished into the wild which retains a fondness for human company – the more so if the animal happens to arouse passions, like a bird-of-prey, or be walking venison. This being sadly so, juvenile evacuees have to be trained to a sensible appreciation of human character, as is covered more fully in the next chapter. Here, however, it can be said that to make rehabilitation more feasible, it helps if the infant becomes attached to just one human during rearing rather than becoming accustomed to seeing a succession of different faces. Once independent, that human should cease absolutely to have any involvement with the animal. At least this reduces the chance of it trotting up to the first human-being it sees after being released.

Feeding and caring for baby deer is not unduly complicated. There are several adequate diets: some authorities recommend whole cows' milk (diluted if diarrhoea occurs), others do not. Even though it has been used for many years by the New York Zoological Society for babies orphaned at birth with no ill effects whatsoever, this does not include experience of the small Roe deer, the most likely British orphan. For Roe kids, ordinary evaporated milk would be a better accessible alternative. Deer which New York remove at birth for

201

hand-rearing are left for 24 hours so that they may gain the benefits of the mothers' colostrum.

Five feeds a day at 3–4 hourly intervals is the general rule, and *never* change a diet once it has been started unless it is inadequate. For the smallest deer, an ordinary baby's feeding-bottle is excellent; larger species will require a larger bottle of some sort fitted with a lamb or calf teat. Quantities consumed vary with age and species, but it is not possible to overfeed young deer as they simply stop sucking when replete – but allow one to resume feeding if it should suddenly break off for a gambol. Roe kids begin with 150ml (5fl oz) per feed. Should difficulty in defaecation seem a problem, gently massage the anus with warm moist cotton-wool.

The five feeds may be decreased as the infant begins to nibble at grass and other vegetation, also at any easily digestible titbits such as peanut kernels, fruit and poultry food. A similar ruse to that outlined for weaning squirrels and leporids is usually effective, the bread in the dish or bowl being replaced by calf-meal. Weaning of Roe kids should be completed by early autumn, but Red and Sika calves go on well into winter. At the appropriate time, milk feeds are reduced to once a day, being grossly diluted if reluctance to abandon them is shown.

The Hedgehog

It may seem an abrupt change to swing from large herbivorous ungulates to a prickly insectivore, but the Hedgehog, happy also with other kinds of food, leads us into the omnivorous carnivores and the true carnivores. Its only actual link with deer is the regularity and predictability with which it supplies orphans.

It seems reasonable to assume that during the months when mother Hedgehogs busy themselves rearing their offspring, the motor vehicle will have a field day. I dare not hazard a guess at the numbers of litters of Hedgehog piglets that die each year from either starvation or cold, or both. The luckiest of the unlucky will draw attention to themselves in or near their nest by distressed, shrill, bird-like piping, and be rescued by people before they are found by predators. Such a call is, I'm afraid, all the evidence that is needed to make it certain one can abandon hope for their mother. First British litters are mainly born – after about a five-week pregnancy – in May or June, a second litter often arriving in August or September. The average size is five.

Newborn Hedgehogs enter the world on their backs; they are pink, blind and deaf. A pimply appearance conceals the first whitish spines,

202

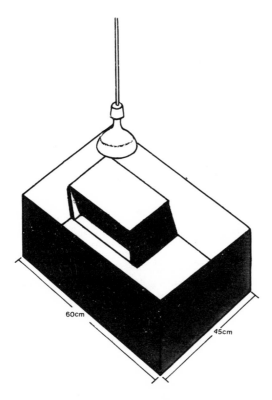

Fig 54 Accommodation for baby Hedgehogs. Aim for a comfortably warm temperature and dim lighting; as the young Hedgehogs grow, enclosures must be dig- and climb-proof

which are soon reinforced by two growths of darker ones. Orphans are inevitably going to be chilled if mother was killed during the preceding night, but their rearing is not really difficult though it is fiddly. Housing is best achieved by an open-fronted box, with an overhead dull-emitter heatlamp, placed inside another larger box with only the top open (Fig 54). This arrangement provides an exercise area and escape should the temperature in the nest rise too uncomfortably.

The chart on page 205 sets out the development of the young. Cows' milk diluted 2:1 with water, plus a pinch of glucose, has been proved a satisfactory diet on many occasions, although the pet product Lactol (Sherley's) is often preferred. The milk should be made up fresh for each feed, or daily and stored in a refrigerator, and it should be fed at blood temperature. The mixture can be given with a 5ml syringe body, ink-dropper (Fig 55) or pipette fitted with a short length of bicycle valve-rubber.

203

Fig 55 Ink-dropper pipettes (see also *Fig 31*)

The ink-dropper idea was proffered in 1974 by Jill E. Jarman who wrote to me about a baby Hedgehog she hand-reared in Lydbury North, Salop. It makes a splendidly controllable feeding device, and the following extracts from two letters show how simple the process can be:

Last summer (July 1973) ... I became the willing foster mother to a baby hedgehog (we surmised about 10 days old) ... the nest contained only one other baby which was dead. We housed him in an unwanted hamster cage standing over, but not on, an electric radiator set on low as it soon became obvious he was very cold without it.

At first I fed him warmed cows' milk from a tiny Indian ink bottle with a nozzle attachment at 2-hourly intervals, but he rapidly developed diarrhoea [*note recommended feeding strengths on page 203*] and I, despairing of helping him to survive at all, went over to feeding on demand – which he certainly did. He tramped up and down his cage making sure the children or I heard him, and clearly this system suited him far better.

I made a practice of feeding him just before going to bed and he used to down his last bottle at an alarming rate and then curl up on my lap to sleep. Endearing, but I felt worried that he was becoming too humanised. Once his eyes were open he recognised the bottle and grabbed it firmly in his front paws ... He lost the desire to curl up every time we came in sight and it was no longer necessary to wear a leather glove when feeding him as he had given up his painful habit of jumping when picked up and throwing his prickles into the palm of your hand.

After about a fortnight we went out in all weathers hunting delicacies for him. His favourite was undoubtedly earthworms which he would attack with incredible ferocity. Once he no longer needed the warmth of the radiator and comfort of the bottle, we segregated him from family and I gave him saucers of bread and milk and his diet of worm, slug etc out of

Age: weeks	Description	Feeding[†]	Remarks
1	at birth – weight 25g (1oz) –naked and pink, eyes closed; white spines soon appear	8–9 feeds daily of 3–5ml every 2hr or on demand. Dusk feeds most important	day 1: suckled by mother; day 2, week 2: covered with nest material when left by hunting mother. Constant warmth needed. Parasites are best removed. Piglets can be cleaned by tissue and baby-oil
2	brown spines begin to show; eyes still closed; able to roll into ball and move about nest	6 feeds of 5–6ml every 2½hr	
3	eyes open; more active movement; teeth begin to erupt	as week 2, but offer dish of tinned pet meat with the mixture poured over	reduce heat if weather is warm. Weight 150g (5¼oz)
4–6	weaning; positive movement; third coat of mature spines grows between previous two	reduce handfeeds consistent with increase in self-feeding	further reduction of heat culminating in curtailment if conditions permit. Guard against cold snaps. Weight 250g (8¾oz)
6–9	fully mobile and independent	cessation of handfeeds and full dependence on tinned pet meat, raw egg, slugs, snails etc in preparation for release	prepare for release in week 8–9 if not too late in year (ie by Sept★) by moving to secure outside quarters. Young may be allowed to self-disperse from home territory if considered safe enough

† They accept food most easily if lying on their backs on operator's lap; slowly dispense until sucking stops.

★ If a second litter, release should not be contemplated until the following spring (March or April). Weight must be at least 450g (1lb).

Development of the Hedgehog (various sources)

sight of the family. Two weeks later and a full month since we had taken him in, we decided regretfully that to be fair to him we must release him back into the wild. It was a hot sunny afternoon as we set out to where we knew there were plenty of other hedgehogs living ...

You will scarcely believe the end of this story. Not 150yds from the house ... we came upon another young hedgehog right in our path somewhat smaller ... though clearly out on his or her own, so presumably independent. We sat ours on the path beside her (or him) and he [excitedly] proceeded to do this curious self-anointing process you mention but between each slobbering over his own prickles he was chewing those of the other hedgehog, which appeared not to mind. It lasted [at least] a good 20 minutes ...

I wonder what his chances were of survival and was he trying to get himself smelling like a wild hedgehog? ... I hope you find this story of interest. I think many of us 'civilised' people get great joy from helping wild animals in trouble. I certainly did.

Mustelids (Including the Badger)

If the Hedgehog is an omnivorous insectivore, the Badger can be regarded as an omnivorous carnivore. But before venturing on to this and other larger carnivores, we must briefly consider their smaller relatives: the Stoat, Weasel, Polecat, Pine marten, domestic polecat-ferrets gone wild (for they are the most likely clients) and the Mink, though the latter is officially a pest. Stoats and Weasels proliferate but are rarely recovered in a live condition at any age. Occasionally, so I'm told, cats will bring home a live infant. In such an event, a diet and conditions similar to those for baby leporids is recommended. If and when the kitten is weaned, a dish of diluted milk ought to be offered; once lapping begins, bottle-feeding can be phased out over a period of about a week. A fortnight after full independent feeding, the kitten can be transferred to outside quarters provided they include a snug bedroom.

Badger cubs do not commonly bring themselves to the attention of the general public. Even though newly weaned ones frequently starve to death, their instincts keep them out of sight. They are born about February and remain below ground in the set until 6–8 weeks old (April), and do not begin to venture farther afield until weaning at about week 11. Although they remain sensitive to noise disturbance, they are probably able to look after themselves in favourable circumstances, as was the juvenile I watched on 12 May 1982 pottering about by the side of a forest track in broad daylight at noon. But they do not usually leave their parents until week 32–35 (September/October). The intervening period is one of education and play in which cubs learn their neighbourhood and society; they do not go far without their parents until high summer. Younger cubs will only be seen to require assistance in the event of deliberate disturbance, and the people who enjoy such work are hardly likely to have the Badgers' best interest at heart. Cubs orphaned by parental accident will either perish below ground unnoticed or be cared for, if of an age, by adult relatives. A chilled cub brought in must first of all be warmed up by being placed in a snug dark box on a nest of torn newspaper next to a well-wrapped hotwater bottle.

E. Jane Ratcliffe has reared many Badger cubs, and for a diet prefers the human invalid food Complan to Lactol, which many other workers rely on exclusively for a wide range of mammals. Lactol is 70 per cent skimmed cows' milk, and manufactured ostensibly for puppies. It will always, she insists, cause a loss of hair in Badger cubs, as may any other food based on cows' milk; this is possibly due to an allergic response or, more likely, a deficiency. Hair loss is more unsightly than a serious problem since a new coat grows after weaning. Phil Hunt, a Westcountry vet who has handled some 200 Badgers since 1975, feels that Complan could be too complex for young cubs, and still prefers Lactol despite cases of temporary baldness. He also cautiously advances Wysoy (Wyeth Laboratories) – a soya-protein food for human babies suffering from allergies. Full-cream evaporated milk and the baby-food Ostermilk have also been used successfully. A Belcroy premature-baby bottle is the ideal feeder; alternatively an ordinary bottle with a premature teat. If other teats are used, care has to be taken to see that the hole is neither too small nor too large. Very young cubs fasten tightly onto the teat, hunching their shoulders; when they realise they are not going to be robbed, they relax and begin to suck. Older cubs may be weanlings; look for signs of canine teeth.

After weaning – between weeks 8 and 13 – cubs may be moved to secure outside quarters since this will be during the equable months of May and June; nevertheless this must still incorporate a cosy den. Hand-feeding is phased out and replaced by one good large solid feed of dogmeat plus a variety of titbits as near as possible to a natural omnivorous diet each evening; more can be offered if in doubt. A bowl of drinking-water must be available. Thereafter the cubs can be prepared for release, which should present few problems if tackled sensibly in a suitable area (see Chapter 10). Cubs are fully independent at about month 6, but in a natural course of events face serious hazards before reaching their third birthday – mainly from other Badgers.

The Fox

Reynard is more of a problem, and in many ways presents the ultimate challenge in rearing: not because it is tricky to feed or dangerous – it is much less so than the Badger – but because of the time commitment and subsequent difficulties which will not be apparent or seem important when confronted by a bewitching cub. These must be understood lest we find ourselves saddled with a full-grown Fox totally imprinted on humans, and an increasingly demanding pet, intolerant of any disruption to normal family life. 'Release' of such a case is in fact quite the reverse, and amounts more to a death sentence due to the peculiar relationship this species enjoys (if that's the word) with *Homo sapiens*.

It is pretty pointless, saddening and demeaning to have to kill an animal that has been lovingly reared just because its face no longer fits, but that is the fate of many. It is none the less so if it is abandoned in strange countryside like a mongrel on a motorway. The 'dump it in "the country", at least it'll have a chance' theory may assuage our conscience, but it is not humane (see Chapter 10). Somewhat luckier ones are often dumped on zoos, as anyone who has worked in a large one will confirm.

Workers with more experience than I of Fox cubs, insist that one brought up in isolation from its own kind has a poor chance of ever making it back to the wild – certainly it is difficult for all higher animals. Those brought up in groups, not necessarily related, stand a much better chance. This is the first thing to consider when presented by fate or someone else with a cub; extensive enquiries should immediately be made through the usual channels (see Appendix 3), culminating, if all else fails, in contacting zoos and wildlife parks.

Depending on such considerations, the job of rearing can either be delegated to someone in a better position or begun. If the latter, be sure to realise that it is a job – assuming the waif has been orphaned soon after appearing out of its earth in May at about 4–5 weeks of age – which will take about four months if we aim for release around September at the time that wild families tend to disperse for the winter. However, it is the young dog Foxes that are forced away by January when mating recommences; the young vixens remain throughout the winter with their mother and into the following spring when she again gives birth. Thus the disturbance hunting causes can actually *make* the Fox a pest (see Chapter 11).

As already mentioned, the actual rearing is not complicated. A litter usually comprises 4–5 cubs, which remain blind until day 19. Unweaned cubs (see accompanying chart), can be successfully reared on Complan or Lactol, as set out for Badger cubs; a syringe, Catac (Fig 53) or doll's feeding-bottle may be used. They begin to lap milk at an early age, and no difficulty should be encountered in transferring

Fig 56 Development of fox-cubs *(after Burrows)*

them to a solid diet of tinned dogmeat etc (see page 108). Phil Hunt has noted occurrences of night-blindness as a result of vitamin A deficiency, this can be avoided by occasional use of supplements or a more varied diet (see Chapter 10). A sturdy dish of water, replenished daily, should always be available. It is imperative that training for release begins immediately after weaning or just before – at week 6.

Age: weeks	Approx dates	Description
born	late March/ early April	moleskin appearance; average weight 110g (4oz)
2	April	chocolate-brown woolly coat shows
3	April	eyes open
5	May	first appear above ground
6	late May	1.1kg (2½lb) red coat develops
7–9	May/June	weaning; leave earth
10	June	1.6kg (3½lb); education begins
12	late June	commence independence
14	early July	fairly independent
16	late July	milk dentition replaced; ¾ grown
19	mid August	3kg (6½lb)
25	late September	adult size but not weight

Wild Fox Cub Development (after Burrows (1968), Hunt and others)

The Wild Cat

Mike Tomkies (1977) has demonstrated that Wild cat kittens can be hand-reared and rehabilitated back to the wild despite an inherent distrustfulness of man and a high degree of ferocity. Tomkies reared two kittens in a fairly conventional way for carnivores and while they grew to accept his presence, they never became humanised. He has collated the following brief information: weight at birth, 120–150g (4¼–5¼oz); weaning begins at week 6, not complete for 2½–3½ months; probably need to run with their mother until month 5 in order to develop fully, learn to hunt (especially at night) and escape from danger up trees.

We conclude our survey of mammal orphans with two types of fish-eating carnivores: the first is, with the preceding subjects, a member of the Carnivora; the second is from a related order, Pinnipedia. The first is much the least likely to come to our attention, for it is shy and retreating.

The Otter

Any enthusiast of the late Gavin Maxwell's books has access to a feast of information regarding Otter/human relationships; Maxwell has done for the Otter what Ernest Neal and now Phil Drabble have done for the Badger. I have a hunch that the Otter is a little more widely spread than generally thought: I have seen one on a semi-tidal marsh in Cornwall where none is supposed to live; moreover, I occasionally hear of similar reports from people of integrity who prefer to keep their observations fairly private. Cubs could turn up as a result of the disturbance caused by the packs of otter-hounds and their human followers. Though they claim now to have turned their attention to the Mink, their activities can do nothing but harm to the Otter.

Otter cubs can, it would seem, be born at any time of the year. There are 3 in a litter – born blind and helpless with a coat of dark silky hair. Eyes open at about week 5, and they remain in the holt for 3 weeks. Rearing is as for Badger cubs until they transfer to a solid diet (see page 108); an adult consumes about 1½kg (3lb) of fish etc each day. Due to the probability of imprinting, Otter cubs should be viewed with as much circumspection as Fox cubs, and treated accordingly.

210

Seals

Though their appearance on certain stretches of coastline – usually as a result of exhaustion or stranding at highwater mark – is not infrequent, they bring with them so many special problems that they are much better off with specialists; indeed there is scarcely an alternative.

As a result of stranding – perhaps over successive high tides on gently shelving beaches – the Common seal (*Phoca*), born in the summer, appears to suffer most from severe dehydration which leads to weight loss, mouth lesions and stress brought on by racking sun and wind. Cansdale and Yeadon, who have supervised much work with this species in Skegness on the Wash coast, have found that most waifs weigh only about 8kg (17½lb) compared to the 12kg (26½lb) which is considered by the Seals Research Unit of the Department of the Environment to be about the minimum viable weight.

The Sea Life Centre (SLC) near Common seal waters at Connel, Argyll has the following *Working procedure for handling abandoned seal pups*, which is reproduced here, with their kind permission, almost word for word:

> When informed of the whereabouts of an abandoned pup people should be advised not to approach it, giving it every opportunity to return to the water of its own accord. On no account should the pup be touched or carried. Taking it to the water's edge or placing it in the water will only reduce its chances of survival. If the pup has been approached at all or if it seems certain that its mother is not nearby, then steps should be taken to bring it into care. People should be advised to keep well clear as any more than two attending a pup will certainly worry it.
>
> The pup should be uplifted as soon as possible and transported in the passenger compartment of a vehicle, preferably with one person to hold and comfort it, to a cool and dull environment (eg a garage floor). This person will quickly become accepted as a temporary substitute mother and should continue to comfort the seal when taken out of the car. No attempt should be made to feed the seal or to give it water as this will only distress it. The pup should be allowed to settle with one person in attendance while the following points are noted:
> 1 Length of umbilical cord.
> 2 Whether or not teeth have been cut.
> 3 Is there any evidence of frothing at the mouth.
> 4 Do the eyes appear to be bright and healthy.
> 5 Does it appear strong and active or generally lethargic.
> 6 Is the heart-beat strong and regular.
> 7 Has it sustained any damage.
>
> Once these points have been noted, the SLC [or other competent body] should be contacted, and an assessment can be made as to whether the pup will be strong enough to withstand a [longer] car journey and if it is a viable proposition to attempt to rear it.

The SLC has pioneered some valuable research into (Common) seal pup diets, and has the following to say on the matter: 'All our pups are, in fact, weaned directly on to an adult diet within a day or so of arriving at the Centre. We are, however, reluctant to divulge the actual method of doing this since, unless all the necessary backup facilities are provided, anyone attempting to rear a pup will get out of their depth long before the pup is ready to be released.' (M. Causer; personal communication).

The demands made by orphaned seal pups are in the main twofold and fairly obvious: firstly a considerable and hygienic seawater environment (especially for *Phoca* if long-stay care is contemplated) and, secondly, an adequate diet. The first is largely governed by finance, commitment and space; the second, despite innovations, is still influenced by imperfect knowledge.

Grey seals (*Halichoerus*) also suffer from mistaken rescue, but natural mortality is high. The Cornish Seal Sanctuary at Gweek takes in 20–60 Grey seal pups a season, and stresses that these pups are much more difficult and dangerous to handle than Common seal pups. At birth, *Halichoerus* measure about 90cm (3ft) long and can weigh up to 16kg (35lb); *Phoca* pups are more than 4.5kg (10lb) lighter and measure about 70cm (28in). But more than differences in size, the location (see Chapter 2) and time of year will unerringly identify the species of a foundling.

Grey seals are born from September to January and remain ashore until independent, but should storms occur before they are 8 weeks old, 50–60 per cent can perish by being washed away from their parents onto rocks. The Common seal has a quite different method of reproduction. Those in British waters give birth about July in shallows or on tidal flats and sandbanks; consequently, their lanugo (the off-white foetal fur or puppy coat) has to be replaced by the adult coat before or soon after birth to enable the pups to swim or at least float almost immediately. The early stages of their lives are, then, predictably hazardous and susceptible to bad weather despite assiduous maternal protection. By day 2 or 3 they are learning quickly, and can swim and dive as opposed to passive floating. At first, pups stay near shore or actually haul out, but by week 6 they are on their own.

The milk teeth of seals grow and are lost before birth, and the adult teeth erupt in a matter of days. In the wild, the weight-gain in pups is astonishing and due entirely to the unique quality of the mothers' milk, which seems impossible to duplicate, and which is rapidly converted to the blubber essential to the survival prospects of pups after abandonment. By as little as 2 weeks old, the birthweight of *Phoca* can more than double to as much as 27kg (60lb); *Halichoerus* should be twice that at about 55kg (120lb), at which time the lanugo is shed.

Of the captive diets variously recommended, recent work has indicated, rather surprisingly perhaps, that initial force-feeding (soon followed by willing acquiescence) of whole Sprats and Mackerel – in other words, instantaneous weaning – yields very good results. At the other extreme, some diets attempt to simulate the mothers' extremely rich milk which comprises over 40 per cent fat and 10 per cent protein. Most techniques fall somewhere between the two. The Cornish sanctuary adopts the emulsified fish diet for its *Halichoerus* pups, prepared by liquidising fish which has been previously skinned and boned. This blend, which looks not unlike milk, is bottle-fed to pups four times a day if they will take it – if not they are force-fed via a stomach tube – until 3 weeks old. Thereafter, they are fed whole Mackerel straight down the throat with the jaws held open so that the fish are not crushed. Starved pups are fed one fish the first day, 2 the second, and up to 10 twice daily at 3 weeks (if the fish are small, up to 30 may be taken). A 6 week old *Halichoerus* still on emulsified fish will take up to 4.5 litres (1 gal). Seals are released when fat and able to catch their own fish etc. When feeding freely, *Phoca* pups will take 1.8kg (4lb) of fish daily, split into 6 feeds. The remarks concerning thiamine deficiency in seabirds at the end of Chapter 8 apply equally to seals; suitable fish are listed in Chapter 4, and young seals naturally eat many shrimps etc.

Cansdale and Yeadon (1975) advise the de-lousing of young seals on arrival at the treatment centre by an insecticidal sheep-dip solution. Some workers routinely medicate each newcomer. Again relaying the successful Skegness method: 1ml of Propen (procaine penicillin: Glaxo Laboratories) is injected immediately on arrival, and repeated 5 days later; one Vitamin Tablet for Fish-eating Animals (Cooper Nutritional Products) plus one 25mg tablet of Benerva (thiamine: Roche Products) and 3 of Sulphamezathine (sulphonamide: ICI) on each of the first 10 days. The tablets are easily administered by insertion into the body cavity of a fish.

Seal cubs in a very poor condition, emaciated and with ulcerated mouth lesions, are often not considered worth attempting to save. But as Ken Jones, curator of the Gweek sanctuary, points out, these are the very animals that hospitals and sanctuaries should exist for – especially, I might add, in areas where the seal population is unnaturally low due to human activity past or present. Gweek loses very few admissions; success rate of 90 per cent is increased to a virtual 100 per cent, once the seals are over the critical first two days. Those never able to fend for themselves are retained for breeding purposes.

10 Convalescence and Rehabilitation

Throughout this book the emphasis has been on a return to the wild as soon as possible. Regrettably, as we will see later, it is not always possible; nevertheless it is the only really satisfactory end to our endeavours, and often our requirement in law. It is the species rather than the disorder which governs this phase of the programme for rehabilitation is reached only in those patients that have fully recovered, and the method varies from group to group. Half-fit or improperly rehabilitated subjects are all too frequently abandoned; so the ability to foresee problems and complete a therapy are prerequisites before any patient is accepted.

The heading of this chapter implies successful treatment, so we omit the chronically sick and the severely disabled, such as the bird with a less than perfect wing. Several things have to happen simultaneously during convalescence. For the animal, it is a period of recovery, conditioning of both mind and body, and unwitting preparation; for the guardian, it is a time when considerable thought and planning may have to go into creating optimum conditions for release, and may well include travel to a distant location.

Given that the species or group is the most important criterion, there is the difficulty of giving specific advice, the more so when we think of the varied geography of the British Isles and the equally varied dwelling places of its human population. What is good advice for the country dweller could be folly for an inhabitant of suburbia. Animals must not only be released in the environment most suitable for them but also in the correct way and in the best part of that environment in the right season, and possibly at a particular time of day or night.

The following are guidelines for the amateur; and they assume some ability to identify species, find the appropriate habitat in a particular locality, and know sufficient about its ecology to work out suitable release times (see also Chapter 2).

Before release, the patient must be brought into a suitable condition to withstand the rigours of its life ahead. As therapy is successfully completed, follow-up or after-care nursing involves routine cleanliness – where appropriate, bathing, changes of dressings and bedding, etc – and a good diet. This latter point is especially important where tissues such as bone are healing and need a good supply of calcium and phosphorus in the correct proportions; the best way to achieve this is to feed sterilised bone-flour as a supplement. Vitamin drops such as Adexolin (Glaxo Products) are also useful.

While the patient's body is recovering its strength and vitality, we should be working out a careful programme, possibly including such factors as reversion to as near natural diet as possible, a check as to complete self thermo-regulation, and an intermediate move to a semi-natural sheltered habitat. It can often be a trying and distressing time calling for great tact and objectivity; for the trust and confidence that might have been fostered in a wild animal during the course of its treatment has now to be undone. While it is to be hoped that imprinting has not occurred, it is inevitable that most wild patients will have become at least partially accustomed to human presence; and even the slightest dulling of a reflex action or releasor can be fatal in the wild. Convalescing animals have to be encouraged to remember their former healthy fear of the human form, but obviously not in so forceful a way as to risk a clinical relapse! There must be no friendly contact and indeed as little sight, sound and scent as possible of humans. For some animals in A1 condition approaching the point of release, a little tactical or peripheral scaring – a little negative stimulation – may be all that is required to bring a subject to 'its senses'. The position with hand-reared orphans is much more tentative.

An adult short-term case can generally re-adapt to a natural way of life. We must aim to release birds *within* three weeks, and specialist/ territorial kinds at *exactly* the spot from which they came. Mammals can take longer, and their release criteria are not quite so critical. Hand-reared subjects must be given time, and encouraged to respond to intuitive behaviour patterns by gradual acclimatisation from a home-base to which they can return for safety, security and sustenance.

During convalescence the worker can, as already mentioned, help prepare the ground by phasing out all direct contact. This may require a move to or near the release point; a different design of cage, allowing

216

'ghost-husbanding'; and possibly the building of a special release pen. These and other devices help to acclimatise the animal from a known position of security to charged insecurity – really a more natural state. With some animals, this is a luxury or unnecessary; with others it is crucial, as the following examples show.

Birds

Passerine birds resident in Britain, in contrast to those over much of Europe, have a healthy but not paranoiac fear of man. Their release, once fit, from our point of view at least, is pretty straightforward. If their exact origin is not known, they should be taken as near as possible to where they were found; failing this, a relatively sheltered or quiet spot in their natural habitat must be chosen. This may well demand a certain amount of fieldcraft, such as a survey to make sure the species is present, and its population density. For the same reasons that captive diurnal birds are best moved from one aviary to another at about midday – because they will have fed in the morning and still have the remainder of the day in which to become acquainted with the geography and find a roosting site – wild birds should be similarly released. Long-stay patients of resident species must not be released in or just prior to either the winter or the breeding season.

The indifference of many small birds to man should not have been seriously endangered by a few weeks of captivity. Orphans which have spent their entire lives in captivity being tended by a potential mortal enemy are a rather different matter. It is contentious and currently a matter of debate whether such cases can ever really be successfully rehabilitated. At least they will need a long period of adjustment, but the law requires they are released even if this means a miserable death. It is a pity that much of the energy which goes into knocking serious aviculture cannot be deployed in decently protecting the Badger and Fox.

In a couple of paragraphs we seem to have dismissed the perching-, garden- and song-birds, possibly our most likely customers. Part of the reason for this is that a mal-released Blue tit can die and perhaps not draw attention to itself in the same way as a starving owl. Whether the owl is or is not more specialised, it seems so; and this specialisation in rarer or more spectacular subjects is a pity because it makes them less adaptable and because they can expect less indifference on the part of man.

217

Of course there are larger birds that have little to fear: the Slavonian grebe mentioned in Chapter 4 is one example. But there are many more which are at risk, more from birdwatchers than hunters. The amateur can find out more about bird/human relationships by reading, contacting local natural history societies and from talking to knowledgeable local people. Rare subjects will attract most advice and support; less glamorous ones are usually either actively hunted (eg species of crows, gamebirds, waterfowl and waders) or ignored. Those species that are not regarded as pests but legitimate quarry, enjoy close seasons during spring and summer; mostly from the beginning of February through to the end of August. The Capercaillie, Pheasant and Woodcock are additionally protected in September; Red grouse may be shot from 12 August, Black grouse from 20 August, to 10 December. The crows will have to take their chances; at least the splendid qualities which get them into trouble may also help them.

Migrators present special problems. Clearly, they must not be released when their kind is on the other side of the world, nor, rather less obviously, must they be released immediately prior to emigration. This is because their chances of having the strength, orientation and resources to enable them to achieve the journey are non-existent. Likewise with passage migrants; unless they can be mended and sent on their way very quickly while the species is still on passage, it may be better to retain them until their fellows return. However, this may well be illegal, and the chances of a passage migrant successfully regaining a normal existence after a confinement lasting longer than three weeks are not good. For these reasons, if no other, it is important to be able to identify species correctly.

Earlier it was said that the species more than the disability governs the release procedure. While this holds good 99 times out of 100, it would be culpably foolish to reintroduce an animal back into the same environment which originally caused its sickness. Poisoned and persistently polluted areas are cases in point; for example a swan, recovered from lead poisoning would not be enamoured of human intelligence were it sent back to a kind of watery death-row. Stretches of heavily fished water are probably best avoided by most aquatic wildlife – fish and all. The victims of oiling, other than in major disasters, generally turn up at a distance from the incident and therefore by the time therapy is through, a more suitable release point can usually be found – probably near a social group or in a well frequented area.

All water-birds are released at the margins of their particular habitat, be it stream, river, pond, lake or ocean. Depending on the species, they can be placed on or near the water, thrown bodily high into the wind, or set down near a cliff edge or on raised ground overlooking the sea. The decision never seems anything less than obvious at the time. Swim-diving specialists such as seaducks, divers, grebes, auks, cormorants etc – some of which can take off only from water – can be floated away from a stretch of suitable quiet coastline, riverbank or lakeside; divers breed on fresh water but move to the coast for the winter, as do some waterfowl. Flying specialists, like the Gannet, gulls, petrels, shearwaters, skuas, terns etc can be boosted into a gentle wind or sea breeze (shearwaters at dusk). Marginal birds, ie rails, waders and herons, should be placed on the ground; whether at riverbank, lake- or pond-side, marsh, mudflat or shore depends on the species. Some, notably waterfowl, gulls, waders and the Grey heron, if convalescing in an open outdoor quarter or let out into one in the daytime, will quite often decide for themselves when the time is right for their departure. Then they will simply vanish one day in just the same way that lost or exhausted racing-pigeons do after a period of recuperation at some stranger's house. At least one always hopes that it was so, and that a rat or some other predator was not involved in the disappearance, for rats and cats can be a real headache where incapacitated birds are habitually kept.

Migratory water-birds need to be assessed in much the same way as their passerine counterparts, although it is very noticeable that geese, for instance, recovering near a flight path will not be able to resist the urge to rejoin their colleagues when the time comes.

Birds-of-prey, as always, are rather a special case. Their relationship with man is very much a love/hate one; and the persecution they have suffered at his hands, together with the bitterness that still persists in some rural areas, on top of their natural nervousness, has resulted in a wary, highly strung creature that under no circumstances must be deposited thoughtlessly in the countryside, however suitable. Their territorial requirements, especially across country which is unfamiliar or less than perfect for them, means that there will be few, if any, vacant niches. Bearing in mind the estimation that only about 5 per cent of young Tawny owls ever live long enough to see their first birthday, the chances of a hand-reared inexperienced owlet surviving its first week, let alone its first winter, are probably zero.

To give all convalescent and first-year birds-of-prey the best

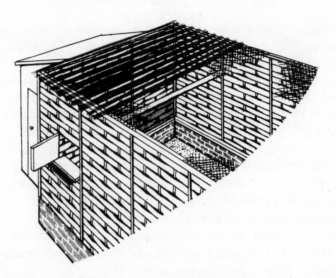

Fig 57 Release cage, with concealed servicing and a release hatch for birds of prey; note the ledge on which food is placed for free-flying birds

possible chance, they should be released only from the aviaries in which they have spent the preceding weeks. Aviaries should be adapted to allow feeding through a small hidden hatch (Fig 57), so that they need not be entered. Water can be poured into a dish from outside, and do not worry about the build-up of excrement. Only in this way can they grow accustomed to an area or a part of it, and have a home base or orientation point to which they can return, for a week, a month, a year or more, and be assured of food and shelter. It is just possible that they will strike up some kind of relationship with wildings. I have found it not unusual for Tawny owls to attract wild relatives who, not always with malicious intent, come and sit on the roof of the aviary. Such contact can only benefit them at the time of liberty. Others workers have noted the same with Barn owls. For this species, pilot schemes carried out by the British Owl Breeding and Release Scheme and The Hawk Trust indicate that by the erection of next-boxes populations can be maintained and, sometimes, increased.

All non-town birds rehabilitate more safely from some form of open aviary. This is most simply made possible by leaving a door or hatch open, presenting no problem from a garden aviary, whether your own or that of a friend living in a more suitable locality. If no such aviary is available, it may be possible to contact a sympathetic person who owns land in a suitable area; failing that, use the contact-points suggested in Appendix 3.

The parks and gardens found in cities and towns are of enormous ecological significance, and much more important to wildlife on account of the diversity and protection they afford than an equivalent area of farmland. However, only species occurring there naturally should be released into a sprawling conurbation.

The ringing *by qualified persons* of rehabilitating birds is strongly recommended, so that evidence can be gained as to the success rates of species and techniques. The British Trust for Ornithology will furnish a list of ringers operating in the different areas of the country.

Mammals

It is easier to be specific because of their fewer numbers; again much will depend on one's own location.

Voles, Mice etc

All smaller subjects of the scuttling, rustling and squeaking variety can be released in a cat-free garden or in any untidied corner or hedgerow away from busy roads. Graveyards, golf-courses and aerodromes for example make excellent nature reserves. Given that the appropriate type of terrain must be found – again the most obvious and sensible thing is to return an animal whence it came – I am not aware that active rehabilitation is necessary, but I am aware that we may be in the Blue tit syndrome again (see page 217). These little beasts seem to know full well how slender hangs their life's thread; and I suspect that they instantly revert – if indeed they ever gave it up – to their timorous existences. Those emanating from aquatic environments, a Water vole for instance, should be returned there. Most such animals are nocturnal and would, were they released in the morning or early afternoon, be at a considerable disadvantage; dusk is correct.

Bats

When releasing a bat to rejoin its home group make sure that it can fly well. Test in an enclosed room over soft material; fast flyers like the Noctule may be wisely reluctant.

The Hedgehog

If they do not make good their own escape first, Hedgehogs should be welcomed by any gardener. But failing safe, de-militarised gardens away from busy roads, an evening trip into the countryside will be a pleasant necessity (see also Chapter 9).

Squirrels

I have already dealt with the Grey squirrel's position regarding release into the countryside, and to comply with the law and as a kindness to trees and squirrels, it really is to be discouraged. Organised squirrel hunts are still part and parcel of forested country, and they no doubt also serve to satisfy the macho pretensions of certain kinds of country dweller. The difficulties encountered in maintaining the Red squirrel mean that no time must be lost in its convalescence.

More for academic reasons than any other, squirrels unavoidably detained over autumn cannot be released until the following spring, for they will have amassed no store of food. Hand-reared specimens have to be released as early in the summer as possible for the same reason.

Leporids

Rabbits and hares must be released as quickly as possible. Without being too dogmatic, I would suggest that the leporids are just about the only prey animals which may benefit by being released quickly before fully fit. They have a habit of suddenly going downhill if kept penned up for too long. With their refined survival techniques, and provided they are taken to pastureland which is little shot over, with cover or dense hedgerows nearby and well away from roads, they can probably look after themselves better than we can. The time for release is similar with orphans – ideally once weaning is completed. Under natural circumstances, the doe abandons her young at an age which seems terribly premature to us.

Deer

Provided deer are not imprinted – which is very likely – they can, with the landowner's permission, be released into an area known to be inhabited by their kind. The rehabilitation of orphans was touched on in the preceding chapter. More often than not, deer which have been influenced by direct contact with man have to go to some form of protected habitat – at best a good deerpark, at worst a poor zoo.

Muntjacs can breed at any time but most deer are produced in May or June. By the end of September, Roe kids and Fallow fawns are just about capable of independence, though normally they would run with the mother until the following year's young are dropped or even until the subsequent autumn rut. According to the Forestry Commission: 'A fallow deer fawn may survive if the mother is killed at the end of

222

September or early October, but it will suffer hardship and even if it survives it is unlikely to make a well-grown yearling. Even November is quite early enough for a fawn to be orphaned.' It may be construed from this that there is no urgency to dehumanise and rehabilitate by the autumn and that a good case could be made for over-wintering them, especially in hunted areas, until the following summer's hiatus. (Male deer are protected in May, June and July; females in March through to the end of October). But this would demand an extensive fenced paddock and supplementary feeding, and clearly the risks of imprinting are that much greater.

What is true for the smaller native British deer is certainly even more so for Red and Sika calves, which take about eight months to wean and are dependent on their mothers until the following year. Young deer suffer severely in hard winters, and so do the old; for instance the twelve-year longevity of Red deer in Scotland can, exceptionally, be as much as doubled in England.

The Badger

This is not a difficult animal to rehabilitate: it has no enemies left in Britain except man (see Chapter 11), and is tough with a high social order.

If for any reason one cannot be returned to its point of origin or released at or near its *own* set, it should be taken to an area known to be free of residents but ideally within reach of one; Badgers can travel many miles in one night so there is no need for excessive caution. As with any nocturnal animal, release should take place at dusk. Phil Hunt is firmly of the opinion that both Foxes and Badgers are best, most easily and most safely released in a disused Badger set – provided one knows the reason for its disuse. His method is to chivvy the animal into the set and to stop up the entrance with a log rammed into the opening, thus preventing a headlong charge out and away into a possibly less suitable area where progress cannot be monitored. After digging its way out, usually in the first night, the evacuee is already to a certain extent habituated. It is tired and therefore more likely to take stock of its situation, exploring the now quiet and deserted neighbourhood, than instantly to flee. Extensive tagging and monitoring over ten years have, time and time again, proved that this is a successful method. A disused barn near a suitable area can be similarly used – retaining and feeding for a few days, and then leaving the door unsecured so that the animal finds its own way out.

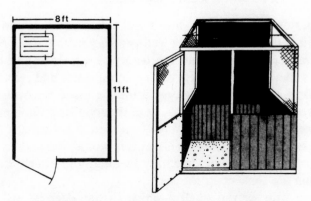

Fig 58 Convalescing quarters for Badger and Fox

Even hand-reared juveniles (see Chapter 9) can be released success-fully with only marginally more trouble. Provided they are properly weaned, feeding independently, and a suitable locality can be found – again preferably with disused burrows, or in an area free of residents where an artificial set could be constructed – their chances of survival are not much worse than those of a naturally reared cub. It will certainly do no harm to get them used to travelling down a decent length of 23cm (9in) drainpiping before release. If, after weaning, they are fed at night, they show no reaction in transferring to a nocturnal routine. If release from the home-run is possible, a Badger may leave in its own good time. A sow will go around her first birthday; but a young boar may well stay much longer, adopting the territory. This is all very well but his lack of fear of humans can mean serious trouble a year or so later when he is mature.

Badgers are immensely strong and able to force their way out through all but the strongest weldmesh. But they will damage themselves in the attempt (see Plate 24), and therefore must be retained behind smooth internal walls with steel sheeting concealing any wiremesh such as on doors. Since they are unable to jump appreciably, they can be retained by smooth walls no higher than 1.2m (4ft), topped by paving slabs to form a small lip. Flooring is a vexed subject; notwithstanding the danger of serious claw abrasion, probably only concrete really satisfactorily covers all contingencies. Phil Hunt's convalescing pens are approximately 3.4m × 2.4m (11ft × 8ft); at the rear there is a screened retreat behind which lies the dustbin which served as the animal's conveyance, which now serves as its den, and which will serve as its transport to the release point (Fig 58).

224

The Fox

In contrast to Badger cubs, young hand-reared Foxes, for reasons already discussed in the preceding chapter, are highly problematical. Jordan and Hughes (1982), having 'reared and released many', recommend that the person who bottle-feeds the very young cubs should after weaning completely withdraw from the scene, and never again be seen by them. The keeper who takes over has a different role to play: he or she must not touch or befriend the cubs in any way and if and when they approach must frighten them away, thus teaching them that humans are not to be trusted. This must be a distressing job, but it is being 'cruel to be kind'.

Gill Hunt tackles the problem from the opposite tack, finding it better, and certainly it is more pleasurable, for one person to undertake the whole programme from bottle-nursing to release. After weaning she alone is seen. The fact that the cubs are imprinted on her does not affect their ultimate prospects because they will never again see her; they are and remain naturally wary and frightened of strangers.

The Hunts firmly believe in feeding growing cubs 'hard' so that they have the best possible start to their first winter – always a time of serious hardship. They must be given a head-start on their wild counterparts, for these not only know intimately the geography of their home-range but have a parental link with it. If the released cubs survive competition from wild-reared juveniles and their parents, plus their first few brushes with man, the hunting season and bad weather with its consequent food shortages, they stand a fair chance of living to breed. A growing Fox can only be helped by lots of good varied food (see page 108). For safety's sake avoid lamb and fowl; instead give road casualties, fur and feather of all other sorts, fruit, *shelled* eggs, invertebrates etc. It will not grow fat, only stronger quicker; and it will not lose interest in food even if fed to repletion each day, nor can you make a Fox lazy.

Release can theoretically take place in any suitable habitat well away from human habitation and farmyards; and avoid heavily hunted, snared and shot areas. Even today it should be possible to find a patch of semi-wild woodland or scrubland with a disused Badger set (see method of release above). Phil Hunt has found that wooded country presents fewest problems, but insists that some research must go into establishing population densities beforehand. Remember the predicament of solitary cubs (see page 208).

225

If one lives in an area known to be inhabited by Foxes (but not poultry etc), liberation from the home-run is an attractive option; this way food can be conveniently left for as long as necessary, and shelter is always available. However, there are usually circumstances preventing this plan. In strange country, the progress of released juveniles must still be monitored and food left: it is the least we can do to nudge them through this dangerous time. An intermediate move outside helps to acclimatise those that have been reared inside. If Foxes escape on their own in a friendly neighbourhood then, in some ways, so much the better; otherwise they require strong fencing, and are able, unlike Badgers, to climb and jump over 1.8m (6ft) fencing unless it has an internal overhang.

Apart from this, the size and plan of their pens can be the same, crating likewise. Foxes are not as robust or resourceful in the early stages as Badgers; they are more intelligent but the inquisitiveness this engenders can bring them into fatal contact with man. So even an unimprinted juvenile must not be dumped cold in strange country, however suitable, if we are to avoid the panic-stricken flight to a less suitable area, and the stress and exhaustion which this would cause.

Adult Foxes do not tame, and those convalescing from injury or infectious disease should rehabilitate quickly. Maximum therapy for a Fox, such as would result from a fractured pelvis, would be about twelve weeks and no difficulty whatsoever should be experienced in replacing a case like this back into its home-range. Any domestication that has crept in will certainly be undone by the removal process. Phil Hunt finds that the added ignominy of being grasped and anaesthetised for tagging purposes confirms the Fox in its opinion of humans.

Other Carnivores

Species of local occurrence, such as the Wild cat and Otter, are unlikely to be kept by amateurs other than extremely keen ones with much local knowledge and connexions in conservation. This being so, general advice here would be futile. Any private individual coming into possession of an Otter must involve the local County Naturalists' Trust or some other reputable body (see Appendix 3), the more so when it comes to considerations of release. The more good conservationists involved, the more chance there will be of deciding on the best locality, and there will be ample back-up monitoring labour. It is quite possible that in the same way that birds are ringed, and Foxes tagged, a researcher into Otter behaviour may want to avail himself of the opportunity of fitting a radio-tracking device to one outward-bound.

What goes for Otters applies here equally to seals, although more because of their size than for reasons of rarity. During the 1970s, advances were made in building up the fat reserves of seal pups so that by three months of age they can be released – preferably near their birthplace, not necessarily where stranded. A forecast of several days of calm weather is necessary, and pups should not be released in the summer near popular holiday regions. Spring or early autumn is much safer in such areas.

Finally, a word must be said about those less fortunate. For those too badly damaged ever again to take their true place in the wild but not so bad that euthanasia is a decent option, our aim must be to turn their tragedy into a virtue. By providing a quality existence or arranging one, it is more than possible to achieve a longevity and fertility far outstripping anything that could be attained in the wild. That, in short, is the trump card of the *good* zoo – and I use the noun in its widest sense, taking in any form of zoological collection from the smallest specialist to the large public sponsored bodies with all the resources they can command.

11 Prevention of Suffering and Mercy Killing

In more ways than one the theme of this chapter is 'leave well alone' for, as mentioned elsewhere, if mankind could just do that to a modest chunk of the globe, the problems besetting conservationists would not seem so intractable.

Coming closer to home, it has also been stressed that young animals found apparently abandoned are usually in no need of help or, at most, only minimal assistance. Safe and useful action can include moving fledgling birds away from the side of a road, say over a wall into a garden, or through a gate into a field, or placing in a hedge out of reach of ground predators. Occasionally they can be replaced in their nests but this, as we shall see, requires care and a certain amount of knowledge and expertise.

Seal pups, if not obviously in distress or lost, may also be best left alone as they are often only waiting for correct conditions before going to sea. Merely to walk between a pup and its mother, who is possibly looking on from just offshore, can cause desertion. The scent of human touch on other young animals, notably young deer, can have the same effect. The same applies to the disturbing of birds' nests, especially during incubation; and it must be remembered that not only is the stealing of eggs illegal, but so is the wilful disturbance of nests whether for worthy reasons such as study or photography, or unworthy ones. Some birds desert almost literally at the drop of a hat – the Turtle dove is such a one, and other columbids can be nearly as bad.

It is impossible for a human to approach a nest without leaving some sign or showing some predator the way. Any sort of path, crushed or disturbed vegetation, broken twigs, a parted screen, can all attract the attention of a cat, Stoat, Weasel, Magpie or Jay.

As much as people should be encouraged to use and enjoy the countryside, many are unable to do so contemplatively or passively, without damaging, capturing, acquiring, collecting or somehow possessing it. Picnickers with armfuls of Bluebells doomed to wilt and die even if they reach water, are a good example of man's peculiar ability to take and destroy something he neither needs nor dislikes. Not only that but he still imagines that the child gathering wild flowers is behaving in a charming and natural way, which is quite untrue. Children are shown and encouraged to thus collect flowers. We all know that a curious child will bend down and pick something up which catches its attention (and which by no means always seems attractive to us!) – this is natural. But collecting merely demonstrates our need to possess and control.

The same kind of insensitivity allows the picnickers to settle down, eat their meal, play and shout and not hear the frantic alarm calls of the Blackbird with a nest of young in a nearby bush, or see its distressed behaviour as it tries to carry on feeding them. By simply being more aware we can all help to lessen the damage man needlessly causes the environment.

Protecting our flora is certainly all part of caring for wildlife, but we must return to the animated variety or, rather, that section of it which is not quite as animated as it ought to be. As already mentioned, the first question always to ask on finding a wild animal of any description or age, save one obviously injured, is 'Do I need to interfere at all?' The chart early in Chapter 5 elaborates this, but the temptation to 'do something' is great. In a broad context, we should understand something of the rationale of human/wild animal relationships and ethology, especially the instinctive fear many adult wild animals have of human-beings, for there are predictable responses following human intrusion into a wild animal's life.

As an example of not interfering, all mild concussion victims ought to be moved merely to a safe place nearby and left to recover naturally, under observation if possible. It will illustrate the point better if we realise that the injured animal may have a dependent family somewhere and that the chances of our finding the litter or brood are slim given the long distances nursing parents can cover.

In case all this seems too negative, let me hasten to say that most approachable birds and mammals, apart from the very young, are in need of assistance of some sort. The very fact that they can be approached testifies to this. The point of this chapter is to see what we can do to prevent some of these disabilities which, as we have already seen, are mostly caused by ourselves (see also Chapter 9).

Birds – Prevention of Suffering

It would be unfortunate if in our trying to replace one adventurous nestling in its nest, the remainder of the brood panicked and fled in all directions. And yet this is more than likely to happen with birds which are near the age of independence. It is unfortunate because any bird which leaves the security of its nest even one night prematurely is subjected to a greatly increased risk – of straying, of poor weather, of starving, and of becoming prey. No bird well-feathered, alert and able to perch should be reintroduced to its brothers and sisters. Do not be fooled by their placid demeanour; if they are eyeing you and are conscious of your approach (Fig 59), the chances are that they will not tolerate it nearer than a few feet and their sudden eruption from the nest is a protective mechanism intended to startle and momentarily disconcert a predator. It is better to risk the life of one than an entire brood, and if the adventurer is so advanced it will stand a good chance if placed high up in a bush nearby.

Younger and obviously immature nestlings which have fallen out either by getting caught up in a parent's feathers, or after being accidentally evicted by their siblings, can be replaced. If in the process the nestlings show undue alarm, they are easily calmed by keeping the palm of the hand gently over the brood for a few moments before calmly withdrawing it; this simulates parental brooding and elicits a sleep response. By the time they have woken up and taken notice, you should have withdrawn out of the critical range.

What else can we do to reduce the dangers to birds caused by our actions? Since there are many good books, notably by Tony Soper, already available on helping and supporting wild birds near our homes, I will concentrate here on the prevention of injury. Matters such as cats, litter, careless driving, agro-chemicals and the dross of

Fig 59 Alert nestlings; these should *not* be approached

irresponsible anglers, are discussed at length in Chapter 1 and need no repetition here except to say that all drivers can do a little to cut down on road collisions. We can dip our headlights when an animal is caught in the beam – nocturnal animals with highly sensitive eyes, such as owls, being easily dazzled. It is often enough to ease up momentarily on the accelerator when birds fly in front of one's car or when one comes upon them looking for food or grit, instead of ploughing straight on. Richard Mabey claims in *The Roadside Wildlife Book* that you can usually tell in which direction birds will take off. Within 1.2m (4ft) of a verge they go to the verge, near the crown they fly in the direction they are facing; but it is dangerous to rely on this blindly as I have not always found it to hold true.

Before moving on to traumatic injury, the dangers of inappropriate and inconsistent bird feeding must be pointed out. It is probably wise not to offer artificial foods at all in the summer or breeding season; in winter, when the provision of good food *and water* is very useful, great harm and distress results when fickle or unthinking people start to feed birds and then go away for a few days or lose interest. Birds quickly get used to a supply of food and come to depend on it, their numbers building up to unnatural densities which can lead to increased aggression, competition, stress and possibly even death if the supply suddenly dries up.

The food, moreover, must be appropriate and certainly not mouldy, for birds with their high-performance respiratory systems are very vulnerable to fungal infection (see Chapter 7). And while peanuts – shelled and unshelled – are an excellent food, salted peanuts would be highly damaging. A certain degree of hygiene is also helpful in preventing the build-up of harmful organisms such as *Salmonella* on the bird-table. Sick, dopey-looking and even dead birds in the vicinity of the table or feeding-station are almost certainly due to this or a closely allied infection. Finches are particularly vulnerable, notably the Greenfinch. Dopey birds characteristically sit hunched up, perking up occasionally to feed before relapsing back into a stupor. Disinfection and regular scrubbing plus alternation between two feeding-points will clear up the incidence.

A perfectly natural crisis that befalls all non-hibernating British residents each year is winter. Its consequences have been mentioned throughout the book but we can be on the lookout to prevent suffering provided we remember that it is a natural phenomenon and that we are interfering with nature's way. It does no harm to be aware of the local weather situation and its consequences: check neighbourhood ponds for instance in icy conditions and if birds appear to be trapped, get help. Do not go on to ice alone; call the local RSPCA or police for assistance; in cases of major importance, contact the RSPB.

Experienced predators and scavengers fare somewhat better when others are suffering, but even they may not be able to escape the effects of prolonged harsh weather. Under thick snow, voles and mice get along quite nicely, not so the Kestrel and Buzzard above. Predators on birds should manage whatever the weather but they have other things with which to contend.

One wonders how many birds die each year from flying into windows. This may seem something we can do nothing about, but though I'm sure it is a problem that is here to stay, there are ways of at least reducing the toll. Most fatal collisions occur when birds are travelling fast, and this is generally not the case when birds fly into the windows of conventional rooms which appear fairly dark from outside. It is the better-lit rooms which cause most trouble, in particular those with opposing windows, which can fool a bird – especially one nervous or fleeing from a predator – into seeing it as a flight-path. Greenhouses too are dangerous, and so are other buildings with a large glazed area or picture windows. A class of infants being taught by a friend of mine was startled by a sudden bang on one of the large windows; on looking outside, a Sparrowhawk was found dead with a broken neck. Usually it is the prey fleeing the Sparrowhawk that falls victim; this time, somehow, the boot was on the other foot.

Such combinations of windows and particular lighting conditions, can claim a fairly regular toll. The threat can however be mitigated by making the glass obvious in some way, just as builders do with newly glazed windows on building-sites. The easiest solution is to stick a transfer or cut-out shape onto those most likely to be struck. The RSPB sell hawk-shaped ones which are doubly effective. Mobiles suspended adjacent to windows may also alert birds to a possible obstruction, and of course net-curtains and venetian blinds, will do the trick. Power cables are a terrible hazard to large birds such as swans. Electricity Boards can fit inexpensive orange foils to deflect birds but seem to need a great deal of pestering first.

Mammals – Prevention of Suffering

The Hedgehog seems to be a particularly vulnerable creature. This is

232

due to a combination of reasons: (a) it is, despite a heavy road toll, still a populous species – in fact, distressing as it is, a high casualty rate indicates a high local population, and so, in one way, a lack of road victims is even more disturbing; (b) it maintains, in the face of the machine age, a touching faith in its prickly armour and is thus not a very timid creature; (c) de-militarised, scruffy gardens make a favourable habitat because of the slugs, snails and earthworms they attract – provided nets are not left lying around or poisons spread about too liberally; (d) it is of noticeable size and habit, and its noisy activities at twilight draw attention to itself and (e) it does have an unfortunate knack for getting into trouble, especially for falling down holes of all sorts from which, notwithstanding its superb climbing ability, it is unable to escape. My worst single discovery so far, in a small square pit dug on a building-site to establish the height of the water-table, has been two dead plus a third past all hope and being eaten alive by maggots. Now I cannot pass a cattlegrid, culvert or hole of any kind without scanning its darkest recesses.

Thanks principally to the efforts of the British Hedgehog Preservation Society founded by Major Adrian Coles in 1982, there are moves afoot and gaining growing support even from hard-nosed county councils, to fit into old cattlegrids and incorporate in all new ones (if they are to conform to British Standard 4008) concrete escape ramps for Hedgehogs and other small blunderers. Something anyone can do on encountering an animal grid is to check it and, if necessary, rig up some kind of escape route. This need be no more than a plank of wood firmly wedged, a length of wire netting, or a pile of stones in one corner.

In 1982 also, the BBC Radio 4 programme 'Today' became a forum over the summer months for ways of preventing Hedgehogs from falling into swimming- and garden-pools and, once in, for enabling them to climb out again before they tired and drowned – for Hedgehogs are competent swimmers. Predictably it was treated in a light-hearted vein, but though it provided exactly the sort of opportunity that many wags cannot resist, some sensible and practical suggestions were aired. To someone like myself, who regards water with a kind of morbid fascination, the thought of anything drowning snuffs out all humour. The simplest means of allowing self-rescue seems to be a length of wirenetting secured and dangling into the water up which Hedgehogs can scramble. Substantial rafts and secured ramps, suitably roughened, on which they can haul out have also been successful. There were also several jocular suggestions for keeping them away from pools; but anyone with a pool or contemplating building one, and who is distressed by the spectacle or prospect of dead Hedgehogs floating in it, can avoid the problem by surrounding the pool-side with a low wall. Even taking into account the Hedgehog's climbing skill, one about 40cm (16in) high, rendered smooth on the outside, will be sufficient.

Hedgehogs also come to grief on account of their penchant for heaps of garden rubbish. Autumn sees tidy gardeners happily engrossed in building mountains of leaves and debris, and Hedgehogs, preparing to hibernate, are on the lookout for just such desirable residences. And then, one crisp, cold afternoon, the gardener feels that a good blaze is a more attractive prospect than a pile of humus, and sets to incinerating nature's goodness, Hedgehog and all. I have even seen garden-owners, presumably delirious, pouring gallons of petrol and paraffin over great mounds of sodden leaves and rotting wood; if I were a Hedgehog I think I'd be a bit choosey about the garden I adopted. Those seen abroad late in the year are probably juveniles from late litters struggling, against increasing odds, to build up their fat reserves. A Hedgehog weighing less than 450g (1lb) will not be able to survive the winter unaided.

Compost-heaps are another favourite haunt of hibernating animals, the Dormouse included – a point (or several) to bear in mind when forking over. A hibernating animal often appears to be dead due to its reduced metabolic and respiratory rate; however it reacts to noise and is very sensitive to disturbance of its nest. The vacuum-like hibernaculum, made of grass, dried leaves and moss, insulates the dormant animal from sudden frosts and, if disturbed, will no longer do the job for which it was carefully built. In any case, in the same way that birds' nests are revealed to predators, a disturbed hibernaculum will probably be sniffed out by a dog, Fox, Badger, Stoat, Weasel or rat, or seen by a crow – all these predators are known to take hibernators. It is thought that four out of five Dormice are eaten in their sleep. They are sometimes found hibernating in birds' nest-boxes – these at least are comparatively safe retreats.

Unless a winter nest is virtually undisturbed, any hibernating animal found should be taken to a sheltered environment where it will be protected from the worst weather and may be observed until it becomes naturally active. British hibernators in fact more resemble species like the Badger and squirrels, which merely become lethargic and undergo periods of dormancy; even the deeply sleeping Dormouse wakes up occasionally and dips into its winter larder. Hedgehogs, like the bats, are occasionally seen up and about even when there is frost or snow on the ground. However, this may be due to melting snow, floodwater or, indeed, the very conditions themselves; for their metabolism is such that if the body begins to cool down to a dangerous level, the heart-beat speeds up, and the special heat-producing brown fat – found in many baby mammals and in some other adults such as bats and various rodents – warms up the body, with the result that the animal becomes active for a while so that it can seek warmer and safer conditions. Brown fat has been described as a kind of electric blanket, but it is rather superior because not only is its use regulated to keep the body temperature just above the danger level, thereby conserving it, it can also be converted from the ordinary white fat laid down in the autumn, as it is used up.

As spring approaches, the periods of winter dormancy – approximately from October to March or April depending on climatic factors – grow less; the periods of wakefulness become more frequent and of longer duration, until the animals are fully active and breeding. Those overwintered in captivity should have access to food and water during mild spells in case they wake up. If kept in warm conditions, they will probably stay awake and active continuously.

Bats are rather different in that they may benefit at times from communal hibernation, and require an equable temperature, and a good degree of humidity and still ventilation such as is found in undisturbed lofts, caves, hollow trees etc. However, our knowledge of bats is so vague that we cannot be precise. Some sleep solitarily, maybe a yard or so from their neighbour, others cluster together densely – mainly, as one would imagine, in colder conditions. John Hooper (1962) writing about the Greater Horseshoe bat, says '[one] found in a cluster one week may be in an entirely different group the following week, or could equally well be found hanging quite alone. These clusters in fact are merely temporary groupings ...'

But bats too are much more active during the winter than popularly supposed. L. Harrison Matthews (1952) puts it well: 'For though a visit to a hibernating cave generally shows all the inhabitants hanging up cold and stiff, another visit a week later will often reveal that many of them ... are hanging in different places.' Never forget though that bats now, more than ever before, require our protection and understanding. Dr Bob Stebbings, possibly the country's leading authority

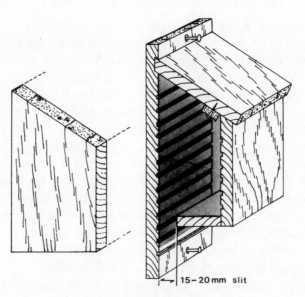

Fig 60 Bat roost box *(after Stebbings and Jefferies)*

15-20mm slit

on bats, tells me that about 90 per cent of all British bats are thought to depend on buildings for their homes. The following extracts are taken from the Nature Conservancy Council's *Focus on bats* by Dr Stebbings and Dr D.J. Jefferies, which I reproduce with the kind permission of Dr Stebbings:

Roost sites in buildings are reduced when access holes, such as ventilators, are blocked and cavity walls are filled for insulation. Retiling and underfelting roofs of old buildings often result in the exclusion of colonies. Remedial timber treatment is probably the greatest threat. Over 100,000 buildings are treated annually with chemicals that are lethal to bats [principally Dieldrin and Lindane]. These woodworm killers are extremely persistent within buildings [for as long as fifty years], and even if bats are not present during treatment they will pick up poison by inhalation of vapour and by contact with treated surfaces.

Trees with holes are important for a wide range of creatures including bats. But such trees are too often regarded as dangerous and mistakenly felled or tidied ...

Conservation measures
Bats will quickly adopt suitable new sites for roosting ... roost boxes [Fig 60] placed on trees or buildings ... can be used by large numbers of bats of most species. A box with each internal dimension about 10cm can hold up to 50 bats. Box shape and size are not critical, but front-to-back depth should not exceed 10cm because bats like narrow spaces. Noctules prefer

236

boxes 20 to 30cm high. Very roughly sawn timber at least 2.5cm thick should be used. Wood can be roughened by making many shallow horizontal saw cuts inside and out ... Entrances should be 15 to 20mm wide and at least 50mm long – or the full width of the box ...

Preservatives must not be used on the timber because they are toxic to bats.

Siting boxes needs care. Generally boxes facing south will be used in spring and summer and those facing north in the autumn and winter ...

Inspect boxes monthly and look for the characteristic crumbly black or brown droppings ... If boxes are not used for two or three years, move them to a fresh site.

Boards attached to walls with battens 20mm thick can provide roosting for large colonies ... on [any side but north] of a building so as to receive direct sun for part of the day. Small slits about 2cm wide and 15cm long made in the soffit against the brickwork near the apex of a south-facing gable-end can give access to bats for roosting above the soffit ...

Timber planking leaning against walls ... can provide additional shelter. Bats squeeze into narrow gaps where mortar has fallen out between bricks and so it is helpful to make such crevices.

Important cave or tunnel roosts that suffer disturbance require grilles. These must be planned and built most carefully or bats may be deterred ... High-tensile, reinforcing steel, 25mm in diameter, must always be used,

Fig 61 Cave entrance with a bat-grille fitted (*after Stebbings and Jefferies*)

with a door at least 50cm square. Vertical bars should be about 75cm apart and horizontal bars should have exactly 17cm air space between them [Fig 61]. It is vital that no paints be used as these drive away bats ... In established bat roosts, grilles should be fixed in May or June immediately after hibernation.

Like bats and the Hedgehog, another insectivore – the Mole – also comes into contact with man in a way that is not altogether to its benefit although its crimes are fairly petty unless you happen to be a groundsman or particular variety of farmer. The hills which mark its presence goad many people into belligerency; but I find that if I cease to regard the molehills on my 'lawn' as mountains spoiling some fantasy that were it not for them the turf would be transformed into a swathe of green velvet, I can look upon them as a privileged insight into the life of this refugee from *The Wind in the Willows*, earnestly toiling away, largely beneficially, tantalisingly just out of sight. To harm such a companionable being, let alone trap or poison it with strychnine, would make me a vandal. I fully appreciate that there are people who do have this need for billiard-table lawns, and to anyone not content to simply rake out the hills and lightly roll, I pass on the following advice heard recently. As soon as a new hill appears, slice it off with a spade, and place a heavy object like a paving-slab or rock in its place; apparently after a cold war lasting several days, the Mole gets fed up and decides to move next door.

Two ethological reasons support and explain this: (a) a molehill is like a volcano – new spoil is pushed up through the core to spill out from the top; and (b) every Mole has a territory to which its activities are more or less confined. However, territories do overlap at times and there is of course movement, so it may mean a series of skirmishes rather than a once and for all war – but then so would campaigns of trapping and poisoning. I have also heard that the Mole dislikes the *Euphorbia* spurges and is also deterred by the vibrations set up by toy windmills stood in glass bottles placed in their runs.

Much of the common misuse and abuse of commercial poisons by which non-target animals suffer and die, could be prevented if the manufacturers' instructions were followed to the letter. Great care and attention should be taken as to exactly where and how bait is laid, to removing leftover bait and poisoned animals so that they cannot be eaten by others, and to discouraging pests in the first place by good general hygiene.

The Fox is another 'popular pest', and in Chapter 9 it was stated that fox-hunting can actually make it so. This, possibly contentious, comment requires some substantiation, for there is a lobby which tries to justify hunting of Foxes on the pretext that they are only tolerated because of it. This may be so in some areas and with some people but we no longer condone slavery just because the abuse of weaker races for the profit of a few traders and masters earns them mere survival.

The work of Phil Hunt on the Cornwall/Devon border has shown that undisturbed Fox families do not break up around July as is usually believed, but remain together until the following spring, with only the juvenile males dispersing in December and January if they need to. The disturbance caused by the actual hunt and all the ancillary activities – cubbing, stopping up earths etc – is much more significant than the relatively low number directly killed, though stress undoubtedly accounts for more; for families are spread asunder, and inexperienced juveniles unable to support themselves naturally turn to easier domestic targets.

The Fox will also make a fine scapegoat if and when rabies reaches our shores (see page 165). Britain has so far been spared the full effects but I, like the environmental journalist Anthony Smith, am more scared of the human psychological reaction to rabies than of the pathological one – awful as it is. Public opinion will be whipped up to a totally disproportionate level of panic, of that I have no doubt. Disproportionate because on the continent, where the disease is widespread and endemic, there are two or three human deaths a year from rabies – infinitesimal compared to the numbers dying from falling off ladders, as Anthony Smith puts it. Vast numbers of people die from other naturally occurring diseases, but these are regarded as facts of life as is, it seems, the carnage wrought by that sacred cow, the motor car.

I fear the devastation to the countryside, and the cruelty to wildlife consequent on futile attempts to clear and maintain buffer-zones. And although the Fox is the most likely carrier, it is by no means the only possible one. In an American equivalent to this book, the authors write almost casually about rabies, the main vectors of which in the USA are species of bats, the Skunk and Racoon. They merely point out the dangers and recommend a speedy visit to a doctor or hospital, and the confinement of the animal for at least ten days, if one is bitten by an animal that is behaving unnaturally, ie too tamely. A bad year in North America results in three human deaths.

I have no wish to play down the horrible prospects of rabies crossing the Channel, but feel that a small plea for rational reaction may not be untimely. The real cost of rabies becoming endemic in Britain would be financial, ie the cost of vaccinating domestic and farm animals. Moreover, it would totally alter human interactions with animals.

Local Conservation

Rabies leads us to more general issues. We cannot here consider primary preventative medicine, in other words global conservation; but what the concerned individual can do is anticipate and help ameliorate human impact on the local environment. If just by living his or her life in an aware way one person can do more good than harm – and this is possible for man need not always be negative, always set apart from nature – imagine the collective good that could come of many people working together either in unison through a Conservation Corps or County Naturalists' Trust, or individually but with common aims.

There is no doubting the influence of the concerted protest group whether it is against luxurious new bypasses and airports, nuclear weapons, hydro-electric dams in Tasmania, or any other manifestation of the excesses of the machine age. We can all monitor and watch over our own patch, be it city park, road verge or country lane, even if we do no more than pick up litter.

Although wild plants grow beyond the periphery of these pages, they support the whole web of life. Much has been done by concerned amateurs, for example in translocating rare plants from threatened sites such as new roads and doomed hedgerows. The flail-mower and its master have mutilated hedges and verges the length and breadth of the land and, even worse, fifty miles are actually uprooted each week. In the first twenty-eight years of my life, and that of anyone else born in 1946, some 120,000 miles have been destroyed.

Flails are a good example of overkill. What should be a useful tool enabling easy maintenance of hedges, albeit with the doing away of an old skill and its provision of employment, has a capability out of all proportion to the need. The great whirling teeth, able to chew up whatever gets in the way, are controlled only by the touch of the operator, which is seldom a sensitive one. So where hedges remain – and some have been reprieved which, in the absence of the flail, would have been grubbed up – they wind incongruously through the countryside, side by side, like two fingers being waved from suburbia.

240

Shelter belts vanish, no young saplings grow up to become trees, nest-sites and cover shrink yet more, small animals get minced up, and the vegetable pulp spewed out over the verge encourages only the ranker plant growth. The worst effect of all on the culture of the countryside, is the tidying up of the only element left of coast-to-coast wilderness. Wordsworth's 'little lines of sportive wood run wild' were once, and should be still, a microcosm of nature. Deep in their hearts, amongst the tangled stems, ancient layerings and woody debris, our smallest mammals find refuge and shelter until they fall prey to the commensal Stoat and Weasel, and the owls and Kestrel overhead; beneath them, larger mammals like the Badger and Fox excavate their homes amongst the roots. To a whole host of birds, insects and plants, hedges are the only link remaining between primeval, tree-cloaked Britain and our present crop factory.

In his lovely book *Trees in the Wild* (1973) Gerald Wilkinson speaks of the 'crying need' for wild, untidied corners. Well, we can all plant trees, leave and protect wild corners, cause less waste, use fewer resources, create less rubbish, drive smaller less polluting cars, cycle or walk more, keep fewer cats, boycott wild animal by-products, support pressure groups, and join local and national conservation societies. We can teach our children, grandchildren and friends' children to be more aware of their surroundings, and show them by example to cherish and not violate it. We should not be too proud to learn from the example of different cultures living closer to the soil. Earth is our planet, but it's a lonely ship spinning in the dark fathomless sea of space; it has no friends save the sun and us, its passengers.

But there are men and women who seem only able to enjoy nature by killing, chasing, harassing or collecting it. Most do it legally, as in hunting, at least according to our present laws, but the sadistic side of man won't go away, and it seems that an economic recession with its consequent unemployment makes the pastimes of bygone days attractive again. Is the veneer of civilisation so thin that hand in hand with the microchip goes the cudgel and the medieval mind? If so, perhaps they come together most neatly in the vivisection laboratory where the cause is more clever and where the cudgels are more subtle.

But while vivisection is beyond our scope, badger-digging and baiting, hare-coursing, illegal snaring for the skin trade and other crimes against wildlife are not. All the same, there is little the compassionate person can do either to help the animals that become

241

the quarry of blood-lust, or to bring a chink of light into the souls of their witless tormentors. The clandestine factor presumably only feeds the thrill for these macho 'countryfolk' who actually usually live in the cities. Genuine country people and farmers, who are vitally involved in the future of the countryside, are urged to support their local Farming and Wildlife Advisory Group, for therein lies one of the best chances of reconciling any conflict of interest.

Some of the horrendous things I have seen and been shown while researching this book have helped me understand the emerging militancy among animal-liberation groups which is born of desperate frustration. We must support those conservation groups that actually appear to be doing something and have their hearts close to the earth. Be prepared to question and discriminate for it is not necessarily the big or most sophisticated establishment bodies with impressive lists of top brass that are the most effective or helpful. Too often, their 'information' personnel appear remote, self-important or disinterested. One senses a jealous guarding of niches as if ecology can be carved up and compartmentalised. Conservation, like politics, can become incestuous. Therefore, before supporting charities and trusts I would suggest writing with a request for specific information, ie something that is not covered by publicity blurb, and see what sort of a response you get – how fast, courteous, concerned, useful, informed and so on.

Away from the rural thugs who regard the Badger as their own personal property to do with as they like, the stoical habits of this creature also send it across the paths of those who wish it no ill. And people and bodies from small farmers to the Forestry Commission, have set aside time and resources to leave Brock some room to move in with safety. Underpasses, for example, are incorporated into new road schemes (see Appendix 4) where they intersect a traditional pathway. The Forestry Commission and other major landowners overcome similar problems by incorporating badger-gates in new fences, or in old ones which are continuously damaged in one place by Badgers on their nightly patrols (Plate 27).

The Badger is bulky, noticeable and, despite the stigma conferred by its role as a scapegoat in the Bovine TB rumpus, is still highly regarded by most people. Not so the lowly frogs and toads, which are equally animals of habit. Early each year, they make their way along ancestral routes to and from their spawning ponds, the treks of toads exceeding those of frogs in effort and distance. Toads travel as much as two or three miles, though one is probably more normal, at a 'speed' of about 46m (50yd) per hour. Where motor traffic now crosses their paths, many thousands of both species are slaughtered each year. At the worst spots, their rescue – a sort of amphibian-crossing lollipop operation – has become something of a traditional event for wildlifers armed with buckets and torches. Frogs spawn first, as early as the beginning of February in the Southwest; toads, later, in March or April. Rainy spring weather, specially at night, brings them out. The lucky ones reach their pond destinations and find them still habitable; frogs prefer the shallow margins, and toads the deeper water.

The senseless slaughter of deer on certain fast stretches of road, mainly at night and despite warning signs, upsets everyone. The idea, borrowed from the Netherlands, of erecting steel mirrors to reflect headlights back over the verges to deter the deer has helped reduce the toll; but of course is not so effective during fog or thick snow.

Mercy Killing

It's a nasty, disagreeable business this snuffing out of life. Not so much the act itself, which is simple enough, but the aftermath, made manifest by the limp bundle we have just sat in judgement on. Having had to despatch many past-hope animals, I still feel empty, inadequate and brutish. And note how we shy away from the word 'kill', and disguise the act and the fact in euphemistic ways – 'do away with', 'put to sleep', 'put down', and so on. But 'mercy killing' should indicate an act of compassion rather than an admittance of defeat, though very often it is either just that or an unavoidable acceptance of hopelessness.

Euthanasia should be a positive act, noble, sensitive, and sensible. Quite often it is a decision for an expert and, where any doubt exists, the merits of the case must be assessed coolly. A repaired humerus may sustain a gull but perhaps not a Gannet hitting the water at 60–70mph as it dives for fish. There are many reasons which, when assessed unsentimentally, suggest euthanasia as the wisest or kindest action. These include preventing the spread of infection, the provision of post mortem evidence enabling the effective treatment of other patients, the conserving of resources where pest or fast-breeding species are concerned. It would be patently absurd to expend resources repairing a Woodpigeon winged by someone over your hedge attempting to protect crops, only to release it to be shot at again. It is reasons like this that makes the thoughtful selection of release sites so important (see Chapter 10).

The rarity of some species encourages therapy and opens all sorts of doors. But however rare or attractive the subject, we must still guard against sentimentality clouding our reasoning. Ignorance too causes suffering. Dr Archie McDiarmid, a world authority, relates the sad story of a deer which, having been involved in a road accident, was treated for her few apparent injuries, tagged and released. Some time later, the doe was shot by mistake in a culling operation. During the autopsy, she was found to be pregnant but with such tumours on the pelvis, caused by injuries sustained in the accident, that the fawn could never have been born. She would have withdrawn into cover to give birth, and there succumbed to a ghastly death. Dr McDiarmid regards this as a cautionary lesson on the ethic of preserving life at all costs, and his professional inclination leads towards the humane killing of most road victims irrespective of species and visible injury. But, as mentioned before, the majority of laypeople and not a few vets will still be unable to resist the temptation to do what they can, and let the animal take the risk of it being a wrong decision.

Being a personal decision, each is a comment on ourselves and supplies an insight into our characters. Vets find it difficult or abhorrent to distinguish between rare and common species, and consider such questions not their primary concern. Their job is to alleviate suffering and promote health irrespective of species just as a doctor treats humans no matter what their status.

From the *Houston Press* in 1983 comes a story of a Sandhill crane which, either to a trap or alligator, lost both its legs at the 'false knee'. After the bird rejected a set of new legs, made from ¾in plastic plumbing tubing fitted inside with rubberised epoxy knee sockets by a factory making prosthetic devices for humans, the experts recommended that it be destroyed. But the bird-hospital took the bird back, its owner saying that it is not her policy to kill birds which are not suffering. A veterinary technician volunteered to help saying: 'If this had been a Whooping crane or some other endangered bird, all the wildlife foundations would be falling over themselves to fund the project... I'm for all animals, not just glamorous ones.' New legs, raising the bird to three-quarters of its natural height were successful. It is planned to lengthen them as the bird adjusts.

Situations such as this are always unique simply because animals are individuals; and they are always a gamble. It is a pity the patient has to be the stake. Policies are always going to be confounded, so each new case must be assessed coolly on its merits, taking fully into account the circumstances and all available evidence, advice and experience. It is easy to act on impulse, and whether ultimately the decision was right or wrong, the way I assessed my Barn owl was certainly wrong.

All too vividly I recall the day about ten years ago when I killed it after it had been brought to me with a mangled wing totally beyond repair. I acted blind with disgust of humans and their machines and with hatred of those who sit smugly behind the wheel mowing down creations that can blend so perfectly in so small a frame both exquisite beauty and mathematical efficiency. Had all its ancestors back along the evolutionary trail, I asked myself, strugged to survive for this? The owl's uncomplaining acceptance of its predicament only made me seethe the more at the guilt of my species, and urged me end the misery I thought I saw in its eyes.

Afterwards, the deed done, the neck hanging limp, my anger dissipated to be replaced by a hollow realisation that the owl could have been saved, that she could have lived contentedly in an aviary, that she may even have bred and that her misfortune would have had some point. For everyone who subsequently looked at her, and enquired about her, would have been reminded of the vulnerability of nature when it crosses the path of our progress. And I resolved there and then never again to act so hastily. The decision might have to be the same, but at least it would be inevitable.

Techniques

Fundamentally, mercy killing is exactly that: the prevention of excessive pain and prolonged discomfort; 'euthanasia' (Greek) means 'painless death'. The following extracts are from the Universities Federation for Animal Welfare's useful booklet *Humane Killing of Animals* and are quoted here with the UFAW's kind permission.

> To kill an animal humanely it is essential to avoid, as far as possible, any actions which may increase its anxiety and awareness of the unusual. Deceptions should be practised. An animal is best killed in an environment [it knows] ...
>
> [True euthanasia] is obviously not achieved if animals struggle or writhe in terror ... or regain consciousness after mutilation. [It] depends on the rapidity with which unconsciousness is achieved and the maintenance of this state until death occurs. Even humane methods may cause suffering if used by nervous or unskilled individuals.

245

Large, difficult or dangerous animals should be referred to a veterinary surgeon or RSPCA inspector by anyone unsure of what to do or if any doubt exists as to a particular species. Those that are unapproachable can be killed effectively only by shooting.

This, however, is a matter for the expert and should not be undertaken without a knowledge of firearms and experience in their use. As a guide … the following table describes the most suitable weapons, ammunition and ranges in respect of the more common species. Wild animals should be shot at as close a range as possible.

Animals	Shotguns min bore 20, max range 22m Size of Shot	Rifles max range 45m Min Bore
Badger/Otter	AAA	.22 Hornet
Fox/Wild Cat	BB	.22 Hornet
Mink/Polecat/Hedgehog	5	.22
Stoat/Weasel	6	.22

Hollow or soft-nosed ammunition

NEVER USE AN AIR GUN TO KILL ANY ANIMAL

In all animals there may be convulsive movements after shooting, but if the eyes are fixed, dull, wide open and insensitive to touch the animal will be unconscious.

Until weakened by haemorrhage the heart beat may continue for some minutes after shooting. If it continues too long or rebreathing starts shoot again and cut the main blood vessels in the neck to encourage bleeding.

Medium-sized birds and mammals of a demeanour which allows handling, can be suspended by the hind legs (Fig 62) and killed efficiently by a sharp and positive downward blow – the 'rabbit punch' – just below and behind the head, breaking or dislocating the neck. Instead of a karate-style hand blow, a heavy stick may be used.

Many birds can be killed by the same 'neck-wringing' method as is universally employed for poultry; but there is a knack, born of experience, in its humane use. Inexperienced executioners, myself included, err on the side of caution and often detach the entire head, which is effective but messy and distressing.

The bird is held by the shanks with the left hand, and kept close to the hips of the operator. The head is held immediately behind the skull between the first two fingers of the right hand, with the thumb under the lower beak. The neck is fully extended by moving the right hand downwards; then by means of a strong downward thrust at the same time pulling the bird's head backwards over the neck, the latter is dislocated at the junction of the cervical region and the occipital part of the skull.

... once the operator is familiar with the technique apprehension on the part of the animal is minimal, death is quick and suffering slight. At the same time it is recognised that many people cannot steel themselves to these procedures and prefer to use other methods. Human feelings, however, should as far as possible not be allowed to influence the use of the most humane techniques. Although these may be distasteful to the operator they are often less distressing to the animal than more complicated procedures involving chemicals and other means.

Birds up to the size of a pigeon are, in my opinion, best killed by bodily swinging the subject and administering a sharp violent downward blow to the back of the head on the edge of a solid object like a rock, window-sill or sink. Very small subjects are humanely killed when hurled onto hard ground.

Snared or trapped animals are sometimes injured and restriction of movement increases their fear ...

Fig 62 Method of administering a sharp, violent downward blow, with fingers extended and the hand held rigid *(after UFAW)*

The physical methods normally used to kill [small mammals] and birds are not suitable for predator mammals, many of which are vicious and extremely agile. A small, stout canvas bag is an indispensable item of equipment for dealing with the smaller animals ...

In the case of rodents, moles, squirrels and weasels, the bag is laid on a piece of flat ground and the animal driven into a corner until the head can be distinguished beneath ... A single sharp blow on the back of the head with a short, stout stick will kill the animal immediately. *This method of killing, however, should not be used for hedgehogs, cats, foxes, badgers, mink and the larger predators.*

In a dire emergency, a violent blow with a heavy blunt instrument to a point above the snout between the eyes is just about the only way of killing a Badger by hand. The top of the skull is protected by a very tough bony crest – the feature which sometimes saves them in road accidents when they turn to face the vehicle and are struck by the underside of it.

Reptiles and amphibians 'should be killed by a sharp blow on the head or by decapitation'.

DROWNING IS SLOW AND CAUSES FEAR.
ANIMALS SHOULD NEVER BE DROWNED.

Glossary

altrices	birds bearing altricial (qv) young
altricial	nidicolous (qv), psilopaedic (qv) nestling which is helpless on hatching (Fig 49)
anorexia	lack of appetite
anus	posterior opening of alimentary canal (Fig 30)
appetitive behaviour	variable introductory phase of an instinctive action
arboreal	tree-dwelling
arbovirus	rather old-fashioned word meaning a virus which is carried by arthropods
artery	vessel which conveys blood *from* the heart
astringent	having power to contract organic tissue
ataxia	inability to co-ordinate voluntary movements
aviculture	breeding birds in captivity
blood plasma	liquid part which includes nutrients, waste products etc
caecal	pertaining to the caecum – a blind gut
cannon bone	formed by the fusion of metacarpals (qv) or metatarsals (qv)
carbolic acid	*see* phenol
cetacean	member of the order Cetacea (whales and dolphins)
chelation	chelating agents bind together toxic metal elements into stable, soluble and non-toxic complexes
cloaca	terminal part of gut of vertebrates (except placental (qv) mammals) into which the rectum (qv) and urinogenital duct (qv) open into one common cavity (eg in all birds, fish and reptiles)
columbid	member of the Columbidae family (pigeons and doves)

commensal	living together for mutual benefit
corticosteroid	drug deriving from the adrenal gland which produces an anti-inflammatory action
corvid	member of the Corvidae family (crows and allies)
cyst(ic)	membrane or sac-like structure enclosing an organism in an intermediate stage of its life-cycle
distal	outer end or extremity (opposite to proximal)
dysfunction	abnormal functioning of an organ
emaciated	lacking flesh; wasted
emetic	causing vomiting
enzyme	catalyst secreted by cells in a living organism, which helps to evoke some metabolic change such as digestion oxidation (qv) without itself being used up. There are many kinds, each usually acting only in certain definite conditions and within narrow limits of temperature
epithelium	thin layer of cells which covers, protects and lines
ethology	science of animal behaviour
fetid	having a strong and offensive smell
gallinaceous	applied to a member of the gamebird order Galliformes (pheasants etc)
gangrene	necrosis (qv)
granivore(-ous)	feeding on grain etc
hack	to rehabilitate a bird back to the wild – usually applied to birds of prey
hepatitis	inflammation of the liver
hirundine	member of the Hirundinidae family (swallows and martins)
indigenous	native from pre-history
insectivore(-ous)	feeding on insects etc
integument	external covering, eg hair or fur, feathers etc
jizz	mien, overall appearance or character of an animal – as an aid to identification
lanugo	embryonic woolly coat of fur or down
larva (pl -ae)	free-living embryo in non-adult form
lesion	injury or wound

ligation	binding or drawing together
littoral	pertaining to the tidal zone of the seashore
metabolic rate	measure of energy expenditure – output of calories per square metre of body surface per hour
metabolism	the chemical changes occurring within a living organism
metacarpals	the bones between the wrist and the fingers (Fig 1) or the corresponding part in a foreleg, ie between the 'knee' and the fetlock
metatarsals	the bones between the tarsus and the toes (Fig 27)
morph	'phase' or variety of a species population subject to polymorphism (ie the existence of two or more distinguishable variations within a single interbreeding population)
mucous membrane	epithelium (qv) which secretes mucus
mustelid	usually applied to a member of the Mustelinae subfamily (martens, stoats, weasels etc); also applicable to other members of the Mustelidae family (ie badgers and otters)
nares	nostrils
necrosis	death in part of a living body
nictitating membrane	transparent third eyelid, widespread in reptiles and birds
nidicolous	nest-confined until virtually mature
nidifugous	nest-quitting at a very young age
oedema	pathological accumulation of fluid in tissue spaces
omnivore (-ous)	feeding on a wide variety of food
oxidation	the act of combining with oxygen
palpate	to examine by touch
parental	avoiding the gut
passerine	perching bird; member of the order Passeriformes
pathogen(ic)	organism or substance causing disease
pathological	relating to disease
peritonitis	inflammation of the membrane lining the abdominal cavity
phenol	carbolic acid, C_6H_5OH, produced from coal

	tar – a mild but powerful disinfectant
physiognomy	assessing character from facial structure
pin-feather	emerging feather still protected by a sheath
piscivore (-ous)	feeding on fish
placental	connected in the maternal uterus (qv) and nourished therein by blood plasma (qv) passed through the umbilical cord (qv); all higher mammals
plasma	*see* blood plasma
pneumonia	inflammation of the lung
poikilothermic	having variable blood temperature
praecoces	birds bearing precocial (qv) young
precocial	nidifugous (qv), ptilopaedic (qv) 'chick' or young bird (Fig 51) able to seek food
prolapse	falling or slipping out of place
prophylactic	preventive of disease
prosthetic	pertaining to artificial parts of the body
psilopaedic	naked when born
ptilopaedic	clad in down when born
pulmonary oedema	pathological accumulation of fluid in the lungs
pupa (pl -ae)	stage in an insect's life between the larva and the adult or imago when it appears to be resting but is in fact undergoing great development
pupiporous	having pupae (qv) developed within the body of the mother
pustule	pimple containing pus
rectum	terminal part of intestine leading to anus or cloaca (Fig 30)
salve	soothing ointment or lotion
spore	usually single-celled asexual reproductive body
styptic agent	astringent
torpidity	lethargy; loss of power of motion
trachea	breathing-tube (Fig 30)
traumatic	mechanical as opposed to pathogenic disease
tubule	narrow tube
tumour	new growth of cells without inflammation
umbilical cord	vascular navel-cord of complex structure which nourishes and supports the unborn

ungulate	hoofed
urethra	tube by which urine is discharged from mammalian bladder
urinogenital duct	common passage for excretory and genital products
uterus	womb
vein	vessel or tube which conveys blood back *to* the heart
venous	that which is contained in veins
ventral	of the side normally towards the ground (opposite to dorsal)
viscid	glutinous, semi-liquid, viscous

Appendix 1

Species of Mammals mentioned in Text

Badger, European	*Meles meles*
Bat: Greater Horseshoe	*Rhinolophus ferrum-equinum*
Long-eared	*Plecotus auritus*
Noctule	*Nyctalus noctula*
Pipistrelle	*Pipistrellus pipistrellus*
Cat, Wild	*Felis silvestris*
Coypu	*Myocastor coypus*
Deer: Chinese Water	*Hydropotes inermis*
Fallow	*Dama dama*
Muntjac or Barking	*Muntiacus muntjak*
Red	*Cervus elaphus*
Roe	*Capreolus capreolus*
Sika	*Sika nippon*
Dormouse:	*Muscardinus avellanarius*
Edible/Fat	*Glis glis*
Fox, Red/Common	*Vulpes vulpes*
Hare: Blue/Mountain	*Lepus timidus*
Brown/Common	*Lepus europaeus*
Hedgehog	*Erinaceus europaeus*
Marten, Pine	*Martes martes*
Mink, American	*Mustela vison*
Mole	*Talpa europaea*
Mouse: House	*Mus musculus*
Wood/Long-tailed (Field)	*Apodemus sylvaticus*
Yellow-necked (Field)	*Apodemus flaviocollis*
Otter	*Lutra lutra*
Polecat	*Mustela putorius*
Rabbit	*Oryctolagus cuniculus*
Rat: Black	*Rattus rattus*
Brown/Common	*Rattus norvegicus*
Seal: Common/Harbour	*Phoca vitulina*
Grey/Atlantic	*Halichoerus grypus*
Shrew: Common	*Sorex araneus*
Pygmy/Lesser	*Sorex minutus*
Squirrel: Grey	*Sciurus carolinensis*
Red	*Sciurus vulgaris*
Stoat	*Mustela erminea*
Vole: Bank	*Clethrionomys glareolus*

Common/Guernsey/Orkney	*Microtus arvalis*
Ground	*Arvicola terrestris*
Short-tailed	*Microtus agrestis*
Water	*Arvicola amphibius*
Weasel	*Mustela nivalis*
Whale: Pilot or Blackfish	*Globicephala melaena*
Sperm	*Physeter catodon*

Appendix 2

Species of Birds with Nestling Periods of Altrices (including Schedule 4 species*)

Auk, Little	wv	*Chough	5–6wk
Plautus alle		*Pyrrhocorax pyrrhocorax*	
*Avocet	p	Coot	3–4d/p
Recurvirostra avosetta		*Fulica atra*	
*Bee-eater, Common	3–4wk	Cormorant	c8wk/p
Merops apiaster		*Phalacrocorax carbo*	
*Bittern	2–3wk/p	*Corncrake	p
Botaurus stellaris		*Crex crex*	
*Bittern, Little	v1–2wk	*Crake, Spotted	p
Ixobrychus minutus		*Porzana porzana*	
Blackbird	c2wk	*Crossbill (+ others)	c3wk
Turdus merula		*Loxia curvirostra*	
*Bluethroat	pm	Crow, Carrion	4–5wk
Luscinia svecica		*Corvus corone*	
Brambling	wv	Cuckoo	c3wk/p
Fringilla montifringilla		*Cuculus canorus*	
Bullfinch	c2wk	*Curlew, Stone	p
Pyrrhula pyrrhula		*Burhinus oedicnemus*	
*Bunting, Cirl	±12d	Dipper	c3wk
Emberiza cirlus		*Cinclus cinclus*	
Bunting, Corn	9–12d/p	*Divers (all species)	p
Emberiza calandra		*Gavia*	
*Bunting, Lapland	pm	*Dotterel	p
Calcarius lapponicus		*Charadrius morinellus*	
Bunting, Reed	10–13d	Dove, Collared	c3wk
Emberiza schoeniclus		*Streptopelia decaocto*	
*Bunting, Snow	wv	Dove, Stock	3–4wk/p
Plectrophenax nivalis		*Columba oenas*	
Bustard, Great	v	Dove, Turtle	±20d/p
Otis tarda		*Streptopelia turtur*	
*Buzzard, Common	c6wk	*Duck, Long-tailed	p
Buteo buteo		*Clangula hyemalis*	
*Buzzard, Honey	c6wk	Dunnock	12d
Pernis apivorus		*Prunella modularis*	
Capercaillie	p	*Eagle, Golden	9–10wk
Tetrao urogallus		*Aquila chrysaetos*	
Chaffinch	c2wk	*Eagle, White-tailed	±10wk/p
Fringilla coelebs		*Haliaeetus albicilla*	

256

*Falcon, Gyr	wv	*Hobby	c30d/p
Falco rusticolus		*Falco subbuteo*	
Falcon, Peregrine		*Hoopoe	c25d
see Peregrine		*Upupa epops*	
*Fieldfare	wv	Jackdaw	4–5wk/p
Turdus pilaris		*Corvus monedula*	
*Firecrest	pm	Jay	±20d
Regulus ignicapillus		*Garrulus glandarius*	
Flycatchers	c2wk	Kestrel	4–5wk/p
Ficedula & Muscicapa		*Falco tinnunculus*	
Fulmar	c7wk/d	*Kingfisher	c25d
Fulmarus glacialis		*Alcedo atthis*	
Gannet	c11wk/d	*Kite, Red	c7wk/p
Sula bassana		*Milvus milvus*	
*Godwit, Black-tailed	p	Kittiwake	c6wk
Limosa limosa		*Rissa tridactyla*	
Goldcrest	16–21d	Lapwing	p
Regulus regulus		*Vanellus vanellus*	
Goldfinch	c2wk	Linnet	c2wk
Carduelis carduelis		*Acanthis cannabina*	
*Goshawk	6–7wk/p	Magpie	c4wk
Accipiter gentilis		*Pica pica*	
Grebe, Great crested	p	Mallard	p
Podiceps cristatus		*Anas platyrhynchos*	
Grebe, Slavonian	p	Martin, House	c3wk
Podiceps auritus		*Delichon urbica*	
Greenfinch	c2wk	Martin, Sand	c19d
Carduelis chloris		*Riparia riparia*	
*Greenshank	p	*Merlin	±26d/p
Tringa nebularia		*Falco columbarius*	
Grouse, Black	p	Moorhen	2–3d/p
Lyrurus tetrix		*Gallinula chloropus*	
Grouse, Red	p	Nightjar	sp/fly ±17d
Lagopus lagopus		*Caprimulgus europaeus*	
Guillemot	c3wk/p	Nuthatch	±24d
Uria aalge		*Sitta europaea*	
Gull, Black-headed	sp	*Oriole, Golden	14–15d
Larus ridibundus		*Oriolus oriolus*	
Gull, Great black-backed	sp	*Osprey	±8wk
Larus marinus		*Pandion haliaetus*	
Gull, Herring	sp	Owl, Barn	8–9wk/p
Larus argentatus		*Tyto alba*	
*Harriers (all species)	4½–6wk/p	Owl, Little	4–6wk
Circus		*Athene noctua*	
Hawfinch	10–14d	Owl, Long-eared	23–24d
Coccothraustes coccothraustes		*Asio otus*	
Heron, Grey	7–8wk	Owl, Short-eared	12–17d/p
Ardea cinera		*Asio flammeus*	
Heron, Night	v	Owl, Tawny	c5wk
Nycticorax nycticorax		*Strix aluco*	
Heron, Squacco	v	Oystercatcher	1–2d/p
Ardeola ralloides		*Haematopus ostralegus*	

*Peregrine	5–6wk/p	*Serin	v
Falco peregrinus		*Serinus serinus*	
Petrel, Fulmar		Shag	c8wk/p
see Fulmar		*Phalacrocorax aristotelis*	
*Petrel, Leach's	c6wk/d	Shearwater, Manx	c9wk/d
Oceanodroma leucorrhoa		*Puffinus puffinus*	
Petrel, Storm	8–9wk	*Shorelark	wv
Hydrobates pelagicus		*Eremophila alpestris*	
*Phalarope, Red-necked	p	*Shrike, Red-backed	c2wk
Phalaropus lobatus		*Lanius collurio*	
Pheasant	p	Siskin	2wk
Phasianus colchicus		*Carduelis spinus*	
Pipits	10–16d/p	Skuas	sp
Anthus		*Stercorarius*	
*Plover, Kentish	v	Skylark	9–10d/p
Charadrius alexandrinus		*Alauda arvensis*	
*Plover, Little ringed	p	Sparrow, Hedge	
Charadrius dubius		see Dunnock	
Puffin	5–6wk/d	Sparrow, House	15d
Fratercula arctica		*Passer domesticus*	
*Quail, Common	p	Sparrow, Tree	±13d
Coturnix coturnix		*Passer montanus*	
Raven	5–6wk	*Sparrowhawk	4–5wk/p
Corvus corax		*Accipiter nisus*	
Razorbill	c2wk/p	*Spoonbill	v
Alca torda		*Platalea leucorodia*	
Redpoll, (Lesser)	11–14d	Starling	3wk
Acanthis flammea		*Sturnus vulgaris*	
Redstart	2–3wk	*Stilt, Black-winged	v
Phoenicurus phoenicurus		*Himantopus himantopus*	
*Redstart, Black	12–19d/p	*Stint, Temminck's	pm
Phoenicurus ochruros		*Calidris temminckii*	
*Redwing	wv	Stonechat	12–13d
Turdus iliacus		*Saxicola torquata*	
Robin	c2wk	Swallow	3wk
Erithacus rubecula		*Hirundo rustica*	
Rook	4–5wk/p	Swan, Mute	p
Corvus frugilegus		*Cygnus olor*	
*Rosefinch, Scarlet	v	Swift	c6wk
Carpodacus erythrinus		*Apus apus*	
*Ruff	pm	*Tern, Black	pm/v
Philomachus pugnax		*Chlidonias niger*	
*Sandpiper, Green	pm	*Tern, Little	sp
Tringa ochropus		*Sterna albifrons*	
*Sandpiper, Purple	pm/wv	*Tern, Roseate	sp
Calidris maritima		*Sterna dougallii*	
*Sandpiper, Wood	pm	Thrush, Mistle	c20d
Tringa glareola		*Turdus viscivorus*	
*Scoter, Common	p	Thrush, Song	c2wk
Melanitta nigra		*Turdus philomelos*	
*Scoter, Velvet	pm/wv	*Tit (=Reedling) Bearded	±11d
Melanitta fusca		*Panurus biarmicus*	

Tit, Blue	15–23d	*Warbler, Dartford	±12d
Parus caeruleus		*Sylvia undata*	
Tit, Coal	16–19d	*Warbler, Marsh	±12d
Parus ater		*Acrocephalus palustris*	
*Tit, Crested	c19d	*Warbler, Savi's	v
Parus cristatus		*Locustella luscinioides*	
Tit, Great	16–22d	Warblers (others)	9–14d
Parus major		*Sylvia, Acrocephalus* etc	
Tit, Long-tailed	14–18d	*Phylloscopus* spp	11–16d
Aegithalos caudatus		Wheatear	15d
Tit, Marsh	16–21d	*Oenanthe oenanthe*	
Parus palustris		*Whimbrel	pm
Tit, Willow	±18d	*Numenius phaeopus*	
Parus montanus		Woodcock	p
Treecreeper	±15d	*Scolopax rusticola*	
Certhia familiaris		*Woodlark	±12d/p
*Treecreeper, Short-toed	v	*Lullula arborea*	
Certhia brachydactyla		Woodpeckers	c3wk
Twite	±15d	*Picus & Dendrocopos*	
Acanthis flavirostris		Woodpigeon	4–5wk/p
Wagtail, Grey	±12d/p	*Columba palumbus*	
Motacilla cinerea		Wren	2–3wk
Wagtail, Pied	c2wk	*Troglodytes troglodytes*	
Motacilla alba		*Wryneck	±20d
Wagtail, Yellow	10–13d/p	*Jynx torquilla*	
Motacilla flava		Yellowhammer	9–14d/p
*Warbler, Cetti's	v	*Emberiza citrinella*	
Cettia cetti			

Abbreviations:

d	days
/d	then deserted
p	precocial
/p	then leaves nest
	(before independence)
pm	passage migrant
sp	semi-precocial
v	vagrant
wk	weeks
wv	winter visitor

NB: Species marked * must be registered and (sometimes) ringed if kept in captivity. For further information about authorisation and details of registered keepers, contact Department of the Environment, Wildlife Conservation Licensing Section, Tollgate House, Houlton Street, Bristol BS2 9SZ

Appendix 3

Contact-Points and Organisations

There are many 'wildlife hospitals' scattered about the country, and countless private individuals with a measure of expertise in looking after injured wildlife. Many are selective, however, and a large number show interest only in birds of prey or rarities. Recent legislation has significantly tightened the law governing the confinement of wild animals, and a snare of bureaucracy now lies waiting to trap the well-meaning but unwary Samaritan (see footnote to Appendix 2).

Local RSPCA inspectors, vets, police officers, zoological collections etc, should be abreast of the current situation in their area, and can help as contact liaison in emergencies. Likewise, the following organisations can give advice and direction even if they do nôt necessarily take in casualties themselves:

Anglers' Co-operative Association (ACA), Midland Bank Chambers, Westgate, Grantham, Lincs NG31 6LE (0476 61008); campaigning against water pollution

Animal Rehabilitation Centre, The Cottage, Hough-on-the-Hill, nr Grantham, Lincs NG32 2BB (Honington 04004 246)

Association of British Wild Animal Keepers (ABWAK), 2a Northcote Road, Clifton, Bristol BS8 3HB

British Deer Society, The Mill House, Bishopstrow, Warminster, Wiltshire BA12 9HJ (0985 216608)

British Hedgehog Preservation Society, Knowbury House, Knowbury, Ludlow, Shropshire SY8 3JT (0580 890287)

British Museum (Natural History), Cromwell Road, London SW7; the Ornithology Dept is at Tring in Hertfordshire

British Trust for Ornithology (BTO), Beech Grove, Tring, Herts (044282 3461)

Cornish Seal Sanctuary, Gweek, nr Helston, Cornwall, (Mawgan 032622 361)

County Naturalists' Trust, *refer to* Telephone Directory

County Trust for Nature Conservation, *refer to* Telephone Directory

Farming and Wildlife Advisory Group (FWAG) *refer to* MAFF's Agricultural Development & Advisory Service (ADAS), local County Naturalists'/ Nature Conservation Trust or the Royal Society for Nature Conservation

Hawk Trust, c/o Bird of Prey Section, Zoological Society of London, Regent's Park, London NW1 4RY (01–722 3333); also re owls

Institute of Terrestrial Ecology, Monks Wood Experimental Station, Abbots Ripton, Huntingdon PE17 2LS (04873 381); contact Dr Stebbings re bat conservation.

Mammal Society, Harvest House, 62 London Road, Reading, Berks (0734 861345)

Nature Conservancy Council, 19–20 Belgrave Square, London SW1X 8PY (01-235 3241); for Regional Officers *refer to* Telephone Directory

Otter Trust, Earsham, nr Bungay, Suffolk NR35 2AF (0986 3470)

People's Dispensary for Sick Animals (PDSA), South Street, Dorking, Surrey RH4 2LB (0306 888291); for local branches *refer to* Telephone Directory

Royal Society for Nature Conservation (RSNC), The Green, Nettleham, Lincoln LN2 2NR (0522 752326)

Royal Society for the Prevention of Cruelty to Animals (RSPCA), Causeway, Horsham, West Sussex RH12 1HG (0403 64181); for local inspector *refer to* Telephone Directory

Royal Society for the Protection of Birds (RSPB), The Lodge, Sandy, Bedfordshire SG19 2DL (0767 80551); contact re major habitat emergencies

Scottish Society for the Prevention of Cruelty to Animals (SPCA), 19 Melville Street, Edinburgh E3 7PL (031-225 6418)

Sea Life Centre, Barcaldine, Connel, Argyll PA37 1SE (Ledaig 063172 386)

Swan Rescue Service, Hill Farm House, Sparham, Norwich, Norfolk NR9 5PP (Bawdeswell 036288 460); mobile radio telephone 24hr nationwide service (Norwich 0603 29444)

Universities Federation for Animal Welfare (UFAW), 8 Hamilton Close, South Mimms, Potters Bar, Herts EN6 3QD (0707 58202)

Veterinary Surgeon, *refer to* Telephone Directory (Yellow Pages)

Wildfowl Trust (headquarters), Slimbridge, Glos GL2 7BT (Cambridge, Glos 045389 333); refuges in many other parts of the country

Wildlife Hospitals Trust, 1 Pemberton Close, Aylesbury, Bucks HP21 7NY (0296 29860); 24hr nationwide service; expert contacts and teams available to help with major problems, eg oil pollution, endangered bat colonies

Woodland Trust, Westgate, Grantham, Lincs NG31 6LL (0476 74297)

Zoos/Wildlife Parks etc *refer to* Telephone Directory (Yellow Pages)

Appendix 4

Badger Crossings under Motorways and Trunk Roads
by E. Jane Ratcliffe

Where their regular routes are interrupted by new heavily trafficked roads, many animals will be killed unless provision is made for them to cross in safety under the carriageway and this regular crossing by animals will form a hazard to motorists.

Compared to the cost of the road, the cost of animal crossings is negligible – for example, if one crossing is provided every few miles, the cost is only one hundredth of one per cent of the total expenditure.

The minimum diameter of pipe suitable for Badgers (and Foxes) is 600mm (23.6in). Although they physically could go through smaller pipes for short distances, the crossing under a major road is quite long and the larger size is needed to ensure that it will be used freely by the animals. Frequently their traditional routes are along valleys where a large rectangular reinforced-concrete or horseshoe-shaped culvert has to be provided in any case to take the road over a stream, and this can make an ideal animal crossing.

Badger-proof fencing is required for at least 200m (220yd) in each direction from the culvert or pipe to ensure that the animals use the crossing under the road and do not cross over the surface. The specification for the fencing is: post and four-rail tanalised timber with heavy gauge galvanised sheep-wire – maximum mesh 150mm (6in) square – fixed to the two lower rails and dug at least 200mm (8in) into the ground; heavily galvanised 75mm (3in) mesh wire-netting fixed to the second and third rails with two strands of galvanised barbed-wire fixed between the third and fourth rails. In most cases this fencing is quite adequate, but if animals are found to be climbing over, two horizontal strands of barbed wire can be fixed on the field side. Close attention to detail is required to make sure the barrier is continuous, that no gaps have been left, and that extra rails and sheep-wire have been used to cross minor depressions in the ground.

For some time after the road is opened, the barrier should be checked regularly to make sure the animals have not exploited any weak places and forced a way through to form a crossing place. Badgers are very powerful animals and will push through or dig under given the slightest chance.

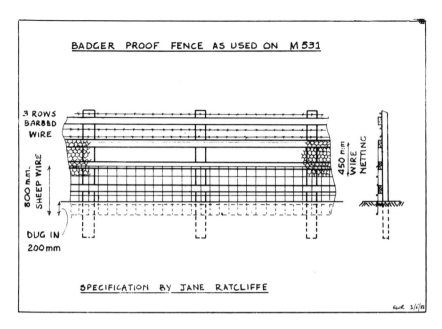

Fig 63 Specification of badger-proof fencing (*above*) and a badger underpass (*below*)
(*E. Jane Ratcliffe*)

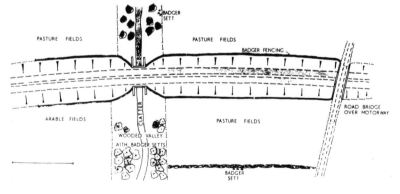

References and Further
Reading

Arnall, L. and Keymer, I.F. (editors). *Bird Diseases* (Baillière, Tindall & Cassell 1975). A standard work

Brink, F.H. van den. *A Field Guide to the Mammals of Britain and Europe* (Collins, 1967). Now superseded by Corbet and Ovenden (1980)

Burrows, Roger. *Wild Fox* (David & Charles, 1968; paperback edition Pan, 1973). An extremely readable monograph

Burton, Maurice. *The Hedgehog* (Deutsch, 1969; paperback edition Corgi, 1973). See also Morris (1983)

Burton, M. and Burton, R. *Purnell's Illustrated Encyclopaedia of Animal Life* (Phoebus, 1978). Useful partwork in 6 vols covering global wildlife

Cansdale, G.S. and Yeadon, J.K.B. 'Hand-rearing Common Seals', *International Zoo Yearbook*, 15 (1975), 250–1

Chinery, Michael. *A Field Guide to the Insects of Britain and Northern Europe* (Collins, 1974). Mainly of interest here for the section on parasitic Diptera flies

Clarke, E.G.C. and Clarke, Myra L. *Garner's Veterinary Toxicology* (Baillière, Tindall & Cassell, first published 1957)

Coffey, David J. *The Encyclopaedia of Sea Mammals* (Hart-Davis, MacGibbon, 1977)

Cooper, J.E. and Eley, J.T. (editors). *First Aid and Care of Wild Birds* (David & Charles, 1979). An extremely valuable and scholarly work, more technical in parts than the present volume

Corbet, Gordon and Ovenden, Denys. *The Mammals of Britain and Europe* (Collins, 1980). Essential on the bookshelves of all naturalists

Corbet, G.B. and Southern, H.N. *The Handbook of British Mammals* (Blackwell, 1977). An expert and up-to-date work

Cowie, A.F. *A Manual of the Care and Treatment of Children's and Exotic Pets* (British Small Animal Veterinary Association (BSAVA, 1976).

Ede, D.A. *Bird Structure* (Hutchinson, 1964). A valuable textbook for the sixth-form and university student

Fitchie, Peter. 'The handling and management of casualty seabirds', *Veterinary Practice*, 15 (March 1983)

Gallagher, J. and Nelson, J. 'Cause of ill health and death in badgers in Gloucestershire', *Veterinary Record* 105 (1979), 546–51

Glue, David (editor). *The Garden Bird Book* (Macmillan, 1982). Largely produced by the British Trust for Ornithology

Harrison, C.J.O. *Field Guide to Nests, Eggs and Nestlings of British and European Birds* (Collins, 1975)

Harrison Matthews, L. *British Mammals* (Collins, 1952). One in the steadfast New Naturalist series now showing some signs of age but still a considerable source of basic information (revised as *Mammals of the British Isles*, 1982)

Healing, T.D., Kaplan, C. and Prior, Anne. 'A note on some Enterobacteriaceae from the faeces of small wild British mammals', *Journal of Hygiene, Cambridge* 85 (1980), 343–5

Heath, J.S. (editor). *Aids to Nursing Small Animals and Birds*, 2nd edition (Baillière, Tindall & Cassell, 1978). Concerned with domestic animals but containing useful information

Hickman, Mae and Guy, Maxine. *Care of the Wild Feathered and Furred* (in UK, Wildwood House, 1980). Aimed at American fauna but charmingly written, if a little twee, and containing much opinion and fact

Hollom, P.A.D. *The Popular Handbook of British Birds* (Witherby, latest edition 1982). A classic condensation of the original 5 vols

Hooper, John H.D. *Horseshoe Bats* (The Sunday Times, 1962)

Hunt, Philip S. 'Anaesthesia of the European badger using ketamine hydrochloride', *Veterinary Record*, 98 (1976), 94

Ivor, H.R. *I Live with Birds* (Souvenir Press, 1968)

Jones, D.M. 'Disease in wild animals and its significance for man and his environment', *Journal Royal Society of Arts*, 127 (1979), 5271: 158–72

Jones, Ken. *Orphans of the Sea – the story of the Cornish seal sanctuary* (Harvill, 1970; paperback edition Pan, 1972). A popular account of the early days of the sanctuary

Jordan, W.J. and Hughes, John. *Care of the Wild* (Macdonald, 1982). The subtitle is 'Family First Aid for Birds and Other Animals' which accurately sums up the content of this book, written by two vets and containing much useful and practical data

Leslie, George. 'Observations on the Grey seal at Aberdeen Zoo', *International Zoo Yearbook*, 11 (1971), 203–4

Lockley, R.M. *The Private Life of the Rabbit* (André Deutsch, 1964). A marvellous account of the life history and social behaviour of the wild rabbit

Mabey, Richard. *The Roadside Wildlife Book* (David & Charles, 1974). Engaging writing from a concerned naturalist

Macdonald, J.W., Owen, D., Spencer, K.G. and Curtis, P.E. 'Pasteurellosis in wild birds', *Veterinary Record*, 109 (1981), 58

Martin, Richard Mark. *Mammals of the Seas* (Batsford, 1977)

Martin, Richard Mark. *The Dictionary of Aviculture* (Batsford, 1983). Basic information on keeping and breeding birds in captivity

Mellanby, Kenneth. *Pesticides and Pollution* (Collins, 1967)

Morris, Pat. *Hedgehogs* (Whittet, 1983). A highly recommended and fascinating account by Dr Morris – a world authority – charmingly illustrated throughout by Guy Troughton

Morris, P. and English, M.P. '*Trichophyton mentagrophytes* var. *erinacei* in

British hedgehogs', *Sabouraudia*, 7 (1969), 122–8

Nature Conservancy Council Report. *Lead poisoning in swans* (December 1981)

Neal, Ernest. *The Badger* (Collins, 1948; 3rd edition 1969)

Neal, Ernest G. *Badgers* (Blandford, 1977)
Neal's books are required reading for students of the European badger

Overend, Eunice D. *Badgers in Trouble – what's to be done about it?* (Overend, Trowbridge, 1st edition 1980). An extremely useful and valuable booklet, privately produced

Peterson, Roger, Mountfort, Guy and Hollom, P.A.D. *A Field Guide to the Birds of Britain and Europe* (Collins, 1954; 4th edition 1983)

Petrak, M.L. (editor). *Diseases of Cage and Aviary Birds* (Lea & Febiger, Philadelphia, 1969). A learned and worthy successor to Stroud, the Alcatraz birdman

Ratcliffe, E. Jane. *Fly High, Run Free* (Chatto & Windus, 1979)

Ratcliffe, E. Jane. *Through the Badger Gate* (G. Bell, 1974; revised paperback edition Dalesman, Lancaster, 1983). To quote the subtitle – the story of badgers, their persecution and protection and of a cub reared and returned to the wild. Jane Ratcliffe's writing makes compulsive reading for all interested in British wildlife

Research Unit on the Rehabilitation of Oiled Seabirds (RUROS). *Recommended Treatment of Oiled Seabirds* (Department of Zoology, University of Newcastle-upon-Tyne, 1972)

Royal Society for the Protection of Birds. *Treatment of sick, orphaned and injured birds* (RSPB, Sandy, 1982)

Salt, G.F.H. and Little, T.W.A. 'Leptospires isolated from wild mammals caught in south-west England', *Research in Veterinary Science*, 22 (1977), 126–7

Shoard, Marion. *The Theft of the Countryside* (Temple Smith, 1980). Important for all concerned with the environment and with the survival of the countryside's integrity

Soper, Tony. *Bird Table Book in Colour* (David & Charles, 1977)

Stebbings, R.E. and Jefferies, D.J. *Focus on bats: their conservation and the law* (Nature Conservancy Council, 1982). This extremely valuable little booklet, which includes advice on the critical problem of timber treatment, is available from Interpretative Branch, NCC, Attingham Park, Shrewsbury SY4 4TW

Thomson, A. Landsborough (editor). *A New Dictionary of Birds* (Nelson, 1964). Twenty years old now but still a useful source of information

Tinbergen, Niko. *The Herring Gull's World* (Collins, 1953). Includes a fascinating discourse on chicks' pecking responses

Tinbergen, Niko, Falkus, Hugh and Ennion, Eric. *Signals for Survival* (Clarendon, Oxford, 1970)

Tomkies, Mike. *My Wilderness Wildcats* (Macdonald & Jane's, 1977). See comments on page 210

Tottenham, Katharine. *Bird Doctor* (Nelson, 1969)

Twigg, G.I. *The Brown Rat* (David & Charles, 1975). At least we must try to understand this animal

Twigg, G.I. 'A review of the occurrence in British mammals of the major organisms of zoonotic importance', *Mammal Review*, 10:4 (Dec 1980), 139–49

Universities Federation for Animal Welfare. *Humane Killing of Animals* (UFAW, 1967; 3rd edition 1978). The UFAW produces several booklets concerned with this vexed subject; obtainable from UFAW, Hamilton Close, Potters Bar, Herts

Watson, George E. and Binion Amerson Jr, A. *Instructions for Collecting Bird Parasites* (Smithsonian Institution, Washington DC, USA)

Wayre, Philip. *The Private Life of the Otter* (Batsford, 1979)

Wilkinson, Gerald. *Trees in the Wild* (Stephen Hope, 1973). Marvellously evocative photographs complete a sublime book

Yalden, D.W. and Morris, P.A. *The Lives of Bats* (David & Charles, 1975)

Yglesias, Dorothy. *The Cry of a Bird* (William Kimber, 1962)

Acknowledgements

A big debt of gratitude is due to my friends and expert veterinary collaborators Jill and Geoff Nute who tolerated and answered all my questions, and provided much of the veterinary information in Chapters 5–7; they also undertook some research for me and thus lightened my load.

Many other people helped, contributed and encouraged me in various ways. There are some in particular I want to mention. Sue and Les Stocker of The Wildlife Hospitals Trust are doing some marvellous work and most generously supplied excellent photographs. Phil and Gill Hunt, veterinarians in the Westcountry who, despite an extremely busy practice, put in a great deal of voluntary hard work in an effort to protect badgers and foxes which are grotesquely persecuted around Plymouth as they are around other large conurbations – no badger set in a twenty-mile radius is safe, and foxes are horrifyingly snared to provide pelts for the illegal skin trade. They read and corrected sections of the script, freely gave helpful advice, allowed me to photograph some charming badger cubs from families demolished by man, and lent me photographs of their own. Dr Archie McDiarmid – a world authority on deer – also kindly gave of his time, checked relevant sections of the text, offered advice and contacts, and regaled me with some fascinating anecdotes. Dr Bob Stebbings from the Institute of Terrestrial Ecology at Monks Wood is deeply involved in bat conservation and with safeguarding Britain's dwindling populations. He kindly allowed me to draw freely on his work, as did Roger Burrows of the University of Exeter. E. Jane Ratcliffe, internationally known writer/lecturer and worker with wildlife, gave me much valuable information – especially on leverets – and some superb photographs. She also wrote Appendix 4.

I would also like to thank S.W. Cooke MRCVS for his help, particularly on the problem of lead-blighted swans; likewise, Len and Sheila Baker of the Swan Rescue Service – two extraordinarily dedicated people. Also my gratitude to Elizabeth Winson, Editor with the RSPCA; Anthony Smith, the BBC correspondent and conservationist; Allen Edwards, Director of the Anglers' Co-operative Association; A.P. Meehan, Chief Biologist of Rentokil PLC; Joanna Vinson, Honorary Secretary of the Dartmoor Livestock Protection Society; Isobel Cameron, Chief Photographer of the Forestry Commission, Edinburgh; Desmond Gunner, Secretary of the Sussex Farming and Wildlife Advisory Group – a stimulating correspondent; Ken Jones and Steve Petherick of the Cornish Seal Sanctuary; M. Causer of the Sea Life Centre; Ruth Robinson of the UFAW; Stella Turk of the Cornwall Biological Records Unit; and Sue Hall and John Pawsey, my editor and agent respectively, for their help in many divers ways.

Closer to home, my thanks to Mick and Jane Lee, Craig and Michael Vernoit, Tim Goggs and, of course, my family – in particular the unquestioning good natures of Sam and little Jo-jo who were and are an unquenchable source of optimism and inner strength.

Index

See Appendices 1 & 2 for scientific names of mammals and birds. Page numbers in *italics* denote figures or plates.

270